THE WAY THINGS ARE

THE WAY THINGS ARE

P. W. BRIDGMAN

HARVARD UNIVERSITY PRESS

Cambridge, Massachusetts

PREFACE

It may be of some assistance to the reader to give some historical account of the development of this book. The impulse to write such a book goes back at least thirty years, when I was writing *The Logic of Modern Physics*. This was written under a definite time limit, so that I could treat only what then seemed to me the most immediately pressing questions, and I had to leave many obviously important lines of inquiry unexplored. In the years that followed, the importance of the individual became increasingly obvious to me, even in science which is sometimes actually defined in social, public, terms. My reason for insisting on the importance of the role of the individual in science was that "proof", without which no science is possible, is entirely an affair of the individual and is therefore private, with the result that any creative science is of necessity private rather than public. In 1939 I wrote *The Intelligent Individual and Society*, in which it appeared that the arena in which I found greatest difficulty in making my intellectual peace with the world was the arena of my relations to my fellows. In the years that followed I became increasingly convinced that there is something radically wrong in the way that civilized man uses his mind, and I set myself the problem more or less consciously of finding out what it was. I began to accumulate notes, some on filing cards and some, more ambitious, in the form of essays up to 20 or 30 pages. The material for these notes was in large part provided by the rapidly increasing tempo of discovery in science, and by the resulting new ideas, both of others and the results of my own reflections. Some of this material found its way into various articles which have been collected in the two editions of my *Reflections of a Physicist*. About four or five years ago I began working over the material which had thus accumulated, classifying it and attempting to get the different parts into some sort of relation to each other.

Two or more years ago I began the serious attempt to weld this material into book form. Some of the considerations which guided this attempt are set forth in the Introduction. As was inevitable, my own ideas changed with the writing of the book, making necessary several rather extensive revisions, particularly of the last three chapters. These revisions were for the most part such as were demanded by the tactics of presenting my argument as I came to see more clearly what was implied in my fundamental point of view. I became more and more convinced of the validity of my earlier vision that the locus of our most important difficulties is the way in which we talk about our relations to each other. At the same time I became increasingly convinced of the necessity of first person report, either by me or by you, if immediate experience is to be communicated with any faithfulness or freshness. At first, as was natural, I attempted to make my own first person report with the linguistic tools of my inheritance. It became increasingly evident, however, that use of the conventional, impersonal, third person language of society makes it exceedingly difficult to express what is perhaps the most important characteristic of my own personal experience, the operational dichotomy between my own immediate experience and that of others, for example, the dichotomy between my pain and your pain. I came to see that this operational dichotomy could be kept in view by the adoption of a comparatively minor conventional restriction in the use of language. This restriction consists in using such primarily introspectional words as "pain" and "feeling" and "conscious" only in their private introspectional mode instead of in both their public and private modes, as is customary. Thus, with the new convention, it is only I that am conscious, and I must not say that you are conscious. The tactics of urging the possibility and desirability of adopting this convention in the use of language went through a course of development which was the primary reason for the several revisions of my presentation, traces of which may still remain. The major initial objective of my tactics was to reconcile my point of view with that of the behaviorists in psychology. I have the greatest sympathy with many aspects of this point of view and I have had many illuminating conversations with my colleague B. F. Skinner on the subject. It seems to me that the behaviorists also solve their problem by using language in a specialized way, namely by refusing to use at all such words as "pain" and "feeling" and "conscious". At first my attitude was that there was room for both points of view, and that there was no reason here for a failure of communication. I thought that I could understand the behaviorist position and that I could talk his language when I wanted to. On the other hand, I argued that there was no inconsistency in my position which would prevent the behaviorist, by the exercise of good will, from talking my language, although he might have reservations about whether it was a sufficiently profitable language. But under the stimulus of repeated conversations and the needs of detailed exposition, my position hardened somewhat and became less liberal. For, although I continued to think that I could talk the behaviorist's language if I wanted to, it became evident that the behaviorists were not capable of talking my language. It seems to me that in consequence they almost of necessity lose part of the picture. I have ended with the conviction that it is not only permissible to recognize the operational dichotomy between such things as my pain and your pain, but that it is mandatory. Whether this operational dichotomy is kept in view by the particular linguistic convention that I have adopted is not of any particular moment, but it must be kept in view by some method or other.

Finally, a word about the title of the book. The title might almost equally well have been "The Way It Is." The title is intended to suggest that the scope of the book is primarily on the descriptive level. I believe that the new insights reach so deep that they demand a fundamental revision at this first and deepest of all levels. The task of a new synthesis in the light of these insights is mostly for the future.

P. W. B.

CONTENTS

THE WAY THINGS ARE

I

INTRODUCTION

In this book I try to find a place for various insights which I have been acquiring over the years. However, nothing could be further from my intention than to erect a closed formal system, and the reader will find that many topics are not mentioned here which would be essential to such a system. Some of these topics, but by no means all, I have discussed in some of my earlier writings, and I shall not attempt to repeat this discussion here.

The new insights for which I am trying to find a place have mostly been suggested by recent experiences in science which I believe have revolutionary implications not appreciated even by most scientists. Two convictions have been growing upon me — a conviction of the importance of a better understanding of the nature and the limitations of our intellectual tools, and a conviction that there is some fundamental ineptness in the way that all of us handle our minds. It becomes more and more impossible for me to read any of the great philosophical writings which have excited universal admiration from the time of the early Greeks — my mind simply will not do the things that it is obviously expected to do. The recent *Treasury of Philosophy* of Dagobert Runes[1] is to me an utterly depressing exhibition of human frailty. At the same time, the importance of putting my finger on what is the matter appears more and more pressing.

In some of my early writings I spoke of the two-fold aspect of the problem of understanding — there was the problem of understanding the world around us, and there was the problem of understanding the process of understanding, that is, the problem of understanding the nature of the intellectual tools with which we attempt to understand the world around us. The implication in my early writings was that the latter is a closed problem which we may hope to solve now to a sufficient approximation, if for no other reason than that we have our minds with us for study and presumably could describe them exhaustively in terms presently in our control, whereas we must always be prepared for the discovery, by yet unknown techniques, of at present unknown structure within the present ultimate particles of physics or beyond the present universe of galaxies. Now this position may still be correct "in principle", although I am beginning to have my doubts. However, it is becoming more and more obvious that the problem of understanding the nature of our intellectual tools offers so many present complexities that it is not profitable to separate the one problem from the other in the way I did. In fact, the problem of better understanding our intellectual tools would at present seem to have priority. Even in pure physics, where the problem does not obtrude itself prominently, it is becoming evident that the problem of the "observer" must eventually deal with the observer as thinking about what he observes. In psychology, as a consequence of recent concern with analysis of brain activity in terms of machine activity, stimulated by the development of super-calculating machines, the problem of understanding the nature of the nervous apparatus with which we understand appears more unavoidable and more formidable. Eventually, when we understand better our intellectual tools, we may perhaps be able to put our finger on what is the matter with human thinking.

Any new insights which I may have been acquiring over the years cannot be dissociated from my constant practise of "operational analysis", which continually reveals itself as a fruitful line of attack. But much remains to be done, and I believe that some of even the more obvious implications of the operational approach have not yet been adequately explored, in particular, the fact that operations are performed by individuals. At the same time, the operational attitude appears as a special case of a more general attitude. It is evident, as its critics have often pointed out and I myself have repeatedly stated, that the operational approach cannot be completely general and that it can by no means provide the basis for a complete philosophy. There are many fundamental questions to be answered, such, for example, as: "What is an operation? On what basis is an operation accepted, or what makes an operation 'good'?" Some of the implications of this incompleteness I have explicitly recognized, as when I have tried to analyze operations into "instrumental" and "mental" or "verbal" and "paper-and-pencil" operations. Or, still more generally, when I have recognized a general and a particular aspect of operations, the particular aspects being those of primary concern to the physicist or other specialist, while the general aspects may be so general that from one point of view they degenerate into tautology. In general, an operational analysis appears as a particular case of an analysis in terms of activities — doings or happenings. In my own case, pursuit of operational analysis has resulted in the conviction, a conviction which has increased with the practise, that it is better to analyze in terms of doings or happenings than in terms of objects or static abstractions. Many professional philosophers will doubtless object that this begs the whole question, for it assumes that an analysis in terms of doings or happenings is possible. Whether this objection is valid in any ultimate sense we leave unexplored, at least for the present, but I believe that it is nevertheless possible to analyze at a level where the immediate emphasis is on doings or happenings, a thesis for which the existence of this book may be taken as partial justification. Furthermore, I believe it is a sort of analysis which everyone can learn to make, by observation of other practitioners if by no other method. Whether it is a more profitable method of analysis than an analysis in terms of things or other static elements can be judged only by the event. For myself I can only report that it puts nearly everything in a different and a fresher light.

Analyzing the world in terms of doings or happenings, as contrasted with analyzing in terms of things or static elements, amounts to doing something new and unusual. I believe that history shows that, whenever human beings find how to do something new, new vistas open. Seeking to discover the consequences of the new doing constitutes an exploration of discovery, the results of which may not be anticipated. This book may be regarded in the light of one of the many possible expeditions of exploration. We cannot tell until we go whether the results the expedition brings back will prove to be important. But even if the results are disappointing, there is still a certain intrinsic interest in finding out something about the nature of the unknown territory.

It was my original intention to present my analysis of doings or happenings exclusively in the first person singular, the doings or happenings being doings by me or happenings to me. My reason for this was, among others, my desire to secure the greatest possible immediacy in description, coupled with a conviction that an essential preliminary to successful analysis is faithful description.

The resolution to use the first person was one of the outcomes of the attempt to see things in terms of activities. A spoken or a written word was spoken or written by someone, and part of the recognition of the word as activity is a recognition of who it was that said it or wrote it. When I make a statement, even as coldly and impersonal a statement as a proposition of Euclid, it is I that am making the statement, and the fact that it is I that am making the statement is part of the picture of the activity. In the same way, when you quote a proposition of Euclid the fact that it is you who quote it is part of the picture which is not to be discarded. And when I quote you it is I that am doing the quoting. Attention to the activity aspect of all our communication inevitably forces mention of the maker of the communication, and in this book it is I that am making the communication.

My feeling of the desirability of giving my analysis in the first person has been with me for a long time, and I have in the past not infrequently used first person report and have even argued to justify it. This argument, and related arguments, I feel have to a large extent been misunderstood, and criticisms of my writings have frequently accused me of solipsism. These criticisms have always puzzled me. However, it is only recently that I have come to appreciate that use of the first person, which is all that I am urging, need involve no commitment whatever with regard to a solipsistic "ego" or "self," the implied existence of which is what I suppose has principally disturbed the critics. My use of the first person in reporting has the neutrality of grammar. That it can have such neutrality I regard as an important observation.

A program of first person report can be carried through by anyone, without prejudice. It is a matter of observation that people can talk to each other, each in his own first person. When my neighbor talks to me in his first person I understand what he is saying, and I take it that my neighbor understands what I mean when I talk to him in my first person.

So much for my original intentions and the justification for them. When it actually came to carrying through the program, however, situations frequently arose in which the urge to use the conventional impersonal manner of speech was strong and use of the first person appeared forced and clumsy. Instead of saying "I see that it is true that — ", or even "We see that it is true that — ", it is simpler, and, with our linguistic background, almost irresistible to say "It is true that — ". I shall therefore not always hold my exposition explicitly to the first person. However, I, and I hope my reader, will be vividly aware that translation into the first person singular is always possible and implicit. When I say "we," I am speaking for myself and, I believe, also for you. That is, I believe that you might be uttering the same words as I. When I speak in impersonal general terms in the third person, this is a compressed way of saying "This is what I would say and I believe it is also what you would say". The question how it comes about that you and I can use the same words in similar situations we may leave for possible future analysis. For the present it is sufficient merely to call attention to the similarity in the brains and nervous systems of all of us, and to the similarities in much of our experience and environment.

In the following, the extent to which I find it desirable explicitly to use the first person will depend to a large extent on the subject matter. In discussing situations in physics or mathematics or any physical science, use of the third person is natural and usually adequate, but, when it comes to situations involving a large social element, it seems to me that use of the first person becomes increasingly desirable, and indeed even necessary, if we are going to bring out into the light features usually ignored.

Insistence on the use of the first person, either explicitly or implicitly, will inevitably focus attention on the individual. This, it seems to me, is all to the good. The philosophical and scientific exposition of our age has been too much obsessed with the ideal of a coldly impersonal generality. This has been especially true of some mathematicians, who in their final publications carefully erase all trace of the scaffolding by which they mounted to their final result, in the delusion that like God Almighty they have built for all the ages. Neglect of the role of the individual, with resulting overemphasis on the social, may well be one of the fundamental difficulties in the way the human race handles its mind.

Attention to activities and the first person emphasizes the insight that we never get away from ourselves. Not only do I see that I cannot get away from myself, but I see that you cannot get away from yourself. The problem of how to deal with the insight that we never get away from ourselves is perhaps the most important problem before us. It is associated with, but incomparably more complicated than, the problem of the role of the observer to which quantum theory has devoted so much attention and regards as so fundamental. We consider this problem more in detail later.

Not only is each one of us as an individual not able to get away from himself, but the human race as a whole can never get away from itself. The insight that we can never get away from ourselves is an insight which the human race through its long history has been deliberately, one is tempted to say wilfully, refusing to admit. But the ostensibly timeless absolutes are formulated and apprehended by us, and the vision which the mystic says is revealed by the direct intervention of God is still a vision apprehended by him. When we talk about getting away from ourselves it is we who are talking. All this is so obvious that it has only to be said, yet it seems to me to have been a major concern of most conventional philosophy and religion to sidestep the consequences of this insight, or not to admit it in the first place. A recent development in technical logic suggests that the consequences of persistent disavowal of this insight may be more disastrous than could have been suspected. The technical development was the formulation of Gödel's theorem. This theorem states that it is impossible to prove that a logical system at least as complicated as arithmetic contains no concealed contradictions by using only theorems which are derivable within the system. To prove freedom from potential contradiction it is necessary to use theorems which can be proved only by going outside the system. This theorem made a tremendous sensation, for at one stroke it stultified the attempts of some of the ablest mathematicians, such as Hilbert for example, who had long been trying to prove by mathematical principles that arithmetic or geometry contain no concealed contradictions. To prove mathematics free from potential contradiction one must use principles outside mathematics, and then to prove that these new principles do not conceal contradiction one must use new principles beyond them. The regress has no end — one has languages and metalanguages without limit.

It is exceedingly suggestive to see in Gödel's theorem an application to our present problem, the problem of discovering the consequences of not being able to get away from ourselves. It is, of course, not a question of any formal and rigorous application of the theorem, but only of something qualitative and suggestive. The essence of the situation presented by Gödel's theorem seems to be that we are here concerned with a system dealing with itself — mathematics attempting to prove something about mathematics. Similar situations present themselves frequently in logic, as when we have the class of all classes, including itself, or contemplate the barber ordered to shave all those who do not shave themselves, including himself, or the map that must contain a map of the map. In all these situations we have systems dealing with themselves, and in all these cases we have paradox, or at best, infinite regressions, and therefore difficulty. It is tempting to generalize Gödel's theorem to read that whenever we have a system dealing with itself we may expect to encounter maladjustments and infelicities, if not downright paradox. The insight that we can never get away from ourselves obviously presents us with a situation of this sort. The brain that tries to understand is itself part of the world that it is trying to understand. It seems that the situation cannot be dealt with satisfactorily in its entirety; the best, and well nigh all, we can do is to operate by successive approximations at different levels, isolating for treatment this or that group of phenomena which experience has shown we may hope to deal with rather satisfactorily so long as we remain within the group, but never forgetting that the concept of isolation is itself rigorously contradictory and impossible. A "level of operation" may be roughly characterized by the things we leave unanalyzed. Analysis can always be pushed further, just as we can always add one to any integer.

The insight that we can never get away from ourselves has been dramatized for me by the "demonstrations" initiated by Ames at Hanover and now carried on by Cantril and his colleagues at Princeton.[2] In these demonstrations cunningly devised stimulations of the sense organs yield perceptions of movements in space with an inexorability that must be experienced to be appreciated, perceptions over which the subject has no control, although he knows that they are incorrect and can correspond to no possible real situation. The question obtrudes itself "What is this mold of space and time into which our perceptions so inexorably pour the world, and is it a good mold?" Evidence is accumulating that it may not always be a good mold, as when we go as far as we can into the submicroscopic world of quantum phenomena or into the world of supergalaxies. If it is not a good mold, can we invent a better? And even when we have invented it, would it not still be our mold?

The Ames-Cantril demonstrations are still the subject of controversy and many psychologists think they are of only minor significance. The insight which I acquired on witnessing the demonstrations was not a necessary or logical consequence of the experience or of the method of demonstration, and the fact that it was not probably explains why some of my psychological colleagues do not see the significance in the demonstrations that I do. Logically, it is perfectly satisfactory to say, when confronted by the physically impossible acrobatics of the cross-bar in the rotating trapezoidal window, for example, that I am not perceiving things correctly in space and time. This statement, by its very form, assumes that space and time are a valid form of perception. My reaction was different and involved the logical jump of saying to myself "It may be, if my brain, which is responsible for perception, can play me such tricks in this special case, that my brain is playing me another trick in casting perceptions into the mold of space and time at all." Although this is a *nonsequitur,* I think it is impossible, once one has the twist that makes one say it, to put it back where it came from and forget the vision.

Another insight is that the conceptual revolution forced by recent physical discoveries in the realm of relativity and quantum effects is not really a revolution in new realms of high velocities or the very small, but is properly a conceptual revolution on the macroscopic level of everyday life. The obvious justification of this statement is that it is still *we* who have the new concepts, and the material which goes into the formation of the concepts still comes to *us* through the agency of the same old senses. In other words, we are macroscopic creatures. It is merely that we have discovered how to make new kinds of instruments and how to do new things with them. This sort of thing is occasionally said by such exponents of conventional quantum theory as Bohr, but an appreciation of the true significance of this situation has only recently been growing upon me. The inescapable implication is that the seeds of all our recent conceptual difficulties were already with us in the way we handled the everyday common sense world, and that if we had only made our analysis acute enough we would have been able to discover them without having to wait for the new experimental evidence. It is, of course, now too late to turn back the hands of the clock, but here is at least a stimulus to make our present analysis as penetrating as we can, to see if we cannot find some of the things that we might have said, but did not. One of the principal incentives back of this book is the conviction that there are still many new and revolutionary things to be said which have escaped us because they are so close, ubiquitous, and constant that we have not been able to see them. A conviction such as this lends a certain excitement to the attempt to make our analysis as penetrating as we can.

Another insight which we shall always try to keep in the background of any analysis is that certainty does not occur, and that sharpness and absolute rigor are unattainable. There is no adequate answer to self-doubt. This applies even to the operations of logic, traditionally supposed to be of absolute certainty. The best that we can attain is relative rigor in a limited universe of discourse and operations. It looks to me as though many philosophers and logicians do not admit this, but their ideal seems to be certainty and rigor. The recognition that these objectives can be attained only in a limited area shifts the focus of interest for me. I can, for example, no longer feel the interest in some of the analysis of symbolic logic that I formerly did. In fact, the whole enterprise of logic appears in a somewhat unconventional light, which many logicians will doubtless find heretical.

It might be thought that one's task in adjusting himself intellectually to his environment becomes easier if one gives up the ideals of absolute certainty and rigor. The exact opposite is the case — every workman knows that it is harder to work with dull tools than with sharp ones. For me, at least, the problem becomes enormously more difficult. There is in the first place the temptation to sloppy thinking — if one knows that rigor can never be attained one is tempted to do less than one's best and let a piece of analysis go that one sees could be improved if one took more time or pains with it. There are situations where a defeatist attitude is too easily adopted instead of pressing the attack to one's utmost. And there is the difficulty that one has no criterion or assurance that one has ever got to the end of the road.

In the elementary geometry of my school days I could write Q. E. D. and stop thinking about it. I can now never stop thinking about any fundamental thing, but always a new idea is possible.

If the insight that one can never get away from one's self has really "got under one's skin" two diametrically opposite reactions are conceivable. Realizing the hopelessness of trying to get away from one's self, one may abandon one's self to an orgy of invention and construction of metaphysical principles and absolutes, on the principle that one might as well die for a sheep as a lamb. Or one may react by trying to get away from one's self as much as possible and to intrude one's self into any situation as little as possible. (An unsympathetic reader will have no difficulty in pointing out that there is very little meaning in the last sentence.) It was the latter ideal that inspired William of Occam long ago in his celebrated slogan that entities are not to be created beyond necessity. This appeals to me as a cardinal intellectual principle, and I will try to follow it to the utmost. It is almost frightening to observe how blatantly it is disregarded in most thinking. I do not know what logical justification can be offered for the principle. To me it seems to satisfy a deep-seated instinct for intellectual good workmanship. Perhaps one of the most compelling reasons for adopting it is that thereby one has given as few hostages to the future as possible and retained the maximum flexibility for dealing with unanticipated facts or ideas.

In the following the various topics are discussed roughly in the order of their complexity, which is also roughly the order of the prominence of the personal element or the degree of involvement of the performer in the various operations. After various preliminaries implied in the universal use of such intellectual tools as language and logic, the physical sciences are examined, in which the results can usually be adequately expressed in impersonal form with no explicit reference to the experimenter or theorizer. After the physical sciences are various topics on the edges of psychology, where we cannot avoid paying attention to our mental processes, but where the interest is in the mental processes of the single individual. Finally are considered some topics pertaining to the reactions on each other of individuals and groups of individuals, that is, topics relating to society. This order of topics is also the order of the magnitude of the revolution in our outlook to be expected if we consistently follow through the implications in the new insights. In psychology, use of first person report will lead to a more consistent use of introspection as a psychological tool than at present. However, introspectional report presents special verbal problems for which a solution must be sought. In the social arena we have the arena of greatest complexity. Most of our social concepts have just grown, like Topsy, with the minimum of deliberate direction. Here it seems to me nothing less is demanded than a new system of ethics, an ethics concerned with the exercise of social pressures by the individual on his fellow.

11

WORDS, MEANINGS, AND VERBAL ANALYSIS

Speech is almost universally employed by human beings and without it activity on the level we regard as human would be all but impossible. By means of it we communicate with each other, thus making society possible in its present form. As individuals, a large part of our mental activity consists of imagined speech with ourselves.

Nearly all the utterances of speech can be broken down, roughly and approximately, into smaller units; it may be in the first instance into sentences, and then sentences into words, and words into phonemes. For many purposes, in the languages which have been most studied, including our own, the breakdown into words is the most significant, the words being the major carrier of the meaning which we wish to communicate. We begin our examination of the nature and limitations of our intellectual tools by considering some of the things involved in the use of words.

There has been a great deal of discussion about how essential the use of words is in thinking. There are some who maintain that their own conscious thinking contains no recognizable nonverbal element, and some even go so far as to maintain that it is intrinsically impossible for thinking to be done without words. But there are, on the other hand, many others who assert with equal emphasis that a large part of their rational thinking contains no recognizable verbal element. I believe it has now come to be accepted that there is enormous variation from individual to individual in this respect. The subject has been discussed at considerable length in Hadamard's little book on the mental processes of mathematicians, where examples are given of all degrees of variation from completely verbal to almost completely nonverbal. For myself, my use of words in thinking depends to a large extent on the subject matter. When I am thinking out the design of a new piece of apparatus or driving a car through traffic my thinking contains no recognizable verbal element.

Whether or not words are an indispensable mental tool, we all are able to use them, and we do use them almost of necessity when we want to communicate with each other. In particular, this book will be written with words. Words have a definiteness and a publicity which fits them to be the subject of a first analysis. In fact, irrespective of the role played by nonverbal thinking in the intellectual processes of different people, most of the important questions with regard to the limitations of our intellectual tools can be made to present themselves in an analysis of our use of words. If we can adequately analyze what happens when we communicate with words, we shall have a very important part of the story, and probably all that we shall need for present purposes.

What, now, is this thing we call a word? Perhaps we shall ultimately be able to formulate some generalizations, but as always we shall have to begin with the concrete. One of the most obvious characteristics of any concrete individual word is that it is able to appear in the most various guises. If it is written, it may be in type or script of any style, in any color, in any size, in shorthand or longhand. If it is spoken, it may be uttered with any audible intensity, fast or slow, at any pitch, and, in most languages, with many intonations. All these so various manifestations may be of the "same" word. In what, now, does this sameness consist? Answers are possible on various levels and of various degrees of sharpness or completeness. For example, the written word which appears in print of various styles may be said to be the same if it is spelled with the same letters in the same order. But we would then have to answer what constitutes sameness in the letters, to say nothing of the fact that sometimes there are different spellings for the same word. Moreover, the philogist understands "sameness" in a word in a very broad sense and talks of the same word in different languages, or traces the history of the same word within a language, following the shifting meaning of the word during the process of linguistic evolution. It would appear, therefore, that the concept of the sameness or identity of a word is a rather loose concept, with recognizably different aspects. The particular aspect which concerns us in any concrete situation may often have to be judged by the context. This, however, is something which we do easily enough in the ordinary situations of daily life.

Our general point of view suggests that whatever it is that gives sameness or identity to a word must in some way be connected with the activities with which it is associated, either as word emitted or as word received. Now the activities associated with the particular word may be exceedingly complex and may vary widely from individual to individual. All sorts of detailed memories regarding past associations may be recognizably called to mind by the word. These may depend to a large extent on the specific experiences of the individual. More than this, a subconscious fringe of "know-how" with regard to usage of the word envelops the word. This know-how has close social involvements. It reminds one of the fringe of knowledge that surrounds our spatial perception of objects, which, among other things, enables us to anticipate and predict our motor experiences when we change our visual relation to the object. By analogy, one may speak suggestively of "verbal perception" in the same way that one speaks of space perception. Unlike our perceptions of space, an extensive social experience would appear to be necessary for the formation of verbal perceptions, but this is only a reflection of the fact that words occur predominantly in a social setting. The full background implied in verbal perception is not articulately present in consciousness, but often may be partially elicited by suitable verbal experiments. One may ask oneself "Would I use this or that word in this or that situation?" and one often finds that the answer comes with astonishing assurance.

The verbal experiment often reveals the presence of verbal compulsion — I feel that I could say nothing else in the situation. I would call verbal compulsion a special case of verbal perception. Verbal compulsion would sometimes appear to reveal the presence of unsuspected tautology. The following is an example. If at the end of an interval of time there is more of something inside a closed surface than there was at the beginning, then I, and I think other people also, feel a compulsion to say that the excess either got in across the surface or was created within the surface during the interval. The concealed tautology here would seem to be associated with the notion of creation. In the absence of an independent definition of creation, and we have not given such a definition, I am not "saying anything" when I say that the excess either crossed the surface or was created inside, but am merely saying in another way what I mean by "create." Another example is afforded by the compulsion which most people feel to say "A statement is either true or it is not true." The compulsion here may arise either because we are dealing with a concealed definition of "not", or perhaps more generally with a tautological tie-in between "statement", "true", and "not". In cases like these we may use the presence of verbal compulsion as a tool for smoking out the presence of concealed tautology.

Most people feel a compulsion in the sort of situation presented by the former traditional point of view toward axioms. These were considered as "self-evident" truths. Here "self-evident" contains an implication of compulsion. It would be interesting to analyze to what extent the compulsion felt here is a verbal compulsion reflecting the presence of concealed tautology. It is not natural to think that the compulsion formerly felt by most people in the presence of the parallel axiom of Euclid arose entirely from a concealed tautology. On the other hand, it is to be remembered that Poincaré[1] viewed the truth of Euclidian geometry as a "convention", and such convention is pretty close to tautology.

The background of verbal perception disclosed by adroit questioning may be of unsuspected complexity and richness. In fact, the complexity and richness are so great that it would be prohibitive to attempt to describe them fully. Furthermore, the total intellectual activity associated with a given word would not be the same for any two individuals: the verbal perceptions of a poet are quite different from those of an engineer. For that matter, verbal perception need not be twice the same for the same individual. What it is that constitutes "sameness" in a word must therefore involve some very restricted aspect of the total activities associated with it.

What we are usually concerned with in words is their function in a social setting as a means of communication, and this is closely connected with the "meaning" of the word. Whatever it is that gives successive uses of a word sameness would seem to be tied up in some way with this question of meaning, except perhaps for the historian or philologist. In fact, for many purposes the meaning of a word is its most important attribute, with all due deference to poets of the school of Gertrude Stein. Now this business of the meaning of a word is not simple — books have been written on the meaning of meaning. "Meaning" may be used in a broad or a narrow sense. I have heard a noted linguist define the meaning of a word as that which is common to all its usages. This gives a first impression of great generality, but when one examines it, it appears on the contrary so narrow as to contain the possibility that it may be self-defeating. For, after the impossible requirement has been met that all the usages have been examined, the possibility remains that no common element may be discernible in all its usages. If one wants this kind of great generality, it would seem to be better to say that the meaning of a word is specified by enumerating all the conditions under which the word would be used. But this would seem to be so broad as to be self-defeating. What we want is something nearer to a minimum than a maximum specification.

The meaning of a word would seem to be located somewhere in the area of verbal perception. Just how much of verbal perception is concerned with meaning appears to be somewhat vague. Many people appear to be satisfied with their command of the meaning of a word if they have a vague feeling that they could, if they tried, tell whether they would use the word in this or that situation, without ever putting the vague feeling to the test of actual trial or usage. This may be satisfactory enough for an individual who does not care to check the success of his communications, but in a social setting it inevitably leads to confusion because the full verbal perception surrounding a word is usually different for different individuals. However, what we shall understand by meaning is associated in some way with successful communication. Furthermore, communication need not necessarily be social — I can talk to myself or I can leave a note to myself on the table to call up the grocer in the morning.

What now is the criterion for judging that an attempt at communication has been successful? It is sometimes a matter of extreme difficulty to know when communication has been successful, but it is, on the other hand, usually comparatively easy to tell when it has been unsuccessful. If the taxi driver takes you to Washington Street, instead of to Jefferson Street, for which you asked, or if you see the stranger who asked you the way taking the first right instead of the first left as you told him, you know that your attempt at communication has been unsuccessful. A general method for checking the success of a communication is to observe whether the recipient of the communication acts in the way you wanted to bring about. In the simplest situations this criterion for successful communication is fairly simple and straightforward, but, as the situation gets more complex, it becomes increasingly difficult to be sure that we have communicated what we wanted, for the communication has not been successful unless *all* the consequences that we intended are achieved. In complex situations it is difficult to check them all. Often the best we can do, when none of the obvious criteria for unsuccessful communication are satisfied, is to close our eyes and hope that we have been successful.

It is often said that all definition or communication of meaning must in the last analysis be ostensive. This, it seems to me, is a gross oversimplification. There is the story of the African explorer who tried to get the native word for table by pointing to one, and who received as many different words as there were natives in his retinue, ranging from "hard" to "round" to "black" to "four-legged", etc. Any ostensive definition can be checked only by usage in many situations, differing in all except the one feature in common which one is trying to isolate.

The consequences that we wish to achieve by our communication are almost inevitably activities of one sort or another — either overt action or mental activity which may or may not result in overt activity. The nature of the connection between the spoken or written word and the activity induced is most complex. In any event, communication between people is obviously something different in kind from the transfer of a physical object from one person to another. The word with which we communicate is not like a physical object. We, in our sophistication, can see this, but there are primitive peoples to whom a word may be a self-existent thing, with an individuality of its own which is often exploited in the practice of word magic.

The activity induced by the word has no immediate or obvious connection with the physical attributes of the word. These attributes could, for example, be given in terms of the coordinates of the groove on the phonograph record which reproduces the word when suitably coupled to a loud-speaker. The factors which determine the connection between the physical attributes of the word and the induced activity involve society and past history, as appears from the consideration that the use of words has to be learned. Speaking roughly, the locus of the most important part of whatever it is that gives a word identity and meaning is in the brains of the people that use the word. Given only the physical word, that is, the sound of the spoken word or the appearance of the written word, neither the activity associated with it or its meaning may be discovered. The association between the physical word and the meaning is almost always arbitrary, and if the continuity of the thread of association in the minds of the people who use the word is broken, the meaning may not be recovered. It is only because the thread of continuity in human brains has not been completely severed that we have been able, by enormous effort, to read the writings of the Mayas or the ancient Cretans.

Whatever the meaning of a word may be, it would seem therefore to be something which does not pertain to the word as such, but to the whole complex environment in which use of the word is embedded, and in particular pertains to the user of the word. From this point of view it is not the word as it stands in isolation on the printed page which means something, but I who read the word, or you who wrote the word, who means something. Emphasis on the activity aspect of the word demands that this not be lost sight of. A simple verbal trick is helpful in this connection. Never ask "What does word X mean?" but ask instead "What do I mean when I say word X?" or "What do you mean when you say word X?" To agree to talk about meaning only in this sort of setting constitutes a considerable curtailment of conventional linguistic usage, which uses such expressions, for example, as "The word X *has* such and such a meaning." An instructive exhibition of the many linguistic contexts in which the words "mean" and "meaning" occur is afforded by a paper by Jason Xenakis in *Methodos 6* (1954), 299–329.[2] But, although we may renounce the possibility of saying many of the things which Xenakis says, I do not believe that we are making any essential surrender if we agree to talk about meaning in this book in such a way that it is only you and I that mean something when we say something, the physical utterance having no meaning as such. I do not have to convince you that it is good tactics to accept this limitation of the usage of "meaning". All that is required is that you admit that it is a legitimate question to ask "What do I mean when I say thus and so?" and that you will be willing to make a serious attempt to answer it. This I think is not asking or expecting too much. In spite of our agreement we may often find it convenient, because it is shorter, to use "meaning" in the common way as something that words *have*. But when I ask whether I understand the meaning of a word I shall understand that this is a paraphrase for "What do I (or you) mean when I (or you) use the word?"

I suppose that my command of the meaning of a word could be called complete if I could exhaustively enumerate the conditions which would lead me to use the word myself and could infer from the usage of the word by you in any particular situation what were the conditions which had dictated use of the word by you. This is what I shall understand by meaning in the most general sense. That is, I shall say that I know the meaning of a word if I can state the conditions which dictate use of the word by you or by me. It would seem that this covers most of what we are usually interested in. It is, of course, only very seldom that we attempt as articulate an analysis of this of our meanings. We are usually satisfied with a vague feeling that we could state the conditions if we wanted to, without ever taking the trouble actually to do it.

I suspect that we are more likely to demand that our neighbor make an analysis for meaning of the words that he uses than to make it for ourselves. When we do get around to attempting such an analysis, I think we discover that we have certain ideals for our meanings; we are not satisfied with a mere factual description of the conditions under which we do actually use our words, but we want our usage to satisfy certain restrictions. The necessity for some sort of restriction is obvious, because we are trying to accomplish some purpose by our verbalizing, usually communication. Some of the restrictions are obvious enough. We would like our meanings to have a degree of stability in time, so that the meaning of a word tomorrow is the same as today. We are not too much disturbed by a slow change of the meaning over centuries — the meaning of many words in Elizabethan English is recognizably different from the meaning today. We would probably prefer that the meanings be unique, although we do put up with many words in English which have multiple meanings. As a special case of uniqueness we would probably prefer that the meaning not depend on the person using the word, although every parent has been able to understand the private meanings of his children while they are learning to talk, and children can talk to each other in their own private code.

There is a special class of words which is of great interest in this connection, of which perhaps the most important example is "I". The particular person indicated by "I" is different for every user. Shall we therefore say that the meaning of "I" is different for every user? Some people would probably say just this; whether we do or not is to a certain extent a matter of choice and a matter of words. I personally would prefer to say that the "referent" that is, the specific object indicated, is different for different users of "I", but that the meaning is the same, because the conditions which determine its use are the same. But there is here a certain vagueness. What shall we understand by "conditions"? Obviously it is not my intention to call the conditions the same only if the actual concrete referent is the same for different users, for this state of affairs never occurs. The sameness of conditions which I fasten on is the *relation* of the user to the referent. "I" refers to the user himself, to whom the user stands in the relation of identity. The matter is not obvious or uniquely necessary, and usage has to be learned by observation of social practise. This is something that we all manage to learn somehow in childhood; from this distance we may be inclined to wonder how we managed to be bright enough to learn it. I find it particularly hard to see how we managed to learn it if those psychologists are right who maintain that the concept of "I" is the last to form, and comes only after much experience in society of other persons. It must be very puzzling for the child to hear other people about him continually saying "I", each person referring to something different.

The meaning of "I" is "relational", and "I" is a relational word. It will be my thesis in later chapters that there are many other similar relational words — many more than are usually recognized — and that recognition of the relational character of many of these words may profoundly alter our conception of such things as the relation of individual and society.

There is an elaborate formal discipline dealing with distinctions such as between "referent" and "meaning" exemplified by the *Theory of Signs* of Charles W. Morris,[3] in which occur such words as "semiosis", "semiotic", "semantics", and "pragmatics". We do not need these for our simple purposes, for we can conduct our analysis without such formal machinery.

Returning to the general examination of meanings, among the many ideals we have for our meanings surely one of the most important is that our meanings be as sharp as possible; absolute sharpness is, of course, unattainable. One of the most potent sources of irritation in daily life is slipshod use of ambiguous meanings. In most cases no elaborate machinery is required for the elimination of the irritating ambiguity; usually it would be sufficient merely that the speaker imagine himself in the place of the hearer and ask himself whether the hearer could reconstruct the situation given only the uttered words. In practice, of course, the hearer has other things to guide him than just the spoken words, so that it does not usually put too onerous a burden on the speaker to achieve a sufficiently unambiguous communication. If only some speakers did not demand it as a right that the hearer figure out for himself what the speaker must have had in mind.

For most purposes we can get along sufficiently well with only casual attention to sharpness, but when real differences of opinion arise, the first thing that should be done is to sharpen the meanings. Every debater knows that a preliminary to any fruitful debate is to define the terms. Ordinarily the meanings are taken so much as a matter of course that often the mere challenge to make more articulate what one means will result in considerable clarification. It is not hard to form the habit of asking oneself as a preliminary to any particular piece of analysis "What do I mean by this or that term?" with consequent disclosure of many factors usually overlooked. For scientific purposes the necessity for a high degree of sharpness is so great as to demand special consideration and the use of special techniques. In those cases where scientific statements can be put in mathematical form the presumption is good that sharpness has been attained merely because mathematics is itself precise. But this is by no means the whole story, because the quantities which enter the mathematical equations themselves have to be obtained by a procedure of some sort, and this procedure may or may not be precise. Consider, for example, Fechner's law in psychology that the intensity of a sensation is proportional to the logarithm of the intensity of the stimulus.

The ostensible mathematical precision of this law is illusory until procedures are worked out for measuring with precision the intensity of a stimulus or the intensity of a sensation.

One method of attaining improved sharpness of meaning which is particularly useful for scientific terms is to subject them to an "operational" analysis. This is a subject which I have discussed in much detail in other places and about which there has been much misunderstanding. There is no point in repeating the details of this discussion here. For the present it will be sufficient to remark that an operation is an activity. Later I shall return to the matter, for there are several questions connected with operational analysis which I have long been waiting a chance to discuss. These include considerations with regard to the nature of the operations themselves, and applications of operational analysis to situations for which I have, up to the present, given no analysis.

For the present we shall assume that enough has now been said about words and their meanings to provide a basis for the attack on the problem of finding the meaning of any concrete word; this in general demands a formulation of the conditions of its use.

There is more to the question of meaning than the meaning of individual words — words are used together in combination, and it is the meaning of the whole combination which usually is of primary interest. New questions arise when we deal with combinations of words. The meaning of a combination is not simply the sum of the meanings separately; that is, the conditions which dictate the use of the words in combination is not the mere sum or the juxtaposition of the conditions which dictated the use of the words separately. There is no simple addition law for the meanings of words combined into sentences, any more than there is an addition law for the meaning of phonemes combined into words. Here we have a legitimate example of "emergence" as opposed to the many illegitimate claims for emergence in biological or social situations.

The combination of words often involves the imposition of additional restrictions by the mere form of the combination. The combination may, for example, take the form of a statement, in which case it is implied that a truth value attaches to the statement. Possibly there is the further implication that there is some method of verifying the truth of the statement. Or the combination may take the form of a question. In this case it is implied that it does not involve logical contradiction to assume that there is a procedure for finding the answer to the question and for checking the correctness of the answer. Furthermore, I think we usually feel that we have a right to demand that one may not ask a question unless he is prepared to say what kind of an answer would be satisfactory. This requirement throws out of court a great many words combined into the grammatical form of a question. For example, many questions beginning with "why" are of this sort. Such, in the context of daily life, are frequently not legitimate questions at all, but are merely invitations to speculation. I think many people ask questions with only the most nebulous sort of an idea of what a satisfactory answer might be like, hoping that when the answer is supplied to them *ex machina* they will at the same time see a little more clearly what it was that they had vaguely in the back of their heads when they asked the question. As a tool of individual enlightenment this procedure may have its justification, but it is a one-sided sort of transaction that cannot commend itself equally to both parties. The asking and the answering should be a cooperative enterprise. It must nevertheless be recognized that it may be a fruitful tool of exploration into new territory to ask oneself questions which seem sensible from their form, judging by past experience, but for which one at the moment has no answer and no idea what sort of an answer might be satisfactory. An example might be "Why does negative electricity attract positive?" The value of asking questions like this is that it affords a stimulus to try to imagine what sort of an answer might conceivably be satisfactory, and under this stimulus fresh aspects of the situation may come to light. One may set oneself to acquiring the knack of formulating scientific (or other) questions useful from this point of view. It is to be considered whether a background of scientific (or other) experience is necessary, or to what extent verbal experience alone will lead to fruitful results. One could perhaps make an argument for the expectation that verbal experience in the individual would be fruitful, since the verbal experience of the individual has as a background verbal experience of the race, and this has been closely coupled by evolutionary adaptation to the external environment. In any event, the actual asking of the question by the individual is a verbal operation, and an important kind of operation, at that. There is, however, the danger that one may remain on the verbal level and this danger has to be continually guarded against. For instance, is the question "Why am I I and not you?" anything more than a combination of words? If anyone has the urge to find something back of his impulse to ask this question it becomes a problem to find the significance of the urge. I suspect that a good deal of philosophy has had its origin in the endeavor to find verbally satisfactory answers to questions that sounded as though they ought to have answers.

Another sort of combination of words in which the meaning of the whole depends on the form of the combination as well as on the words individually is a command. "Eat your spinach" means more than could be inferred from the meanings of the three words separately.

Grammar is the name of the discipline that deals with aspects of the ways in which words may be combined if the combination is to have meaning as a whole, but grammar is not coextensive with the whole question of the meaning of combinations of words. There are grammatical combinations of words that have no meaning — "Virtue is blue" — and there are ungrammatical combinations that are meaningful — "Women is nuts". We do not need to attempt a necessary and sufficient characterization of what grammar is — roughly it would seem to be concerned with the rules governing the permissible association of certain types of words with other types. Grammatical speech can largely be learned by observation of the grammatical speech of others without the articulate formulation of the rules. It is an interesting exercise for the imagination to try to reconstruct the historical steps by which grammar developed. Which came first — individual words or combinations of words? It would seem probable that the usage of words and of combinations of words developed hand in hand, and that only after the language was an accomplished fact did some contemplative grammarian see what had happened. There are languages, such as some of the North American Indian languages, in which the analysis into individual words is much less clean cut than in the Indo-European languages, and what corresponds to a sentence is more like a single long compound word put together by the successive addition of separable prefixes and suffixes.

The question of why it is that utterances are analyzable into words is similar to the question of why words are analyzable into phonemes, a fact which made possible the invention of the alphabet. Perhaps both these questions are only invitations to speculation, but, at any rate in the case of the second question, a glimpse of what might constitute a satisfactory answer is afforded by a consideration of the physiological constitution of the biological machinery that utters the words.

The subconscious feeling of the limitations imposed by grammar on combinations of words is contained in what I have called the fringe of verbal perception that surrounds a word — it is formed only after long experience and is by no means the same in different people.

Perhaps the most sweeping of all the rules of language is that words of one language may not be combined with words of another language. This, of course, at once brings up the question of what is a "language." The answer is not sharp — there will not always be agreement about whether some local pattern of speech should be called a dialect or a language. Neither is the rule sharp that words of one language may not be combined with those of another — the rule is often consciously violated by those who would achieve a meretricious elegance in their style. But the rule may be violated for better reasons. Only in the simplest cases are words in one language completely equivalent to those in another. Usually there are recognizable differences in the perceptual fringe that surrounds a word in different languages, so that seldom is an exact translation possible from one language to another. It may be that English, for example, possesses no word of the precise shade of meaning that a particular situation demands, but that some foreign language does. In this case a meticulous writer will not hesitate to insert the foreign word in the English sentence.

It is interesting to ask about the order of events in a situation like this. Would the shade of meaning of the English word be felt unsatisfactory if one did not already have at one's command the foreign word? Or does one have some vague criterion, not formulated in language, which the word must satisfy, and then does one seek for it in any language at one's command? The deeper one probes into the mechanism by which one fits a word to a situation the more convinced one will become of the importance of unformulated and even unconscious mental processes.

Vaguenesses with respect to what a language is do not make much trouble in practice, but it is usually clear enough what we have in mind when we talk about a language in the context of our every day life. But when we want to achieve greater sharpness we have to refine the everyday notion of a language as being predominantly a speech pattern practised by people associated with a restricted geographical area. It turns out that it is profitable to make distinctions depending on the subject matter, and we talk of the "language of physics" or the "language of biology". The decision of subject matter is fairly straight forward in the case of usage like this. The matter becomes more sophisticated, however, when we try to characterize the subject matter in logical terms. We may, for example, want to understand by a language all those words which can occur in a single logically consistent system. By a logical system we may understand all those statements that can be deduced by the rules of logic from a set of fundamental postulates in conjunction with a set of terms that are accepted as unanalyzed. In the "language" of this logical system it would not have meaning to ask what is the meaning of one of the undefined terms. But with a different set of postulates and a different set of undefined terms the term in question might be analyzed and so a meaning given to it. The language of the second logical system thus enables us to ask questions about the first which the first could not ask about itself. The second language is a "metalanguage" with respect to the first. The metalanguage may in turn have a language "meta-" with respect to it, and in fact it would be possible to construct an unlimited hierarchy of successive metalanguages. Precise analysis of the construction of the first logical language and the succeeding metalanguages has been carried to a high degree of refinement by professional logicians and is most important for logical precision. An example of the sort of situation to which analysis in terms of metalanguages leads is afforded by Tarski's celebrated analysis of truth.[4] According to this analysis the *statement* "snow is white" is verified if snow is white. The second occurrence of "white" is in the metalanguage with respect to its first occurrence. But when we have done our best and have constructed the last metalanguage necessary for our purpose we find that we are still using English words (or the words of whatever happens to be our native tongue), so that the system of metalanguages is embedded in the single language of daily life. We are still left with the problem of understanding our language of daily life and discovering what the meanings are that can be expressed in that language and what degree of sharpness we can hope to attain. For our purposes in the following we shall not bother much with metalanguages but shall address ourselves directly to what seem to me more immediate problems.

The fact that we are going to try to get along without the formal machinery of metalanguages does not mean that we can close our eyes to the basic characteristics of situations that invite the analysis into hierarchies of language. It is only that we shall try to be less formal. Furthermore, an analysis into metalanguages would have for us the disadvantage of implying the possibility of unattainable precision. In any event, we shall often find ourselves operating on one or another "level", and the different levels correspond roughly to the different metalanguages. But the levels are not sharp, and we shall find it almost impossible to avoid shifting back and forth from one level to another, even in the same sentence. This suggests that "level" may not be a very good figure for describing what actually happens, but it does have the advantage of suggestiveness.

The structure of language is not always such that it facilitates recognition of different levels, and considerable logical practise may be necessary to specify them. Facility in handling the affairs of daily life would often be hampered by stopping to recognize the logical niceties, so that for some purposes a language may be better fitted to survive if it does not offer a machinery by which these nice distinctions may be made. A simple example will illustrate. Ancient Babylonian had different words for a letter and for the character that represents the letter. Modern English ignores the difference; in fact it is hard to say in English that the letter, as such, is not the same as the character which represents it. Yet there are situations where the Babylonian distinction naturally presents itself to the user of English. For instance, we might want to say to a stone-cutter, "The 'A' which you just carved in that inscription is too small". It is easy to imagine that the desirability of making the distinction arose in Babylon precisely because of the enormous labor required to make cuneiform records on clay tablets. At any rate, here is an example of the use of a word on two levels in English, and two distinct words in another language corresponding to the two levels of English.

Often a writer or speaker may be conscious of operating on a level different from the usual one, and he may find it desirable to call explicit attention to it by using some special device. Thus, in the case of the letter A above, he might say "the letter, as a letter", or, if he is writing, he may enclose the letter in quotation marks, as we did above. This situation often occurs with respect to individual words; we may be concerned with them in their capacity as words and this may be indicated by the use of quotation marks, a device which I shall often use. A word handled in this way functions as a noun, irrespective of what part of speech it may be in ordinary usage.

The situation presented by two levels in the usage of "letter" is suggestive of a very broad class of situations. We often have occasion to talk about talking, and there are many words in English for use on just such occasions. The situations thus presented are of indefinite complexity. For not only can we talk about talking by the use of words devised for the express purpose, but then we can talk about our use of these new words, or, otherwise expressed, talk about talking about talking. The regress has no end. The regress occurs whether we look at the situation in static existential terms, as we imagine the Babylonian, did, or whether we look at it in terms of activity, as we may when we consider that talking itself is an activity which continually creates itself as we talk, so that the very act of talking itself creates new topics for conversation which did not exist before we started.

It is surprising to discover, on making the detailed analysis, how many of the puzzling questions occur in a context of talking about talking. The simple terms of logic are of this category, such as "if" and "or". Or some of the simplest terms of daily life, such as the "past" or the "future," are of this class. For what is the past more than a word which we use in talking about events that have already happened, or the future more than a word that we use in discussing plans? Even if one maintains that there *is* much more to past or future than this, nevertheless for most purposes we do not need this something more, for we can get along perfectly well without agreeing on a formulation of what more it is.

About all that one can do about talking is to talk about it. Here again we have a system dealing with itself. How shall we understand our tools if the only tools of understanding are the tools themselves? It seems doubtful to me whether such situations can ever be dealt with in a completely satisfactory way or whether we can ever lay the ghost of the infinite regress. One questions the fundamental validity of the whole enterprise of language. At best it would seem that there must be limitations of some sort here, and one of our problems is to find what they are.

Many of the puzzling issues of daily life, which we unconsciously realize we have not learned to cope with, are on the verbal level. For example, the age-old problem of the freedom of the will is on the verbal level. We *say* that we are free, but there is no objective proof that we really are. The problem of the freedom of the will is to reconcile this that we say with other things that we say, such as that everything is subject to law.

On the legal plane such concepts as human rights and justice are mostly things that we say about our relations to each other. The problem of the critically minded lawyer is to a large extent to discover how he can weld the things that we want to say about these relations into a consistent verbal edifice whose parts are logically tied to each other.

Two of the most important human enterprises are almost entirely on the verbal level. The first is philosophy. Certainly the part of philosophy which is open to observation is verbal — what is written in books or what is said by one philosopher to another. The philosopher uses no material instruments — he does not go into the laboratory or even collect statistics. His primary concern is to get our experience into as verbally satisfactory a form as possible. Most philosophers do not like to have the predominantly verbal nature of their enterprise insisted upon. They apparently feel, in my opinion unnecessarily, that this implies a pejorative attitude toward the importance of what they do. The favorite tool of the philosopher is the verbal experiment. He tries this or that form of expression and he asks, "Would you regard this way of talking about it as satisfactory?" Even if we try to go beyond the verbal level and ask what it is that the philosopher is trying to get into words, we see that the philosopher is primarily interested in a particular sort of subject matter. He is interested in an aspect of human activity, as distinguished from the unlimited activity of the whole external world that characterizes the interest of the physicist or the chemist or the biologist. This aspect of human behavior primarily is thinking, and we may, if we think it is more consistent with the dignity of the philosopher than insisting on the verbal aspect of what he does, say that the philosopher is concerned with thinking about thinking.

But even so, he is interested only in certain aspects of thinking, the aspects which find their most immediate expression in verbal behavior and not in the explanatory and descriptive aspects which concern the psychologist. Of course the dividing line is not sharp, as shown by the fact that formerly psychology was treated as a subdivision of philosophy. Roughly, the primary concern of the philosopher seems to be how he shall talk about what he thinks and what he says. In doing this it seems to me that he is sometimes tempted to treat verbal activity as a self-contained activity, worth pursuing for its own sake. It seems to me that he is inclined to hope that there must be some meaning in any grammatical combination of words, particularly when they deal with abstractions, and that he regards it as one of his problems to discover what this meaning may be.

The second great human enterprise, almost exclusively verbal, is logic. Simple observation shows that this, as well as philosophy, is conducted almost exclusively on the verbal level. But logic is subject to a control that philosophy is not, the control of "truth", for logic offers a method of passing from initial statements to other statements of such a nature that if the initial statements are true the statements to which one passes are also true. This puts the enterprise of logic in a special category — we reserve further discussion of logic, particularly the truth aspect of it, to a later chapter.

It would appear that in general a large part of the serious enterprise of the race is precisely to discover how the various things that we want to say can be welded into a verbally consistent whole. Individuals differ widely in their attitude toward this human enterprise. Many act as though they take it with a deathly seriousness and regard the successful solution of the problem as of transcendent importance. I suspect that most religious fanatics and a good many lawyers are this type of person. To others it does not seem so important that everything should be got into a verbally consistent whole, provided only that they can deal with each new situation as it arises. This attitude is fortified by a certain cynicism with regard to the possibility of carrying out so ambitious a program of getting *everything* into a verbally consistent whole, a cynicism which has a certain justification when the haphazard origin of the whole human linguistic apparatus is considered.

Eventually, of course, we have to stop talking about talking — the regress cannot actually be carried to infinity. Where we stop is almost as important as what we say before we stop. For example, the "ultimate particle" of physics probably only marks the place where the structure of experimental knowledge forces us to stop talking. Other fields of verbal activity are not so fortunate in having an externally imposed cut-off point and, in consequence, may never make their emergence from the verbal level. In general, our verbal machinery has no mechanism for automatically shutting itself off beyond its range of applicability, a feature which, as I have emphasized in some of my earlier writings, also characterizes mathematics.

In spite of all the limitations which we can thus see in the verbal process I shall not hesitate, when it suits my purpose, to exploit the verbal nature of many of our activities. This is to a certain extent making a virtue of necessity, for it is an inexorable fact that the written page which I am now writing and which you are now reading is composed of words. I as I write and you as you read cannot get away from words, any more than I can get away from myself. This is a simple matter of observation. Any effects which I can here produce on you must be through the medium of words. It is a tautology to say that our verbal communication, which includes nearly all significant human communication, cannot get away from words. It may strike the reader as surprising that I would be willing to adopt so tolerant an attitude toward the purely verbal by admitting this necessity of operating on the verbal level, if he remembers that I have often insisted on the importance of an eventual emergence of our operations onto the nonverbal level. This necessity is still as imperative as ever, particularly for the physicist when he attempts to form concepts which will be useful to him. However, on the printed page I am compelled to express this nonverbal emergence in verbal terms. This is accomplished by the use of different types of words — the referents for some kinds of words are non-verbal activities, it may be operations in the laboratory with instruments, whereas the referents for other words are recognizably still verbal activities. The words in which the physicist defines the meaning of such concepts as "length" must be of the type that have nonverbal referents — no more can be demanded. And even here we have to get back onto the verbal level if we wish to communicate the results of our nonverbal operations. Verbal operation is thus a pretty pervasive thing, and it is important to understand what is involved as well as we can.

The advantages, on occasion, of concentrating attention on the verbal nature of communication and thought are that in many contexts we do not need anything more for our purposes and can save ourselves many of the embarrassments that arise when we imply that there is something more. In this way we can automatically keep out many of the questions that I call metaphysical. For example, in discussing such things as length or velocity or momentum, usually and perhaps always, we need only to be able to specify the conditions under which we would use the *word* length or velocity or momentum. We do not need to ask "What *is* length or velocity or momentum?" a form of question which often has unfortunate metaphysical implications. However, a nonmetaphysical meaning *can* be assigned, when the context makes it desirable, to the question "What is length", for we can say "Length is a number obtained by a special instrumental procedure" and we can specify the procedure if required. The two approaches are not inconsistent, however, for we can paraphrase the instrumental operational approach by saying "I use the word length to indicate that I have obtained a number by such and such an instrumental procedure". We are here obviously operating on different levels and it does not seem possible to keep them sharply distinct. The physicist will not be comfused by all this, but will still realize that the number and the procedure are the important things for him.

Going still further, abstractions in general can be dealt with on the verbal level. Thus we can always say, when pressed to say what truth or time or existence or any other abstraction *is,* that these are words which we use under such and such conditions. Or, instead of asking "What *are* external objects?" we find that it is quite sufficient to ask "What do I mean when I say that there are external objects?" It is surprising, when one tries it, to find how many situations can be adequately dealt with in this way, and how seldom we need anything more. This is obviously true in most situations involving communication, for most communication is verbal. Whenever it turns out that this is all we need, it would appear that there "is" nothing more.

I think a great many people feel that a verbal approach to abstractions is so superficial that they will be unwilling to make it. For instance, in trying to answer the question "What *is* virtue?" they will be unwilling to answer by saying "I use the word 'virtue' in such and such circumstances" because of their feeling that so much essential is disregarded in such a statement. I think most of the prejudice to such an approach can be overcome if such people could learn to say "Whatever virtue may 'really be', it *at least* has its verbal aspect" and learn to realize that they have not mastered their understanding of virtue until they can account for all its aspects, including the verbal. When they have learned to make this approach I think they will be surprised to find how often it meets all their needs. And I believe that everyone is capable of learning how to make this verbal approach.

There are certain types of situation which language, as conventionally used, cannot deal with without an embarrassment that comes pretty close to being the embarrassment of self-contradiction. Some of these are self-reflective situations in which we try to say that there are certain situations that language is incapable of dealing with. The embarrassment comes when we attempt to say what the situation is, which we usually feel an irresistible impulse to do. But, manifestly, it is impossible to express in language a situation which language is incapable of expressing. As an illustration we may take the example probably originally due to Kant, although it seems to have been independently discovered a number of times since, that it is impossible to distinguish in words alone between a right- and a left-handed screw. If one tries, he will find that it is impossible to make the distinction without pointing to some concrete embodiment of right- or left-handedness. This example is often hailed as one of unusual profundity, but I believe the profundity is fictitious. For language is never capable of specifying in terms only of itself the concrete referent for any word whatever, but always we have to point eventually, and the pointing itself becomes significant only in the context of indefinite repetition in a fixed cultural background.

Some people like to say that the success of language in dealing with the world around us is due to the similarity of structure of language and the world. If the structures were not similar, they say, language would not be capable of dealing with the world. The late Count Korzybski and his disciples were particularly prone to say this. To me, if there was ever a glittering generality that is repudiated by simple observation, it is this one.

There is another type of situation in which conventional language is embarrassed. These are the situations discussed, for example, by Quine in his *From a Logical Point of View*[5] under the heading of "nonbeing". We cannot say that such a thing as a square circle, for example, does not "exist" without implying by the mere fact that we are using the words and talking about "it" that a square circle has a certain kind of existence. What kind of existence this may be has provided philosophy with a topic of discussion for thousands of years. The quandary presented by this situation we can see is one which naturally arises in the Indo-European languages — it would be interesting to know whether it is felt as a quandary in other types of language. It seems to me that the situation can be adequately dealt with by reducing it to the purely formal verbal level. If we say "The combination of words 'square circle' has no referent either in the objective external world or in the conceptual world of logically consistent objects", it seems to me that we have said all that we need to say. I do not see why philosophers are not willing to say this and dismiss the topic from serious consideration.

A somewhat similar paradoxical and embarrassing situation arises whenever we make a statement of the form "The statement A has no meaning". For if the statement A did not have a meaning of sorts, we would not be able to assent to the statement that it has no meaning. We may recognize this "meaning of sorts" as a second kind of meaning, which may be defined in terms of the response elicited when the statement is made. If the response elicited is always the same or if the different responses have recognizable elements in common, then it may be socially useful, and it may be in accord with the usual implications of language, as used, to admit a second sort of meaning. The primary meaning of meaning would then be sought in the purposes and operations leading to the usage, and the second meaning of meaning in the response actually elicited in the given cultural context by the particular verbal combination. We might be able to get along with this sort of situation, and I think popular usage as a matter of fact does, but we would have to admit such questions as: "What is the meaning of the meaningless statement A?" Although perhaps possible, it seems to me that it is too confusing to admit this second sort of meaning, and I shall endeavor to find other ways of talking. I would be willing, for example, to speak of the implications of the meaningless statement A, reserving "meaningless" for a somewhat restricted technical use which does not correspond to its full usage in everyday life. In later chapters we will encounter examples in which I think we are, as a matter of fact, concerned with this second usage for "meaning". Some of these are of the greatest social significance.

The situations with which language deals are in a continual state of flux, yet language forces us to deal with them with a vocabulary of a finite number of discrete words with approximately fixed meanings. One may anticipate infelicities and ineptnesses; the wonder is that we are able to get along as well as we do. Our use of static words is analogous to our analysis of the world around us into things — individual, discrete, constant, and static — whereas it has been obvious from at least the time of the Greeks that "all things flow". It must be that it is a necessary characteristic of human thinking machinery to operate with fixed elements which recur. It is meaningless to ask how the world would appear if we did not see it in terms of things that recur, or what our thought would be like if it were not tied to language.

The structure and the use of language are such that we seem forever condemned to get along with only a partial description of what introspection reveals is happening. Our sentences do not leap instantaneously and full grown into being, in spite of the fact that we usually treat them as static complete structures, but they are uttered in time, and we can see that things are happening during the uttering. Meanings grow in time, and this growth implies transient effects which we seem to be incapable of getting into adequate verbal expression. Popular usage is not completely unaware of this situation but recognizes that the order in time of the component words in a sentence is not a matter of indifference. Nearly everyone can see that it is better to say "Please pass the butter" than to say "Pass the butter, please". Social success may depend on the recognition of niceties of this sort. It is a problem for the future to devise an introspectional microscope to reveal the "fine structure" of the transient detail.

The language of much of daily life — the language of the family and particularly the language of women — comes much closer to being an instrument which recognizes the fluent nonrecurring nature of things than the somewhat idealized academic thing which has been the subject of our discussion. In this language of daily life words do not have a frozen meaning, but much greater flexibility is attained. Speech in daily life is often obviously only part of a process, and it may have significance only in the immediate context. Language is thus used to suggest what is going on at that moment in the mind of the utterer, and the utterer, particularly if a woman, expects that the listener will accept the speech in the spirit intended, and try to deduce what was going on in the utterer's mind. The same word, used a second time in a later sentence, naturally does not have the same context as on the first use, so that there is no assurance that the meaning is the same on the second use as on the first. In fact, under conditions such as these, there is no reason why even the principle of contradiction need govern the successive uses of a word or successive enunciations of the same statement. Examples of the failure of the principle of contradiction have probably been observed by everyone in family life. I recently encountered a particularly glaring example in which my wife was not even embarrassed when it was called to her attention — on the contrary. Such usage of language is more of an art than the ordinary man can achieve, and when I was asking above for a method of using language better adapted to dealing with the fluent nature of experience I had hoped for a somewhat different sort of solution.

I I I

MORE PRELIMINARY METHODOLOGY

OPERATIONS IN GENERAL

If our analysis is to be concerned with happenings or doings or activities or operations we must consider what is needed in order to specify our happenings, doings, or what-not. In general, since a happening or doing is more complicated than a static object, it will take more to specify it than to specify an object. For example, activities take place in time and the component parts of the activity must be performed in a specified order. Or, again, doings require a performer, and for a complete specification the performer must be specified. We must be prepared to find that it may make a difference whether the performer is myself or my neighbor, a consideration which is usually neglected, but which I believe is vital in many social situations.

I shall not attempt a precise specification of the differences in shades of meaning between "happenings", "activities", "doings", and "operations". Some of these words are sometimes used interchangeably, but at other times with differences in shades of meaning which it would probably be impossible to make sharp and which often can be sufficiently well inferred from the context. In general, "happenings" has the broadest connotation and "operation" the most restrictive. My "operation" perhaps comes closest to a "doing", understood in the sense of implying a doer, and this in turn usually implies a conscious purpose. In the following we shall be concerned with specific questions in specific contexts, and it will usually make little difference whether we talk about activities or doings or operations — happenings being more general can usually not be used interchangeably with the others.

In a recent book, *Operationism*,[1] Professor Benjamin has subjected the operational point of view to an elaborate examination. He introduces a sort of "generalized operation," which he describes as one or another of the fundamental kinds of process which are involved in "cognition". His analysis suggests that there are five of these. Just what the elementary processes or operations (in this sense) are will depend on one's analysis of cognition, which I suppose is what Professor Benjamin means by "theory of cognition", which he says is necessary in order to give a clean-cut concept of operations. In my own usage I have not felt the need for a prior "theory of cognition", but the operation, in my usage, may occur in describing what I see is happening during cognitive activity. My "operation" is thus recognizably not the same as Professor Benjamin's "operation". In the following I shall be concerned to some extent with some of the other points brought up by Professor Benjamin in his book, but, since these other points occur in other contexts also. I shall not always try to make the reference to Professor Benjamin's book explicit.

A complete specification of an activity would determine it uniquely, for any actual activity is individual, unique, and does not recur. In particular, a complete specification must specify the time and the place. Such meticulousness in specification, however, goes beyond ordinary practice and implication, because we do talk about performing the same operation twice, and in fact the value of an analysis into activities or operations lies precisely in the fact that we do use the "same" operation on demand. For example, the length of an object is defined as the number which we obtain by a certain operation, the operation being performable on demand and in conjunction with any object permitting the operation. Speaking meticulously, therefore, what we are usually concerned with in practise is *classes* of operations rather than individual operations. The length of an object is a number obtained by an operation belonging to a certain class of operations. Usually, however, we need not be as careful as this and we run little danger of being misunderstood if we say that the lengths of different objects are determined by the "same" operation.

In practice the concrete specification of the operation often discloses whether we are concerned with what is strictly a class of operations or not. In particular, if the specifications carry no reference to time or place or person, then we may be sure that strictly we are dealing with a class of operations. The implication in a specification given in such terms is that it is immaterial at what time or place or by whom the operation is performed, all such operations being lumped together for practical purposes as the same operation. Most of the concepts of physics are defined in terms of such operations.

In general the fact that we do not attempt to make our specification exhaustive, but lump together as a single operation all those which meet the requirements of the specification, implies a background of purpose in our prospective use of the operation, with the further implication that the details omitted from the specification are immaterial. Thus we may think of length in a context of Euclidean geometery, in which perhaps our interest is to fit objects together in a material structure, as in a house, and the fact that we do not specify time or place or person in specifying the operation for measuring length implies that all lengths of the same objects obtained at any time or place or by any person all fit equally well into the same structure.

Our willingness to use any operation of a class can be justified only on the basis of experience. We do not mention time or place or person because experience has shown that these make no difference, that is, no difference in the context of our present purposes. But in the beginning we must start with the most cautious and noncommittal viewpoint and recognize that time, place, and person, until proved to the contrary, *may* make a difference.

In other words, in our formal analysis we start with the point of view that all we can do is to describe, and that the world around us is an aggregate of individual events which never recur. Even at this level we soon discover that good description is difficult. Later, with our description before us, we pick out features that recur and allow ourselves to make generalizations or to say that such and such a factor makes no difference. This prescription for formal procedure contains no implication that historically, in childhood, my developing capacity to deal with the world proceeded in such wise.

Logically there is an interesting point here. Let me imagine myself starting with virgin innocence of any informing experience and describing what happens to me as a succession of unique happenings. In what terms can I give my description? Surely language is not possible without a background of informing similar experiences, nor would an artificial symbolism of any other sort be possible. The concept of unique individual happenings can only occur in the logically inconsistent context of nonindividual repeatable happenings. It looks like a vicious circle. However, I reflect that logic is my construction, and these considerations suggest that logic may not be as widely applicable as I would like. In any event it would seem that what we are here concerned with is better described as spiraling approximation rather than a vicious circle. This is probably characteristic of every method of successfully dealing with the world. Or, if we prefer, we can talk about operation at different levels.

Actually, it has never been proved that there are *any* operations completely indifferent to time and place — it is only that we know that any effect of these factors is so small that we can usually ignore it. It is to be remembered that the effects of high velocities on various phenomena which underlie Einstein's special theory of relativity were for a long time too small to detect by contemporary methods of measurement. *Verb. sap.*

How, now, shall we specify our operations in detail? A full answer to this question would take us much further into the general subject of operations than I intend to go, and furthermore would duplicate many considerations which I have already given in other places. We confine our attention here to only a few aspects of this general question.

In the first place, we may confine our attention to specifications given in verbal terms. This rules out, for example, specifications given ostensively, as, "do as I do". It is perhaps arguable that all specifications were originally ostensive, as also all language. But we shall suppose ourselves far enough away from the primitive situation so that there has been time for the development of a vocabulary, and that we have learned how to translate the ostensive specification, if such there was, into words. Similarly, if the original specification should have been given in any other manner, we assume our ability to translate it into words. There must be very few specifications not so translatable. Perhaps an orphan bird building its first nest by instinct is following some kind of untranslatable specification. But we in this book or in any other kind of written exposition are certainly confined to verbally translatable specifications.

The verbal specification must preferably have permanence — we would not like to trust to memory and mouth-to-ear transmission because of the danger of cumulative changes. Verbal permanence is to a high degree mechanically attainable — we can get the specification from a phonograph record which can be played on demand, or we can put it into writing on paper and read the paper on demand. It would appear that we meet all present essential needs if we specify an operation as that which is described on some indicated phonograph record or which is written on a definite piece of paper. Such a definition would be analogous, for example, to the definition of the meter as the distance between two scratches on a particular bar of platinum, a definition which has been found workable, although it suffers from inconveniences which have stimulated search for a substitute and has now been superceded.

Let us agree, therefore, that in the following we shall think of our operations as at least formulatable, if we wanted to, in this way on a permanent record of some sort, and that we name the operation by referring to the record. All the operations performed to satisfy the specification on the permanent record shall be by definition the "same" operation, disregarding the fact that from another point of view it is merely one of a class of operations. There is, however, one important exception, to be examined in detail later, when the specification of the operation mentions a person who might himself be the operator.

We now have to ask whether there are any inherent limitations in operations so specified, and what are the implications in the assumption that an operation can be specified in this way at all? Among any such limitations must be those implicit in any use of language, such, for example, as are implied in the analysis of the first chapter. No language, in its capacity as an instrument of communication, is autonomous and self-contained. In fact, the mechanically given language is only a small part of the story, the major part of which is concealed in the terribly complicated structure of the brains of the users of the language, which again depends on past history. Part of the "know-how" concealed in brains is general, the possession of all those who know the particular language of the specifications. Part of the know-how, however, may be special and may involve technical competence which demands special abilities and special preparation. No science, or other specialized discipline, for that matter, can be completely public. In practice and today, the limitations imposed by this feature of the verbal specification of operations are not onerous and, in fact, are hardly perceptible.

There is concealed here, however, a question of principle. We have already commented on the fact that there are many examples in English of the slow secular change of the meaning of a word. What happens when such a word gets into one of our specifications? And can we have any guarantee in advance that any specific word of our specifications will not be subject to this secular change of meaning? If so, what is the earmark of a word susceptible to this sort of change? Perhaps the question will some day be answered, but I do not believe there is any present answer, nor have I even seen the question raised. Until we can give some sort of answer I think we have a right to feel uncomfortable in the presence of any operation for which limitless unrestricted applicability is implied.

It is for reasons like this that I mistrust the point of view back of Einstein's general relativity. Here we have asserted the equal status of all reference systems. We assume no difficulty in transporting the mechanically written specifications of the operations from one system to another. But how do the equations and the operations themselves that give meaning to the equations and the specifications get transported from one system to another? Perhaps there is no difficulty with the equations as such, but surely there is difficulty with the operations. For instance, as we pass from one system to others moving with progressively higher velocities, what we originally hear as sound we eventually see as light. How shall we cover this sort of thing in our specifications — how shall we decide when to stop giving our specification in terms of sound and switch to light? It would appear to be obvious that we cannot write our specifications once for all on a piece of paper, which we can take with us and follow, come what may. For the same reason the "cosmological principle" as usually formulated appears to me highly suspect — the principle that the universe as a whole appears the same to an observer situated in any part of it, neglecting "small scale" local irregularities. How does the observer get from one part of the universe to another without subjecting himself to the possibility that the meaning of the specifications experience some sort of continuous change, analogous to the secular change which we know sometimes actually happens? It seems to me that neither the general principle of relativity or the cosmological principle have the slightest intuitional appeal as being "really true". Their virtue is heuristic, in providing new parameters to manipulate in our attack on unknown territory. (It is to be remarked, however, that a cosmological principle apparently can be formulated in terms not requiring the equivalence in principle of all observers. For example, Professor Arthur

G. Walker[2] of the University of Liverpool has set up an axiom system such that it is always possible to recover the original unique observer.)

Another question connected with the general specification of operations was not discussed earlier because of its wider involvements. There is one very broad sort of specification which I have usually rejected as illegitimate, namely, a specification of the operation in terms of its result instead of in terms of the specific activities which together make it up. One obvious reason is that the method of getting a particular result is often not unique — there are more ways of killing a cat than choking it with cream. Another reason is that we cannot always be sure that the result is attainable "in principle." It may be that when our measurements become more accurate a result is vitiated which we had thought to be valid — this is the situation that gave rise to the special theory of relativity. As an example, if we specify an event on Mars by saying that it is the event which is simultaneous with the outburst of a certain prominence on the sun, we encounter a situation of this sort. However, I do not believe that any sharp or complete elimination of the use of results or properties is possible in making our specifications, but that implicit in the assumption of our intuitive ability to perform various elementary activities there is an identification or naming of the activity by reference to certain simple results or properties. Consider a very simple example. We might specify the operation by which the length of an object is to be measured in this way: "Place the end of the meter stick bearing the zero graduation in coincidence with one end of the object and read on the meter stick the number where the other end coincides with the stick". The notion of coincidence is, for the purposes of this specification, accepted as primitive and is not analyzed further. But there is no notion which we may not try to analyze further in other contexts, and in particular the notion of coincidence. What we mean by "Place the end of the meter stick in coincidence" is the same as "Place the end of the meter stick *so that* it coincides, and so forth." That is, we are specifying the operation with the meter stick in terms of its result. But are we not making an assumption when we assume that this can be done? In fact, it is obvious in any concrete case that the coincidence is only approximate. What, then, is the justification for the assumption except previous experience with methods of not indefinite sensitiveness?

In the end, when we come to the place where human weariness

and the shortness of life forces us to stop analyzing our operations, we are pretty much driven to accept our primitive operations on the basis of a feeling in our bones that we know what we are doing.

In all our dealings with the world of objects there is one operation which we always assume can be performed, namely, the operation by which we attach an identity to the object. Some such concept seems to be almost a "necessity of thought" in dealing with the world. Even if we know that actually and theoretically there is no such operation, as when we deal with a continuous fluid, nevertheless we talk about the particles of such a fluid as possessing identity, and we imagine that we could do something to establish their identity even if we are unable to specify what it might be. I have discussed certain aspects of the concept of identity in the *Logic of Modern Physics*. I wish to add only one comment here. This is that we always suppose that the operation by which we establish identity has no reaction back on any of the other operations which can be performed, or, in slightly different words, that the property of the object through which we establish its identity is independent of its other properties. For instance, suppose we are applying a probability analysis to the drawing of black and white balls from an urn. We are interested in only one aspect of the ball, its identification as black or white. We assume for the purposes of the analysis that the ball may be either black or white with absolutely no effect on any of its other properties, in particular, on any properties which might affect the drawing. Or when we draw a parallel between the shuffling of a pack of cards and the universal increase of entropy we are assuming that the markings on the cards are without effect on the shuffling process. What we are effectively doing here is to "isolate" one set of properties or operations, namely those through which the object is identified, from all its other properties or operations. But when we push our analysis to the limit, as we shall see later, the operation of isolation is never exactly performable, and the concept of isolation is one which makes only approximate contact with what happens. It can only be a matter of experience that the approximation is good enough in so many situations.

GOOD OPERATIONS AND CONVENTIONS

There is no limit to the number of operations which we might invent and apply to the world around us. A complete characterization or description of the world would be one that would enable us to know the result of any one of these so infinitely numerous operations. Nor can we claim to understand the world completely unless we can predict how it will react to everything that we can do to it, including all possible experiments with all possible instruments. We should also know how to fit the world which we thus discover into our verbal structure, and in particular we should be able to answer any meaningful questions about it, for verbal activity is a special form of activity, and our general problem is to find how to act in the face of the world. But in practice we never attempt such extreme generality. For practical purposes we regularly utilize only a limited number of operations, and we give our description of the world in terms of these operations. If our description is adequate we then should be able to know what would be the result of applying any one of the infinite number of nonused other operations. In fact this is what we mean by giving a complete description. Whether or not it is possible to give a complete description in terms of a limited number of operations has to be established by experience. I do not believe that the answer to this question in its full generality is known. In the sphere of everyday life the answer is obvious enough, but if we go beyond daily life and enter the field of nuclear physics the answer appears to the physicist to be by no means self-evident.

The world which we want to describe or reproduce is in the first place the world of direct sensation. Our description is not complete unless we can specify what we see or feel or hear or smell or taste. What is more, this world which we are to describe is dynamic rather than static. What our senses give us changes with time, not only if we stay still, but more especially if we ourselves move about or manipulate. As we wait or move about or manipulate we find certain correlations between the reports of our different senses, or between the reports of the same sense at different times. The establishment of such correlations is the first thing we do in getting order and understandability into our world. The thesis that there are such correlations is perhaps the broadest "scientific" thesis that we can formulate.

The fact that there are such correlations implies that it is not necessary, in order to completely describe the world, to tell the results of every conceivable movement or manipulation on our part, but that a smaller number are sufficient. A large part of our early experience was devoted to establishing correlations, perhaps most importantly between the reports of our visual and motor senses. When we say that we see a thing out there in space we are exploiting correlations built, by experience and repetition, into the structure and functioning of our brains. Because of these correlations the aspects of the world to which we need to attend in order sufficiently to master our environment become greatly reduced in number, so that we are left with a degree of complexity with which we can cope. The necessary aspects fall into classes. There are, for example, all the geometric aspects of the world. We may, if we like, define the geometric aspects as those dealing with the positions of objects, although the concept of position is itself by no means primitive but must have taken much experience to form. Even so, after the formation of the concept of position, we still are dealing with an infinity of high order, because every object has a position with regard to every other. It is an enormous simplification to discover that all the relative positional aspects of any and every object with respect to every other can be reconstructed if we are given the position of every object with respect to only one other, which, when we become sufficiently sophisticated, becomes the framework of our coordinate system. The coordinates are lengths measured along the axes. These lengths are the result of certain operations — operations chosen from the infinitely many possible operations.

The operation for measuring length is a "good" operation precisely because it enables us to correlate so much. This would seem to be typical of operations in general. Those operations survive in use which enable us to express as simply and conveniently as possible the correlations which we commonly exploit. Now when there are correlations there is a multiplicity of operations — the operations involved in determining the various terms which enter into the correlation. And when there are such correlations and multiplicity of operations, we can substitute one operation for the other by means of the correlation. In other words, we have two methods of getting to the same terminus. I believe that it will be found that all those operations which have survived as good or useful are operations applicable to situations in which there is more than one, and perhaps many, methods of getting to the same terminus.

An example may make this more concrete. Given a system of fixed points and the Cartesian coordinates of each point in any arbitrary fixed coordinate system, the "distance" between any two points may be defined through the Pythagorean theorem as the square root of the sum of the squares of the differences of the respective coordinates. We have a perfect right to define distance in this way (it is an operational definition), but so long as it is this and nothing more, it is merely a conventional definition without further significance. But now comes the discovery that "distance" defined in this way is also the number that we get when we stretch a string between the two points and measure the length of the string by successive application of a measuring rod along the string. "Distance" now becomes something that could have been equally well obtained by either of two procedures — by the Pythagorean procedure or by the stretched string. That is, we can get to the same terminus, distance, by either one of two operations, and our "distance" loses its character of a pure convention. Of course, in this simple case there are innumerable other operations for giving distance, such, for example, as defining the coordinates in any other system, or any complicated method of triangulation whatever.

Notice that the equivalence of the two methods of getting to the terminus was established empirically, by observing that the results were the same, or, in other words, by observing that the geometry of objects is Euclidean. This brings up a question in the methodology of operational analysis. I have always insisted that in the first instance operations must be uniquely defined, which means, from the point of view above, that they are conventions. The number of such possible conventions is infinite. Among this infinite class of operations those are now selected for use, that is, those are recognized as good operations, which the present state of experimental knowledge enables us to combine with other good operations in getting to the same terminus by different paths. And the better the operation the more ways there are of getting to the terminus. There is an obvious parallel here with the redundancy discussed by communication engineers. A redundant communication system has an advantage in lessening the danger of misunderstanding by allowing checks on the assumed interpretation of the message. Most of the concepts of daily life, such as "material object", are defined redundantly.

In common usage all the different operations (for example, all the different "distances") which lead to the same terminus are lumped together as defining the "same" concept. But when greater rigor is required I think the necessity for the unique specification is obvious, for otherwise we cannot guard against the future experimental discovery of new small effects vitiating the supposed equivalence of the different operations. Furthermore, in all cases in practise where we lump together into a single concept a number of different operations established by experiment to be equivalent, we should be able to pick out from the many possible operations that one to which we shall hitch the concept in any analysis which is formal or pretends to rigor. Thus in the case of distance we might, and usually do, single out for our unique fundamental definition the number obtained by measuring the length of the string stretched between the two points in question. Or, the effective "interval" between two different events in general relativity theory is the ordinary three dimensional distance in that coordinate system in which the events are simultaneous.

There is an interesting special situation here in which the implications of getting to the same terminus by different paths have stimulated much discussion. This concerns the concept of force. It has often been claimed that Newton's law of motion, force equals mass times acceleration, does not have its ostensible significance, but is in actuality only a concealed definition of force. The ostensible significance of an equation that describes an experimental situation is that if one determines by the appropriate experimental procedure the number representing the left-hand side of the equation, and similarly determines by the appropriate procedure the number measuring the quantity standing on the right, it will be found that these two numbers are equal. That is, an equation is ostensibly a statement of the possibility of getting to the same terminus by two different paths. Now apply this to "force equals mass times acceleration". The right-hand side can be determined, because we can measure mass and acceleration by suitably specified operations. But how shall we measure the force on the left if we are, for example, dealing with a heavenly body not accessible to experiment in the laboratory? The answer often given is that there is no way of giving independent meaning to force in a situation like this, so that the equation becomes a definition of force rather than a statement about an experimental situation that is subject to check. There is a certain amount of formal justification for this position, but I believe that nevertheless it does not reflect what was probably in the mind of Newton nor does it suggest the full complexity of the experimental situation. I believe that Newton thought that he was really saying something in his equation and that he did have some sort of feeling for the force on the left of his equation entirely apart from the right-hand side. It may be that this feeling was recognizably anthropomorphic, as those critics have maintained who claim that the concept of force is nothing more than a glorification of the sensation of muscular tension. But there are certainly factors here which are not anthropomorphic and I believe that Newton had them in the back of his head. Thus, if the equation is applied to a freely falling body at the surface of the earth, this force does have independent physical meaning and can be determined with the use of a spring balance applied to the body when it is at rest. Or if a body is tethered to a fixed point by an elastic cord and is rotating about the point with uniform angular velocity so that it is accelerated toward the center, then the force acting on the body is independently measurable by noting the extension of the cord, and it will be found that the force so measured is in fact equal to the product of mass and acceleration, independently determined. In the case of a rotating heavenly body I have no doubt that Newton thought of the gravitational force on the satellite as just as "physically real" as the force exerted by the elastic cord, and he doubtless made the mental experiment of imagining the rotation suppressed, then measuring the force which he would have to apply to the satellite to keep it from falling into the central body, and finding that the force so measured was equal to the force demanded by his formula when the body was rotating under gravity only. Viewed in this way the force of gravitational attraction is a "physically real" thing and by no means a convention to be defined in terms of observed accelerations. The feeling for "physical reality" becomes overwhelming when it is observed that all the $n(n-1)$ mutual forces in a system of n gravitating bodies can be expressed in terms of only n parameters, one associated with each of the bodies individually.

It thus appears that "force" is far from a matter of definition, and that in the situations in which we are concerned with force there are two (or more) methods of getting to the terminus. But in spite of this I think the situation is not so simple as this analysis might suggest, but that there *are* elements of conventional definition here which it is not easy to disentangle. Consider, for example, our statement that the force on a freely falling body at the surface of the earth can be found by bringing the body to rest and hanging it from a spring balance. How shall we answer our critic who wants to be told how we know that the force acting on the body does not depend on its velocity? If we think of the gravitational field as like something that gets a grip on the falling body, then it is not unnatural to anticipate that it may not be able to get so effective a grip on a moving body as on a stationary one. We have to recognize that the question of our critic is a sensible one and that we ought to be able to answer it in some way.

How now shall we measure the gravitational pull on a body in motion? We can make shift to deal with this situation after a fashion. Thus we can experiment with different falling bodies, to which we have imparted different initial velocities, and we find that at any given height above the earth all the falling bodies, no matter what their velocity in that point, are moving with the same acceleration. If we are content to define force as mass times acceleration we have thereby proved that the force is independent of velocity. But was this what we wanted to do, and are we satisfied? We would like somehow to refer to the independent definition of force in terms of the reading of a spring balance. And we can do this merely by attaching the weight to a spring balance and impressing a constant velocity on the balance. The system presently comes to equilibrium with the weight moving with the same velocity as the balance and therefore without acceleration. We now find that the balance reads the same as before and independently of what particular velocity it may have. We would seem to have answered our question, until our critic asks us how we can show that the functioning of the spring balance is not affected by its velocity. Perhaps we can think up a new kind of experiment to answer our critic on this point, such as constructing our balance of different sorts of material, of different moduli of elasticity, and showing that no matter what the material of which the balance is constructed its reading of gravitational attraction is independent of its absolute velocity, and arguing that it is unlikely that if there is any real effect of velocity it would be the same on different sorts of material. Our critic may now give up this line of attack and ask us how we can be sure that the force on a body in a gravitational field is not affected by the acceleration of the body. Might it not be a complicated function of the acceleration, such that when the body is not accelerated at all the force is that recorded by the stationary spring balance, and when the body has the full acceleration of free fall it again has a force numerically equal to that of the stationary balance, but for intermediate values of acceleration it has some other value varying perhaps in some complicated way with the acceleration? I suppose that we would make some attempt to eliminate this possibility, but by this time I think we would have the pessimistic conviction that our critic could find some other point to attack. In practice we do not pay much attention to all these fine points, but omit any reference to velocity or acceleration from our operation of measuring force. In so far as we do this tacitly, without considering the possibility of an effect of velocity or acceleration or any other usually ignored factor, we are in effect setting up a conventional definition of the gravitational attraction as something independent of these factors. The definition is formally conventional because we cannot justify our neglect by some independent experimental procedure — that is, we have no other method for getting to the same terminus.

This I believe is typical of our procedure in most physical situations. When we push our analysis far enough we shall in the end run into a convention in the way we actually proceed, because we have thought out no way of proving or even making probable that our neglect of velocity or acceleration or what-not was justified. In practise there is always an end of this sort merely because of human frailty and the necessity of getting on with more pressing business. But in spite of all this I do not believe that any physical situation can ever be completely reduced to a pure convention, although it is easy to get such an impression from the writings of Poincaré and others. For, no matter what the place where we have stopped our conscious analysis, once our critic has ventured to make his criticism specific, we always can make shift to deal with that specific situation somehow on a physical basis, as has appeared in the examples above. I do not believe that we are ever reduced to *pure* conventions. It is for this reason that I have an instinctive mistrust of Einstein's reduction of the force field of gravity to a matter of pure geometry. The gravitational field cannot be exhaustively characterized by the local curvature of space — if this were all there is to it the force would be a pure convention. But always there has to be something to give the space curvature — gravitating bodies somewhere in the background — and it is these that remove the element of pure convention and give physical reality to the force by providing a second method of getting to the terminus.

DIFFERENT ROUTES TO THE SAME TERMINUS

This business of getting to the same terminus by more than one path is a pretty pervasive thing. In a purely verbal context it may mean only two different ways of talking about something. It is only because of this that we are able to "say anything" about things. Whenever we have a system in which there are relations that can be expressed by equations we have such a situation, the two sides of the equation representing two methods of getting to the same terminus. Not every formal equation, however, is of this sort. For we may have equations of conventional definition, although I believe there are not as many of these as often supposed, or we may have equations of specification. An example of the latter is $l = 10$, which is a method of stating that the length of some object is ten units.

The field of arithmetic is full of getting to the same terminus by many routes. For example, the law that the sum or product of two numbers is independent of their order, or any of the associative laws express the same thing. We have already seen that the field of geometry is the same sort of a field, in which, in particular, the distance between any two points may be found in numerous different ways.

Certain aspects of the importance of being able to get to the same terminus by more than one path are instinctively recognized in the transactions of daily life. It is for this reason, for example, that flat contradiction, without attempt at other justification, is usually such a sterile tactic. There is a purely verbal aspect to the situation. As long as the force discussed in the last section is defined as mass times acceleration we have not said anything. If we want to have anything to talk about we must get beyond the pure convention by finding some second method of getting to the terminus. If we have found such a method we can at least say something not trivial in saying what the second method is.

Although this business of getting to the same terminus by more than one route is pervasive and of the greatest utility in enabling us to free ourselves from the purely formal conventional aspect of definitions, the situation is nevertheless often fuzzy and it is not always clear what the terminus is that is the same or what constitutes two different routes for getting there. There are situations where the concept of "invariance" gives a better characterization of what is involved. Suppose, for example, that we define the thermal conductivity of a given substance at any point as the number which we obtain by dividing the heat flux by the temperature gradient. In the first instance this is a purely formal definition and the thermal conductivity so defined is a pure convention. Consistent with this purely formal character, we have to demand that the definition apply only to a particular point of the body and for a particular heat flux and a particular thermal gradient. But now the conventional character is removed by the empirical observation that there are bodies in which it is immaterial which point we choose or what the magnitude of heat flux or of temperature gradient is. The "same terminus" which we reach here is the numerical value of the thermal conductivity, and the different routes by which we reach it are the different conditions (different points, fluxes, and gradients) under which we compute it. Another way of expressing the same situation is to say that the conventional character of the originally conventional thermal conductivity has disappeared because of its invariance under change of flux, gradient, and position.

So much for thermal conductivity — it has lost its conventional character and become a physical parameter of the body. But what about heat flux? Is it a pure convention, or may it acquire a more substantial existence by participating in two or more methods of getting to the same terminus? Notice, in the first place, that even should it have to remain a pure convention, it may nevertheless be a useful convention. We may make our original definition of heat flux in terms of the drop in temperature of a reservoir and the simultaneous rise in temperature of a sink when there is heat flux through a member which joins source and sink. With such a definition it is true that the application to any concrete situation has to be through pretty impractical "thought" experiments, but we may for the present disregard any possible embarrassments arising here. So long as we are interested only in the rate at which heat is transferred from one body to another there are many situations in which such a purely formal definition of heat flux is useful. There is one way in which the attribute of pure convention could be removed, namely, if we could devise independent means of giving meaning to heat flux by the construction of other sorts of instruments. But this is something which in the present state of technology has not been done — there is no instrument which can be inserted into a body at a single point and indicate, by the position of a pointer on a scale, what is the heat flux at that point. But, if we accept the concept of thermal conductivity as independently given, then we have a method of removing the conventionality from "heat flux" by joining the reservoir and the sink of the definition through connecting members of different thermal conductivity and observing the independence of the relation stated in the definition. This, of course, is what we usually do, namely, to think of thermal conductivity as independently determinable in its own right. But I question whether the two concepts can be completely disentangled, and I believe that the situation is more complex than it usually appears.

The thermal conductivity is actually more complicated than suggested by the analysis above. Heat transfer in a stationary substance (that is, a substance in which there is no convective flow) takes place by at least two independent mechanisms, pure thermal conduction and transfer by radiation. Our definition above makes no recognition of this and leaves us uninformed about whether the conductivity determined according to the definition has some component contributed by the radiation. This is indeed the case, and the situation can be straightened out only by considering other factors ignored in the definition. Thus, not only does the definition ignore the prevailing temperature gradient, but it also ignores the intensity of the radiational field. The justification is that under usual conditions the effect of radiation is negligible. But strictly it is not negligible; the "thermal conductivity" obtained with different radiation fields is not quite constant, and correction for the variation with radiation provides the method of separating the true conductivity transfer from the radiational transfer.

It is to be noticed that we could have been put on the track of these matters by following our purely verbal impulses. It is natural to ask "Does thermal conductivity depend on thermal gradient or the radiational field?" and, in the endeavor to implement these sensible-appearing questions physically, we may get the clue to features in the physical situation that we may not have thought of before. Verbal experiments doubtless have their use, but a physical background helps.

There are other situations in which the analysis is less obvious than in the case of thermal conductivity. One such is presented by a conductor carrying a current of electricity in the presence of a temperature gradient. The phenomena involve thermal and electrical conductivity and Thomson heat. I have not thought of any method of deciding, and I know of no one else who has brought up the question, whether thermal conductivity and Thomson heat are each affected by the current, but in such a way that under the circumstances the effects appear to neutralize each other. Until some independent method has been thought out for answering this question the usual definitions of thermal conductivity and Thomson coefficient have the status of conventions so far as independence of current is asserted.

Getting to the same terminus by two or more routes is often exploited as a means of verification or of checking against mistakes. Thus, we add a column of figures up or down — unless we get the same result both ways, we know that we have made a mistake. Or we measure the width of a room first from north to south and then from south to north. One of the most frequently used methods of verification is simple repetition; in fact, this is often the only practical method. At first it might appear that this is not a case of getting to the same terminus by two paths, but reflection will show that actually it is. Because we have here two different operations, namely, the "same" operation performed at two different times. We know that the result of such an operation should be independent of the time at which it is performed, and we are here using the actual establishment of this independence as a method of check or verification.

The physicist has, and the rest of us should have, a temperamental aversion to *ad hoc* constructions in his theorizing. I suspect that the principle reason is that so long as the construction remains purely *ad hoc* there is no second method of getting to the terminus and therefore no method of verifying that the construction corresponds to anything "real". As soon as the second method of getting to the terminus, or other method of verification, appears, the construction loses its *ad hoc* quality.

It is not to be concluded from all this that purely conventional terms, which correspond to only one method of getting to the terminus, are to be discarded from our conceptual machinery. Such terms often have a well defined use, as, for example, in enabling us to recall or reconstruct specific situations.

OPERATIONS OF VERIFICATION

The subject of operations of verification in general here suggests itself. The subject is important because verification, or checking, or confirmation, is basic to every scientific enterprise, and also to every enterprise in daily life in which it is important to be sure that we are making no mistake. There are intimate connections with meaning and with truth. In general, in order to know the meaning of any term it is sufficient to know what operations to apply in order to verify in any concrete instance that the term has been properly used. The meaning of truth is to be found in the operations by which truth is "verified".

The context in which verification occurs is invariably human — processes of verification do not occur in nature apart from human beings. Computing machines are sometimes so constructed that they "verify" the result of their own operation and cease to function as soon as a "mistake" occurs. But the mistake is not in the machine, but only in the conjunction of machine and human purpose. No machine as such ever malfunctions or makes a mistake, but at every stage of its operation it is doing exactly as it should and as it has to (neglecting quantum effects). The malfunctioning of a loose bearing, say, is not a malfunctioning from the point of view of the machine, but from the point of view of the man who wants it to do something for him.

Not only is verification a human operation, but the sort of verification in which I am usually interested is verification by *me*. Your statement that you have verified something is indifferent to me unless I believe that I could make the verification also. There is evidently a close connection between verification and proof, which is a private matter.

There is no unique operation of verification, and the concept is not sharp — in fact, it is an unusually fuzzy concept. Nevertheless, in any concrete situation nearly every human being will respond in some way to the demand to verify what he is saying or assuming, and because of this there is probably something common in all these situations which we can make the basis for the meaning of "verification". It would seem that in general I verify when I give myself (or you) assurance that a situation is really the way I (or you) think it is. This is pretty nearly equivalent to saying that verification occurs when I give myself assurance that I am not making a mistake, because a misconception about the nature of a situation may be described as a mistake on my part. The degree of assurance that I can give myself varies greatly. There are situations where only a vague and nebulous assurance is possible that nothing is violently wrong. Verification may thus be of quite different significance in different situations.

Nearly any method of establishing that any particular aspect of a situation is as I think it is may be, and is, exploited as an indirect method of presumptively verifying that the total situation is as I think it is. It is inherent in any such process of verification that it is incapable of giving certainty. If the attempted verification fails, then we may be sure, subject to a limitation to be mentioned later, that we are in the presence of error or misconception of some sort, but, if the verification succeeds, then we have presumptively enhanced our confidence that nothing is wrong, but we cannot be sure. Everyone must have had the experience of struggling to find his mistake in adding a column of figures, making the same mistake in every verificatory repetition of the process, and he probably has even had, less frequently, the experience of checking his addition by getting the same result adding up and down, only to find later that he had made a compensatory mistake in both additions.

Logically all that one ever has are the two premises: "If the situation is as I suppose, then such and such follows", and "Such and such is the case". One would like to draw the conclusion "The situation is as I suppose," but this is obviously not permissible logically, but only the weaker conclusion is justified, "The situation *may* be as I suppose". The situation here is closely allied to the situation with regard to establishing general laws of nature. A single exception will invalidate a proposed general law of nature, but no number of compliances can certainly establish it.

We consider now some of the special situations and procedures that commonly occur in verification. I verify both in predominantly social and predominantly private situations. Consider the social situations first. One of the commonest of such situations is when I verify that I have correctly heard what my neighbor said. The need for such verification may arise from various factors, some of them residing in my neighbor and some in me. The commonest method of verifying that I have heard correctly is to get my neighbor to repeat what we said. Usually the repetition is made under more favorable circumstances than at first, perhaps he takes pains to enunciate more distinctly or perhaps I listen more attentively, so that usually the repetition leaves little doubt. If the repetition agrees with what I thought he said at first, then I have verified my first hearing. If it does not, I am usually willing to believe that I made a mistake in my first hearing, but not always. Sometimes my neighbor's repetition is of what he thought he said, not of what he actually said, although I may find it difficult to convince him of this. That such is the case can sometimes be given irrefutable proof when there happens to be a concealed dictaphone somewhere in the vicinity. Sometimes he will admit that he did not say what he intended the first time. Or it may be, on the other hand, that the repetition convinces me that I misheard him the first time, because I can see that his words have a resemblance to others which I may have been anticipating for some adventitious reason.

Having verified for ourselves that we have correctly heard our neighbor, our enterprise of verification has only just begun. For we usually wish to verify also the content of what our neighbor says. This applies preeminently to statements by our neighbor, and we will confine our attention mostly to them. We do, however, verify other forms of utterance of our neighbor. Thus, he may give us a command, and we may want to verify that he really intended to tell us to do what his words seemed to imply. Or he may utter an exclamation of surprise, and we may verify that what surprised him is what we think. Or he may make a prediction. In this case we may verify the prediction itself by waiting, if we are willing to admit the operation of waiting, or we may attempt to verify his prediction in the present after analyzing what can be the present meaning of his prediction about the future. It would appear in all these cases, in which we apparently have to do with other forms of utterance than a statement, that we could paraphrase the point at issue and throw it into the form of a statement. For example, in the case of the command, we could substitute for the command "It is my intention to ask you to do such and such", and the statement, as such, is subject to verification. In general, wherever it is a question of verifying our neighbor's intention, we can throw the point at issue into the form of a statement.

What, now, do we do to verify statements by our neighbor? Notice in the first place a verbal point here. We might have said "verify the truth of my neighbor's statement" and started off on a long analysis of the concept of truth. It seems to me that this is not necessary for our purposes. We have said nothing more when we talk about verifying the truth of a statement than when we talk about verifying the statement itself. "Truth" is here merely a verbal artifact, incidental to the construction of our language and our verbal habits and entirely dispensable. It cancels out from our completed action as a quite unnecessary intermediate term.

We might also make a distinction between verifying a statement and verifying the fact which the statement is about. Thus, in Tarski's famous example, "The statement 'snow is white' is true if snow is white", I think we have to recognize that not only is the *statement* "snow is white" subject to verification but also the fact that snow is white is subject to verification. Now in some contexts it is doubtless profitable to distinguish between the verification of a statement and the verification of the fact which the statement is about, but it seems to me that usually the primary interest is in the verification of the fact rather than in the verification of the statement. For it is undeniable that we do verify facts as such, independently of their involvement in statements. A statement is usually the social aspect of a fact — statements are usually made by our fellows, and the verification of the statement is subject to the limitations of its social origin, including, for example, all the implications of language. But verification of a fact as such is something more primary and personal, and scientific protocol demands that facts be capable of private verification, every man for himself.

There is one quite general method of verifying the statements of our neighbor which we always adopt by preference if it is applicable. This is to repeat for ourselves the steps which led our neighbor to make the statement and see whether we would make the same statement. This procedure of verification is of most value when our neighbor's statement was made on the basis of his first-hand experience, but is also of some value when our neighbor is only repeating hearsay evidence. For by going to the same source as our neighbor we can at least verify that he did not garble the report in transmission. All purported general statements, as contrasted with individual nonrepeatable episodes, are of this character, in particular most of the statements of science. The statements that we read in textbooks are included here, for obviously a printed statement is as much a communication from my neighbor as a statement directly uttered by word of mouth. It is the ostensible ideal of science to accompany its statements with sufficiently specific description of the processes which led up to the statement to permit anyone else to repeat the process and thus to make his verification. Here the difference between verifying a statement and verifying a fact is pretty tenuous. Experience has shown that there are a great many situations of this character, and that we are therefore dealing with a practical method of verification.

There are, on the other hand, many situations in daily life, particularly the situations that are the concern of the philosopher or the theologian, which are not of this character. It is true that the utterer of the statement may attempt to reproduce for us the activities which led him to make the statement, but often he will not be able to describe them in sufficient detail so that we could perform them also. In fact, it will often occur that, even given the full details, we are not able to repeat the experience of our neighbor. For example, a form of argument may appear cogent to him which we are unable to accept. Too often it will happen that all our neighbor can do in the way of describing for us his activities is to say "If you had my background and had lived my life you would feel as I do in this situation". Doubtless there will be many people who have had the same background and who, therefore, are able to say that they verify the statement, but such a verification is obviously of less significance than a verification which everyone of admittedly sound mind can make. In fact, the verification may have little more significance than the discovery that under such and such circumstances the human animal reacts in such and such a way, different human animals reacting in the same way merely because there are so many common features in the construction of all human animals. Verification by consensus is always to be accepted with extreme reservation.

The verification of statements of scientific fact by methods publicly applicable is perhaps the most satisfactory form of verification and leaves least open to question what courses of action are made permissible by the verification. There are other kinds of statement and other kinds of verification in which the human element obtrudes itself more obviously and in which, therefore, the significance of the verification is more obscure. An example is a statement involving a logical process. How, for example, shall this sort of statement be verified? "Given premises A and B, the conclusion C follows logically". The answer to this involves the whole question of the nature of logic, which will be discussed in greater detail in the next chapter. For the present we are content with the observation that verification of statements involving logical conclusions is a different thing from verification of statements with regard to matters of fact and that therefore the significance of the verification is different. Logical statements are more concerned with human behavior, although of course the element of human behavior can never be entirely removed from anything which concerns us.

There are other sorts of statement which we subject to a process of verification. For example, there are statements about happenings in the past. How shall we verify such statements as, for example, "The sun rose yesterday"? Here the verification must perforce be indirect, but I think that any such indirect verification still comes under our general formula that verification involves assuring ourselves that previously unperceived and inferred aspects of the situation are really as we suppose. The most immediate verification about the rising of the sun, and as near to a direct verification as it is possible to come for a past event, occurs when we can say "The sun rose yesterday because I remember seeing it rise". The chain of verification is here pretty direct, but nevertheless involves recognizable intermediate steps, such as: "If I saw the sun rise it must have risen, and if I remember seeing the sun rise I must have seen it rise." In spite of the directness, there is here obviously an element of inference and check on the correctness of the inference. The inference is contained in the statement "If I remember seeing the sun rise it must have risen". Even here the verification is not absolute, for we have the problem of guarding against hallucinations or dreams. A second kind of indirectness in our verification is exemplified by the following sort of situation. "The sun must have risen yesterday morning because I remember seeing it in the sky at ten o'clock". The same remarks apply about memory as before. The new feature is the implicit inference "The sun could not have got high in the sky where I saw it at ten o'clock unless it had previously risen". Now this inference is one that everyone in his right mind would accept, but nevertheless it is obviously an inference based on a more complicated past experience than the direct seeing of the sun rise. That is, we here base our verification on the consistency of our statement with our whole scheme of correlating our experience. The weight which we attach to the correlation will be the greater the more vividly we appreciate the way in which the event in question is involved with all our other experience. Thus, I have no doubt that the astronomer feels a greater degree of confidence in the rising of the sun yesterday than the man in the street, because the astronomer knows that if the sun had not risen it would have involved a suspension of the laws of mechanics which, so far as he has observed, are manifest in every moving thing.

In general, indirect verification seems to be accomplished by examining the involvement of the suspect thing with the rest of our experience and finding whether it presents us with a picture which is consistent with what we expect. It is almost inevitable that our theoretical outlook determines to some extent what we expect. The more thorough the verification, the more varied and larger in number the involvements which we examine. This sort of indirect verification is all that we can apply to the events of the past. The chain of involvement always has to be prolonged until it touches the present, for our verifications, like our meanings, must be verifications now.

The smaller the number of involvements, the less complete or satisfactory the verification. Public events have a high degree of involvement and are susceptible of a high degree of verification. But the sensations or memories of sensations, as I find them in introspection, have fewer involvements, so that their verification is more difficult and less satisfactory. This topic will be expanded in greater detail in the chapter on psychology.

We have seen that verification is never final or complete — even the most elaborate verification of a simple arithmetic addition is subject to the possibility of a highly improbable occurrence of compensatory errors. Publicity and consensus as methods of verification are subject to the possibility that the entire human race, because of some common kink in the structure of all of us, is deceiving itself together.

There is no absolute defense against this kind of thing — the best we can do is to make the verification better and better by exploiting an increasing number of involvements. In practice we cease extending the process of verification when we are tired or content, but in principle we could usually at any stage of the proceedings extend our verification further if we wanted to. There is one situation, however, in which this sort of thing is not possible and verification is not possible, even in principle. Self-doubt is always possible, and there is never any real answer to it. The integrity of our mental processes is a fundamental assumption in our dealing with the world. How shall we go to work to assure ourselves that we have not suddenly gone insane, or, for that matter, how do we assure ourselves that we are not now dreaming? We can give ourselves some assurance that we were not insane in the past, because our memories fit into a consistent pattern, but how do we know that now, before the last occurrence in our brains has had a chance to become a memory, we have not suddenly gone insane? Or how to be sure that we have not had an insane lapse for a moment and have now recovered our sanity? This is the sort of limitation referred to on page 57 which prevents us from being *sure* that we are in the presence of a mistake somewhere even when our attempted verifications fails.

The recognition that certainty is not possible, perhaps for some reason such as the impossibility of verification, is becoming rather widespread. This situation is sometimes described by saying that the only sort of knowledge we can have is *probable* knowledge. It seems to me that there are dangerous implications here. The situation here is not unlike that presented by quantum theory when we attempt to formulate rigorously the Heisenberg principle. The Heisenberg principle is *not* to be formulated by saying that nature is so constructed that we cannot simultaneously measure position and momentum with any desired precision, with the implication that a particle "really has" both position and momentum, but that they are inaccessible to us. Similarly, with regard to "probable" knowledge, the implication is too likely to be that somewhere there is such a thing as certain knowledge, but that we, because of our human limitations, cannot acquire it. The further implication is usually present that by some appropriate procedure, perhaps statistical in nature, we could make some sort of numerical assessment of the degree of probability of our present knowledge. These implications, it seems to me, are illegitimate. It is the nature of knowledge to be subject to uncertainty. One may, if one wants and understands what one is doing, underline this aspect of knowledge by speaking of probable knowledge, but only with the understanding that he is coining a new kind of compound word, "probable-knowledge", which may not be separated into components. If one properly understands the situation I think one will prefer to get along with the simple unadorned "knowledge".

THE OPERATION FOR JUDGING SAMENESS

Let us now pass to a more detailed consideration of more specific operations. In our discussion above we have continually talked about the "same" operation. What is the operation by which we judge of sameness? Here we touch on something pretty fundamental and pervasive in our dealing with the world, and we should stop and look. Under what circumstances do we use the word same, or what is this concept of sameness which we use so often? We need not stop here for any hair-splitting examination of how we pass from the adjective "same" to the abstraction "sameness". For us the abstraction "sameness" need be nothing more than an artifact of our grammar; our verbs like to be transitive, and when I talk about situations in which I use the adjective "same" grammar makes it convenient to talk about "sameness". For instance, to see that two objects are the same is to recognize sameness in the objects. We shall use the adjective and the abstract noun interchangeably according to the grammatical exigencies of the moment.

What, now, are the conditions under which I use the word same? The application of the word is broad. I may apply it to objects, as when I say "That tree which I now see from my window is the same tree which I saw yesterday from the street". I may apply it to sensations, as when I say "The same crick in my back which I had yesterday has come back". I may apply it to activities, as when I say "Man of War is the only horse that ever won the same race five years in succession". I may apply it to thinking, as when I say "You have the same idea which I have". Sometimes the application of the idea of sameness is more questionable and indirect, as to a shadow, or the wind, or a wave. We use "same" with either spatial or temporal connotations. All the Ford cars at this instant on the road are examples of the same make of car, and the Ford now in my garage is the same car which I drove into the garage last evening.

It is paradoxical that with all the examples which we can invent for the use of same, we can never construct an example in which the sameness is complete, or in which my adversary cannot force me to admit that the purported examples of sameness do not exemplify complete sameness. When I make my analysis fine enough, the tree which I now see is not the same as the tree which I saw yesterday, because the sap has been rising from the roots and evaporating from the leaves. Or, no activity ever exactly repeats and therefore cannot be exactly the same when the full context in which it is embedded is considered, if for no other reason than that on the second occurrence the clock on the wall reads differently than on the first occurrence.

It appears, as we analyze our examples, that nontautological characterization of what we mean by "sameness" continually eludes us by getting pushed further and further into the background. We define what we mean when we say that a complex object remains the same by saying that all its recognizable parts remain the same, and the best we can do when asked to say what we mean by saying that the smallest recognizable parts remain the same is to say that we can detect no difference. From the point of view of the psychologist it is doubtless necessary to make a distinction between perceiving sameness and perceiving absence of difference, but for our present purposes the difference would seem to be pretty sterile. Back of all our usage of "same" there would seem to be something pretty primitive and unanalyzable. The recognition of recurrence, or the feeling of familiarity in an experience, would seem to be fundamental to memory and rational thought, and our recognition of sameness in the complex situations of daily life would seem to be built up from this primitive recognition. The edifice that may thus be erected may be of astonishing complexity and may have the precision of mathematics, as when we describe in equations the motion of some complicated mechanism. Any such description involves in the background the use of measuring rods and of clocks, which may not be specified except in terms of fixed objects which retain their identity, which in turn means continued "sameness".

The sameness which we encounter is always a sameness of aspects. I do not know to what extent this statement is tautological, or what an "aspect" of a situation is except something about the situation which remains the same. The total number of aspects which must be the same in two situations in order that we be willing to say that the situations as such are the same depends on our purposes of the moment, and on occasion may include only a minor part of all the recognizable characteristics. For instance, when we say that the Derby which was run yesterday was the same race that was run a year ago we are neglecting a host of features that in other contexts can by no means be neglected — the horses which ran yesterday were not the same as those which ran a year ago, nor the crowds that watched them. Only the name of the race, the auspices under which it was run and perhaps the specifications of the prizes have remained the same. Yet, because it is these which are of primary interest to us, we say that it was the same race. "Sameness" is a relative concept — relative to our purposes — and usually a very complicated concept. It is usually more complicated when applied to activities than when applied to objects because the specifications of an activity are usually more complex than the specifications for an object and usually imply them. The concept of the sameness of the motion of two particles is more complicated than the concept of the sameness of the particles themselves.

A unique sort of exemplification of sameness is myself. "I" remain the same, but, on the other hand, I recognizably change. It appears extraordinarily difficult to specify with any precision what aspects of "me" I would regard as essential to the propriety of saying that I am the same person now as last year. Persistence of the "same" body, which however is known to renew itself every seven years, is doubtless a factor, and almost certainly memory. A physiological basis is the persistence of the structure of the brain, but our conscious thought is innocent of any knowledge of the brain or of structure in it, and the connection is elusive. At any rate, the invention of an entity, an "ego", to explain the situation does not get us anywhere, and those people who have to have an ego seem to me to be ascribing an unwarranted significance to an impulse probably primarily verbal in origin.

THE FUTURE AND THE OPERATION OF WAITING

Let us now consider another concept of great generality, which I have not attempted to analyze hitherto, and which involves an important general principle with regard to operations. What is the operational meaning of the "future"? What are the operations in terms of which it may be specified? Or, rather, what are the operations or activities necessarily involved when we talk about the future? For the future is palpably not an "it". Or, under what conditions do I use the word future, either explicitly or by implication? Consider a concrete special case. What do I mean when I say "It will rain tomorrow", tomorrow being a special case of the future? An easy answer is to say that if I *wait* until tomorrow I shall find tomorrow that it is raining. That is, it would appear that the meaning of the future may be made to involve the operation of waiting. The important question that now presents itself is whether the operation of waiting is a legitimate operation. If we are to answer this question we must decide what it is that makes an operation legitimate or not. To ask whether an operation is legitimate might seem to imply that an operation may have an absolute property of legitimacy. I believe, however, that the implication is false. The matter would seem to be largely in our own control — we can admit or not different classes of operation as legitimate, recognizing that if we do there are specific consequences. For instance, if I am willing to admit the operation of waiting it would seem that I must also admit the possibility that statements may not have meaning now, but may acquire meaning after the lapse of sufficient time. For the operation of waiting is not an operation that can be consummated now, although I can begin to wait now, so that the meaning, which involves performance of the operation, cannot be a present meaning. But are we willing to make this sacrifice in order that we may include the operation of waiting as a legitimate operation? I personally am not willing. I have a very strong inclination to demand of a meaning that it be a meaning now. I want to be able to say "Although your statement may acquire fuller meaning in the future, you are making the statement now and it must have some meaning now". It seems to me legitimate to ask "What is the present meaning?" In fact, I would be willing to restrict the meaning of meaning to present meaning. If this restriction is accepted, meanings must be found in operations presently performable, and the operation of waiting must be ruled out. This, it must be recognized, is a personal preference, and others may admit operations in the future if they are willing to pay the price. For example, Schlick[3] of the Vienna School has been very explicit in admitting the operation of waiting. I shall not do this, and in this book admit only present operations. If one adopts the other point of view and admits future operations it is questionable whether one can properly ask the meaning of "future" at all, but must rather treat it as primitive or unanalyzable. For it would seem highly probable that the implication that "future" is understood is already smuggled into any possible specification of those future operations which purportedly are to give "future" meaning. In particular, one can hardly avoid specifying *when* the operations are to be performed, and the notion of "when" involves the future.

If one admits only present operations one has also introduced difficulties and complications. For example, what is the meaning of "present"? It is obvious that every operation requires *some* time for its performance, and that the whole enterprise of making definitions and checking that the definitions are applicable involves sequences of activities in time. In the first chapter we have already mentioned the growth of meanings in time. There are probably two things to distinguish here — growth of apprehension of meaning in the mind of the recipient of the communication, and the performance in time by the speaker of the operations which determine meaning for him. This sort of consideration has not obtruded itself to any perceptible extent, however, in conventional analyses of meaning, so that we may assume that there is a large realm in which such considerations can profitably be disregarded. For our present purposes we shall do this and understand by "now" the psychological present as distinguished from the physical present. The latter is capable of enormously finer subdivision, by the use of instruments, than the psychological present. The question of what we mean by psychological present has been the subject of analysis by others, for the matter is not obvious. We can give a very crude answer by saying that we shall consider that we are dealing with the psychological present when we are dealing with situations in which the successive occurrence of activities in time is not directly perceived, the use of instruments is ruled out, and the whole conscious situation can be sufficiently characterized with no reference to the flight of time.

Assuming that the "present" makes no serious difficulty, there is another consideration which fortifies my resolution to demand that my meanings be meanings now. Go back to the concrete question that started this discussion: "What do I mean when I say that it will rain tomorrow?" We previously accepted this question in good faith. But when I have my wits about me and give a little consideration to the implications of what I am saying, I, as a matter of fact, never say "It will rain tomorrow", but I say instead, "I expect it will rain tomorrow". That is, an intrinsic component of the concept of the future is the recognition that the future can by no means be certainly anticipated, and furthermore that what the future brings can only be accepted, no matter how it may run counter to our expectations.

I believe that this attitude toward the future, namely, that it cannot be predicted with certainty and that the only possible present attitude is to accept it when it comes, is the attitude of everyone, even of those who accept the operation of waiting. This has priority over the attitude that the future may be predicted by projecting the regularities of the past.

A couple of other consequences of the inscrutable character of the future may be mentioned. I personally do not think that one should speak of making statements about the future. For me, a statement implies the possibility of verifying its truth, and the truth of a statement about the future cannot be verified if we are to accept only present operations. I would prefer to say that a combination of words in the grammatical form of a statement is only a "pseudo-statement" when it purports to be about the future. This is not a serious matter and to a large extent is only a matter of words and convention. People like Schlick maintain that statements can be made about the future. I could perhaps bring the two points of view a little closer by saying "I have no *right* to make statements about the future" and by eliminating any such statements from my serious consideration, as involving an error on my part.

The language of daily life does, as a matter of fact, often deal with situations in this way. In the present case the difficulty is that "statement" has no clean-cut unique meaning when handled in this way.

The second consequence, perhaps more remote, has to do with the popular attitude toward the predictive function of a theory. It is frequently said that that one of two theories is to be preferred which correctly predicts the larger number of phenomena. But no theory can, here and now, be correctly predicting. The present properties of a theory cannot be described in terms of prediction of the inscrutable future. To "correctly-predict" is a verb which has only a past tense. And whenever any two theories present themselves as rivals for present acceptance they both must have predicted equally in the past, because a theory is rejected, except perhaps for heuristic use, when it turns out to have made an incorrect prediction. The superiority of one theory over another in the present is not to be described in terms of superior prediction, but rather in terms such as greater simplicity or superior versatility in suggesting and foreseeing the results of radically new lines of future experiment. What we have here is a linguistic trap — it probably is not a very great calamity if we fall into it.

PROGRAMS

If we phrase our meanings involving the future in terms of expectations, we have at least thereby secured that our meanings are meanings now, because our expectations are now. It is possible, I believe, to put the matter on a somewhat broader basis. I believe that we can give meanings to our futures in terms of *programs* of action. Drawing up a program is a present activity, but it is indissolubly tied to the future. The heavy reference of the program is always to the future. I can be drawing up a program now for future action, or I may now be in the process of carrying out a program which will be completed in the future. Like the century plant, the program dies when it has flowered in action. The completed program is no longer a program.

A program may have certain of the properties of an object. For a program may be written on cards and filed. Alternate programs mean simply several cards with instructions when to follow the specifications on the cards.

What constitutes a "program"? Among other things it is a schedule for a sequence of actions in time, but it is more than a schedule. It would seem that the element of "intention" is necessarily involved. So far as my schedule of action constitutes a program it is a program that I intend to follow. But we may have tentative programs and alternative programs. A tentative program is a program which I intend to follow if certain occurrences eventuate in the future, or alternative programs are programs one or the other of which I intend to follow in the future according as this or that other thing happens.

Alternative programs contain a strong component of the concept of "if", and the meanings of "if" and "alternative" are coupled. We intend to follow this or that of alternative programs if this or that happens. It is perhaps possible to analyze what we mean by "if", but mental indolence urges us to accept it as a primitive concept. Formal logic also appears to accept it as primitive and unanalyzed. It would seem that there are at least some situations in which we can dispense with "if". Instead of saying "Do such and such *if* such and such occurs," I could equally well say, as far as any resulting action is concerned, "Do such and such *when* such and such occurs". "If" seems to be a word which marks the occurrence of certain verbal situations and is merely a short hand way of signaling the occurrence of the situation. It may be that if one were willing to make a sufficiently involved circumlocution the use of "if" could be avoided altogether. We can see, in any event, that the concept of "if" arose out of a complicated experience — perhaps out of our endeavors to plan for the future, coupled with the experience that we very often fail to anticipate the future and that often the edge can be taken off our failure if we have alternative plans for action. We can to a partial and limited extent do our thinking ahead of the event, provided, of course, that we have had pertinent past experiences. We can thus save ourselves the time necessary for thought in an emergency where quick reaction may be vital.

Certain types of counterfactual statements in terms of "if" can be translated into statements of actual fact with regard to programs. Thus, "If Mary had come home last week I would have kissed her" may very well be a statement of actual fact about my program last week. However, it would seem that not all counterfactual statements are of this type. "If it had rained yesterday the streets would have been wet" appears to be a concealed statement about an observed regularity in the functioning of nature and an expectation as to its continued functioning under circumstances not yet encountered. Or, "If it were raining now I would not like it" conceals a general comment on my behavior, with the implication that the conditions which have in the past determined this sort of behavior now prevail.

In general it would seem that counterfactual statements should be dealt with on the purely verbal level, for they are in fact verbalisms. Thus, what I mean by saying that " 'If it were raining now' (which it is not) is counterfactual" is partly covered by saying "The combination of words 'it is raining now' does not correspond to experience". The further implication in the counterfactual conditional, namely, the conclusion following on the "if" is to be taken, as above, as a projection of past experience.

The view that in dealing with or talking and thinking about the future (are not the two the same?) we are concerned mainly with programs or expectations is opposed to the very commonly held opinion that we are dealing with commitments or beliefs. For example, it is often said that the scientist can operate only on the assumption that nature obeys laws, so that the mere fact that he is a scientist means that he "believes" or has "faith" that there are laws of nature. This it seems to me is a false position. It is to some extent a merely verbal matter and our definition of faith could be changed by agreement if we wished, so that from this point of view it is not of too great importance. But beyond this, and not so innocent, it is palpably bad description of what happens. The scientist can draw up a program of action in which he postulates that there are laws of nature, and he can start to follow that program while still recognizing that he may run into some unexpected snag which will make it impossible to complete the program. He may follow a program assuming that there are natural laws in the spirit that that is the best bet, but only in the spirit of the best bet. When pursued in this spirit a program that assumes that there are natural laws becomes only a special case of a broader program, namely the program to discover as many uniformities as he can in natural phenomena. This latter is a more accurate description of how I operate, and I am convinced it is also a better description of how many of my fellow scientists operate, or how they might all operate if they took pains to think carefully about the matter. In the assumption of a best bet I can see very little in common with what seems to me to be implied in "faith". The scientist has no place for "faith".

Consider now some further examples in which the meaning of the future is to be found in programs. What, for instance, do I mean when I say "In one thousand years the day will be one second shorter"? I shall be dead in one thousand years and my programs for action in one thousand years are merely marks on paper. Or if one makes the objection that I cannot certainly say that I shall be dead in one thousand years because no "statement" about the future can be made with certainty, we may rephrase the issue by asking what I can mean when I say that I believe that the earth will continue to revolve on its axis after I am dead. Such a statement can have no meaning in terms of any program of waiting by me, but it may nevertheless be given an indirect meaning, and a present meaning at that, as we have demanded that all our meanings shall be present meanings. For example, my son will doubtless be able to adopt the program of waiting and observing whether the earth continues to revolve on its axis after my death, and we may say that the statement has present meaning for me in terms of his present acceptance of his program. Present meanings may be even more indirect than this. What shall I mean when I say "I believe the earth will continue to revolve on its axis after the last living being on it has died"? The programs involved in making a statement like this are even more esoteric and remote — such programs, for example, as are contained in the equations of motion of the astronomer which connect the period of rotation at future times with the present period, equations in which allowance is made for tidal friction, for example. Now these equations contain no reference to any living beings, and so far as they can be checked in the present day they are valid equations. The implication is that it makes no difference to the rotation of the earth whether there are living beings on it or not, so that, in particular, when all life has ceased, the equations continue to be valid. The operational meaning of a statement like this about the future has thus become indirect, namely that the programs in terms of which we now deal with the rotation of the earth contain no reference to life. Doubtless this will seem unsatisfactory to those who may want to maintain that we really do mean "something more" than this. To which we may reply, sidestepping the question whether one *can* mean more than this by asking whether we *need* to mean more than this. Cannot we say everything that has factual reference if we restrict our meaning in this way, and have we thereby deprived ourselves of any potentialities except that of talking in certain ways?

What do I mean if I say "I believe there is a life after death"? Some people think they attach an ordinary factual meaning to this and consider that the statement is verified by seances with mediums, and so forth. But what shall I mean as applied to myself if I say "I believe that my conscious existence will go on after my physical death"? This statement is to have present meaning. It seems to me that such present meaning is very simply and adequately given in terms of programs which I may now follow, such as going to church on Sunday or refraining from certain actions which I regard as wicked, a restraint which is rationalized as making more probable my comfort in the future, but which in the present results in following a certain program of action. If one wants to mean more by his statement than this, I would again ask him what more he needs to mean unless he insists on the use of certain verbalisms.

The meaning of my statement, "I believe that my conscious existence will continue after my physical death", has features in common with the meaning of "I believe that I shall be alive tomorrow". It seems to me that the meaning of the latter is obviously contained in my present programs for future action. There are, however, also obvious differences in the two statements. My belief for tomorrow involves a projection of past experience with no radical break in it. In the case of life after death I do expect a radical break with the past, but in spite of this adopt the program that my consciousness will continue.

In general, it seems to me that the drawing up of programs is one of the most important of operations, and that the application is wider than merely in giving meaning to the future. For instance, the concepts of probability acquire much of their meanings in terms of programs; this will be discussed in detail later.

A program for action may or may not contain within it instructions about when to stop acting according to the program. If it does not contain such explicit instructions, the program may be of such a sort that it automatically terminates itself, as when I form the program of counting the apples in a certain basket. Or it may be that the performance of the program never cuts itself off, but it may be carried on indefinitely. Perhaps the most familiar of such non-self-terminating programs is the program by which we name the successive numbers as we count. We could keep on counting forever, and no matter how far we had counted, we would know what to call the next number provided only that we know what we have called the last one. It is my somewhat heretical opinion that all we can mean when we talk about "infinite" numbers is concealed in the properties of the non-self-terminating program by which we generate the numbers. Surely no one ever saw or handled an infinite number, but everyone has operated according to the program. It is not the infinite numbers which have the properties they are said to have, but the program by which they are to be generated.

THE ROLE OF THE PERFORMER OF THE OPERATIONS

Although most specifications of scientific operations are given in impersonal terms in the sense that no explicit mention is made of the performer, a performer is nevertheless pretty close. Specification in the form of a command, as above, "Place the end of the meter stick, and so forth", could equally be phrased "You place, and so forth", and the person appears. Although some personal reference thus appears unavoidable even in scientific specifications, the effect is to a certain extent sterilized because the person is directed to concern himself with nonpersonal things of universal reference, such as meter sticks. There are, however, some situations in physics in which it seems to me that the performer of the operations is an essential part of the picture although his role is concealed. Situations of this sort are presented by general relativity theory or by the "general cosmological principle". Already, earlier in this chapter, various objections have been made to the conventional formulations and understanding of these principles. The essence of these objections is that the role of the performer of the operations is overlooked.

Turning from the narrower field of physics to the broader field of psychology it seems to me that we do encounter situations here in which the performer of the operations is of vital importance. Discussion of such situations will be given in a later chapter.

Any program of operations which I can adopt is subject to one obvious and universal limitation, namely, it must be performable in my lifetime. A program which by implication assumes the performance of certain operations by me after I am dead is self-contradictory, and meanings defined in terms of such a program are nonexistent. It is easy to let our thoughtless chatter go on with no regard to this — our verbal machinery has no built-in cutoff. As a trivial example, I may not form the program of calling my daughter's attention to the notice of my death in the *New York Times*. A somewhat similar limitation is that I may not form a program which demands mastery of detail greater than is physically possible in a finite organ with the number of atoms in my brain. I can have only a limited number of experiences. I must not, for example, assume that it means something to talk about the simultaneous position of all the atoms in the world. Such limitations seldom intrude themselves, but I believe they may on occasion be decisive. This is one of the reasons that no concept can be absolutely sharp and that absolute certainty is a self-contradiction.

The demand that any program of operations which I adopt be one which I can perform in my lifetime and be within the physical possibilities is only a special case of a limitation to which all our operations are subject. We, being finite creatures, are not capable of an infinite number of operations, but the operations which we employ must be chosen from a universe of operations. We usually do not feel this as a restriction, nor is the observation that our operations have to be chosen from a universe of operations usually a particularly helpful observation. A reason is that it is usually impossible to formulate in advance what the universe of operations is, in view of the possibility that our operations may grow as we proceed, compounded out of operations that we have already performed. The result is that usually, when we strive for the greatest generality, we tactically assume that our universe of operations is all the operations which we can perform, and we let it go at that without attempting further specification. There is, however, at least one situation in physics in which the universe of operations is definitely not all the operations we can perform and where the assumption that it is may get us into trouble. It is assumed in the classical thermodynamics basic to physical chemistry, that is, in the thermodynamics of Willard Gibbs, that the atoms of chemical compounds are inviolable. This means that the universe of operations of physical chemistry does not include the operation of taking the atom to pieces. No one thought of the possibility of such an operation when Gibbs started the subject, but now we have learned how to do it, and inclusion of the operation entirely alters the fundamental picture. The concepts of equilibrium, temperature, and entropy fail in the new universe of all the operations which we can perform. The third law of thermodynamics no longer holds if the zero of entropy has to be taken as a configuration of electrons and protons rather than as a configuration of atoms. At ordinary temperatures the entropy change to be expected under indefinitely great pressures is entirely different in the new universe — this has an obvious bearing on cosmology. I think there is room for further work in finding what becomes of thermodynamics in the wider universe of operations now open to us.

LEVELS OF OPERATION

The discussion so far, fragmentary as it has been, is, I think, sufficient to suggest how terribly complex the whole situation is when we try to get under a single point of view all the sorts of thing we want to say. The difficulties are greatest when we are dealing explicitly with ourselves and what we do, as when we talk about talking. I personally do not believe that there is any consistent method for dealing with the complete situation, but that we are forced to a spiraling approximation or to operation on different levels. That we are forced to something of this sort need not be too surprising if we have taken to heart the lesson of Gödel's theorem. There can, of course, be no sharp line of demarcation between the different levels, but we may make rough distinctions as follows. There is in the first place the almost completely public "objective" level of classical physics, chemistry, and the other nonbiological sciences. On this level we pay no attention to the performer of the operations, as such, and do not talk about feeling or thinking. We never push the analysis to the point of self-doubt. This does not mean that the subject matter has to be completely nonbiological, for there are certain generalizations that apply no matter what the nature of the material — conservation of the center of mass applies to two fighting tomcats as well as to two colliding billiard balls. Of course an operator is demanded if there are operations, but we think of him as little as possible. The specifications for the operations may be given verbally, and at this level all operations specified verbally have complete objectivity and publicity, because the specifications may be put in writing, and the writing may be stored in a library for all to read and act on at any time. This is the level of most science as it is taught. For many purposes the criterion of publicity as that which can be spoken or written is a most useful one, and it would seem to be what people principally have in mind when they talk about the publicity of science. But even here it is recognizably not the whole story. Intelligent teaching and learning include more than lecturing or listening or reading and remembering. The pupil must "see" the point before he can learn, and seeing the point is something which no one can do for him. Neither does public science include creative science — the process of discovery cannot be put into words, for when it is got into words the discovery is over and we are dealing with history.

It is a question whether mathematics is to be included on the same level as physics and chemistry. Certainly the theorems of mathematics are couched in impersonal terms, and a universal meaning and significance is usually ascribed to the symbols and operations of mathematics. How one shall classify mathematics and locate it in a hierarchy of levels is to a considerable extent a matter of taste, since the levels are not sharply defined. Personally, the matter of proof bulks so large for me in the enterprise of mathematics, and proof is so completely a personal matter, which cannot be communicated, that I would put mathematics on a level of lower "objectivity" than physics or chemistry. Mathematics is peculiarly and exclusively a human enterprise, and it will always "smell of the lamp", scrub it as we may. Logic is in much the same situation as mathematics. Logic is usually thought of as the archetype of an impersonal discipline, but I suspect that the social value of logic largely lies in the fact that different performers are involved. The performer who performs the operations involved in the premises is not necessarily the same as the performer who draws the conclusion. This topic will be expanded later.

The biological sciences may perhaps be put on the next level beyond classical physics, chemistry, and so forth. There is a hierarchy of such sciences, perhaps beginning with descriptive botany and culminating in human psychology. As one ascends in the hierarchy there is an interesting departure from the stark publicity and definiteness of the first level. There is in the first place the vagueness associated with the idea of life itself. No one appears to have formulated a definition of life which covers everything that one would like to mean by it, and it is evident that the concept of life finds its value only in a vague and general setting. Added to this, the specifications of the operations of the biologist increasingly lose their universal applicability, insofar as time or place are not specified, and increasingly refer to specific occasions, even though the person of the performer remains indifferent. The situations of biology seldom, if ever, repeat. The initial material for a biological experiment is never twice the same, different members of the same species differ and the species itself has no permanence — every gardener has witnessed the rise and running out of some popular brand of flower, so that the specification of biological material demands the specification of a date and, it may be, also a place. Statistics and probability become increasingly a tool for describing biological results. At the upper end of the hierarchy, human psychology, many people want to talk about such things as feeling and thinking and consciousness. However, the difficulty of getting these satisfactorily into public terms is so great that some psychologists prefer not to talk about these things at all.

We digress here to look at an issue which arises only with the biological sciences, the question, namely, whether any new principles are involved in the biological sciences as compared with the sciences of the nonliving exemplified by physics and chemistry. A vitalist gives an affirmative answer to this question. Not many biologists today are vitalists in the original sense, and by the principle of the excluded middle this might be taken to imply that they would give a negative answer to our question. But, nevertheless, the negative answer would seem to require a little further sharpening. One way of effecting this sharpening is through what I have called the thesis of the sufficiency of atomic description. This thesis will be examined in some detail in a later chapter. Briefly, the thesis states that a living organism can be fully specified by completely specifying the state of every constituent atom. The present interest of this thesis is that here we have a particularly important example of the operation of forming programs. For the only meaning that can be given to the difference between the vitalist and the nonvitalist is in terms of a difference of programs. With present techniques it is hopeless for the nonvitalist to attempt to specify the state of every atom in a system. "Specify the state of every atom" is at present merely something that we say — its meaning is to be found in a program of action. But, even so, the essential difference is not so much with their programs, as such, but with the almost inevitable human accompaniment of every program, namely, the accompaniment of expectation. The nonvitalist expects that if he could follow his program the results would be as he states, and similarly the vitalist expects that the finding would be different. So far as present practice goes, neither position makes much difference — the vitalist is not able to exhibit what "else" there is that makes life, and the nonvitalist can only lend probability to his position by saying that there is no presently known fact inconsistent with it and that the vitalist historically has been playing a losing game, being in continuous retreat from one obstinately defended position to the next in the rear.

After biological phenomena, the next level in the hierarchy is the level of social phenomena. The operations which give meaning to many social concepts involve in many cases the performer of the operations. For instance, the law that is "social" law as distinguished from "natural" law is a body of permitted practise, originating in specified ways in the activities of certain individuals who are designated as competent to make laws, and enforced by other individuals also specially designated. The law could not arise in a context in which there were not different individuals functioning differently, and it is the interplay of these different individuals that gives the law its meaning. The need to specify the performer of the operations in legal and other situations arises primarily because of an opposition between myself and my fellows. It is usually my fellows who make the laws and I who obey them. It is when the opposition between myself and my fellows begins to be important that it begins to be important to specify the performer of the operations. This usually means distinguishing between operations by me and operations by somebody else. However, the necessity to make the distinction does not arise sharply on crossing the line into the realm of social relations, but already in human psychology it is necessary to recognize the performer. Some of the consequences of this will be examined in detail later.

With the recognition of different levels in the specification of operations we are provided with a scheme of arrangement for the further discussion in this book. The details of this arrangement have already been sufficiently indicated in the introduction.

I V

LOGIC, PROBABILITY, AND RELATED TOPICS

GENERAL CONSIDERATIONS

In previous writings I have examined some of the aspects of logic.[1] It will not be necessary to repeat this examination here. Perhaps the most important point was that logic cannot give the absolute sharpness or the absolute certainty that many often attribute to it. It is, for example, a fundamental tenet of Catholic theology, and many non-Catholics holds the same opinion, that conclusions reached logically have absolute certainty. The "formal" element in logic is sometimes made the keystone of this situation. Logic, according to this view, is a purely formal discipline, devoid of any dependence on experience, in which the conclusions reached are already implied in the premises, so that a logical process gives nothing new and is essentially concerned with tautologies. As a consequence, logic is said to contain no necessary human element. In further proof of this is adduced the possibility of constructing machines which can grind out logical conclusions quite automatically when the premises are fed into them. I do not believe that this point of view can be maintained; certainly not with respect to logic machines. For how shall we be sure that the output of such a machine is logically correct? If we have to assess each particular conclusion as it is delivered by the machine, we have surrendered our point. Furthermore, the answer to this question can never be given merely by inspecting the output of the machine, no matter how apparently reliable. We might be inclined to say that if it has functioned correctly in a million cases it must be a true logic machine, but on the other hand we know perfectly well that we could construct a machine such that it would give an incorrect conclusion every two million times. How else, then, shall we have confidence in the output of the machine unless we examine its construction and assure ourselves that a machine so constructed is capable of functioning only in accordance with the dictates of logic? The machine itself cannot know whether or not it is so constructed — it is we who have to know it. It seems to me that the human element in logic cannot possibly be by-passed. But much worse than that, I do not believe that the private personal element can be by-passed, or that logic can be put on a completely public basis. We have already seen that "proof" is a private matter, and without the conviction of proof logic is empty.

Logic is a form of rational human activity, and the implications of the activity aspect of it are to be kept clearly in mind in any analysis. It is difficult to delimit all that one would like to include under the general term "logical". Certain activities would probably be classed as logical in character although not to be included in conventional logic. Always some form of transformation seems to be involved. One starts with an apperception of some sort, an observation, or a statement, or a recognition of a relationship, and transforms it into something else which is of interest to him. Logical activity is usually on the verbal level — one starts with certain statements and winds up with other statements. But this does not cover all the usage. If one wants to know what the thermal expansion of water is, and in consulting a library to find out goes, without conscious consideration, to that section of the library containing the books on physics, one has thereby implicitly used the notion of "class" and has therefore engaged in an activity that many would want to call logical, although it may never have got onto the verbal level. The line of separation of rational action in general from rational action that we would, in particular, want to call logical is fuzzy. If a monkey puts two sticks together in order to reach a banana that he otherwise could not get, I think we would call the action rational, although we might perhaps not be sure whether we would want to call it logical. However, for our purposes it is not necessary to attempt to sharpen the distinction. It will be enough to consider only the verbal aspects. In the following we shall be concerned only with that aspect of logic by which we pass from certain verbal situations to other verbal situations. These verbal situations are not completely general, but are subject to restrictions imposed by the use we want to make of the verbalism which is the terminus of our verbal activity. The overriding interest in all logical activity seems to be that the verbal terminus should stand in some sort of usable correlation with the world of experience. In practice this very general requirement gets narrowed down to the requirement that the verbal terminus be of such a form that it is "true" when applied to experience. Narrowing still further, but still retaining great generality, we may say that logic provides us with true statements by transformation of other statements. It would, of course, be desirable if we could find some method of making true statements starting with any sort of material, true or not, but this would probably be asking too much. We therefore restrict our demands to something we have found to be attainable, and still further narrow our requirement to demand that logic shall provide us with true statements given other true statements to start with. This requirement is often made the basis of a formal definition of logic, as when Bertrand Russell defines logic as the science of drawing necessary conclusions, which is merely another way of saying conclusions which are true when the starting point is also true. In making this definition we have, however, smuggled something extraneous into the situation. The verbal conclusion is taken to be a statement concluded from the initial statements by a process called by the general name of deduction. It is not necessary, however, that every method of arriving at the truth should be a deductive process. Another possible and useful method is by the exhaustive enumeration of all special cases. Suppose, for example, we have a table of the physical properties of all known liquids. In this table we find that water has a density of 0.99987 at 0° C and 1.00000 at 4° C. We also find in the table that water is the only such liquid. We further find in the table that water freezes at atmospheric pressure at 0° C. Whenever now we find a liquid which has a density of 0.99987 at 0° and 1.00000 at 4° C we draw the conclusion that this liquid freezes at 0° C (we also draw the conclusion that the liquid is water). This process, consulting the table, is a process which yields true statements but would not, I think, be called a process of logic.

The requirement that a process yield true results is then not a sufficient condition that it be called logical, but it is a necessary condition. If logic does not provide the only method of arriving at true results the question arises of how indispensable it is for successful living or for survival in general. The question is not merely rhetorical, for, although it is unquestionable that conventional logical processes play a large part in our western culture, there are cultures which do not habitually use conventional logical argument. It is fundamental to all western logic that the notion of "class" is involved. We group the objects of interest in some definite way into classes, and from the mutual relations of the classes draw certain conclusions, again in terms of class inclusion. This is illustrated by the conventional example from the old Aristotelian logic of the syllogism: "All men are mortal, Socrates is a man, therefore Socrates is mortal". Now there are languages and cultures which do not express the class concept; there are, for example, primitive languages which have no word for tree. It follows that such languages cannot formulate general statements of class inclusion, and therefore cannot express a syllogism. Yet such cultures manage to get into effective enough contact with the environment (at least if their fellow humans will let them alone), so they must have some method of getting at "truth" not formally logical. I shall not stop to inquire in detail how it is that cultures like those of many of the North American tribes manage to get at the truth without syllogistic logic, but shall content myself merely with remarking that since syllogistic reasoning is recognized to be tautological in character, that is, to be a method for bringing to light features which were already concealed in the starting material but which were not explicitly stated, it is not too surprising that there should be other methods of taking effective possession of what one already has.

For us in our western culture with our Indo-European languages and with our characteristic use of conventional logical processes it becomes of great importance to understand how "truth" gets itself attached to the accepted processes of logic. Professional logicians recognize a purely formal aspect of logic, that is, the formal rules by which one combines systems of symbols with other symbols, the symbols themselves having no specific interpretation. It appears to be a fact that the formal processes satisfy our demand that if we start with truth we end with truth, but what is the guarantee of this and what is the mechanism by which it is brought about? Is the statement that any process which satisfies the demands of formal logic is a process which produces truth out of truth a statement that is capable of proof, and, if so, what kind of proof is it? The formal process of logic, as such, is completely divorced from any connotation of truth. For consider this syllogism: "Water is a solid, all solids freeze at 0°, therefore water freezes at 0°". This satisfies the formal requirements of the syllogism, yet the only connection with truth is in the conclusion, which is true by accident. What, then, is the nature of our insight that the formal processes of syllogistic reasoning yield truth? This insight was not an insight unique in the mind of Aristotle, but is an insight possessed by every user of the syllogism. I have spent a good deal of time trying to analyze this insight, but without success. One can at least say that the insight is in no way connected with the formal process as such, as just shown by the example of freezing water. Here there is none of the feeling of compulsion or necessity which we find when dealing with true premises and their validly deduced conclusion. I have not been able to do better here than merely to say that we see that it must be so. When we keep clearly in mind all that is operationally involved in the premises, we see that the conclusion is only a report on some aspect of what we do: we *see* that if we have gathered together all men and observed that they are all mortal and have also observed that Socrates is a man we have incidentally observed that he is mortal. I believe that it is probably impossible to go deeper into the meaning of truth than seeing that something is so, or to go back of our report of what we find. I have gone through Susanne Langer's book on symbolic logic[2] pretty carefully, examining all the situations in which the question of truth presents itself, and can find nothing more. The basis on which she makes a statement of truth is always an intuitive basis, involving *seeing* that it is true, quite apart from the logical process. What is more, she takes the whole thing for granted, and nowhere raises the question which is bothering us here.

If any one will examine a situation in which he can say "I *see* that it is so", I think he will realize that this "seeing" is a purely private activity which he has to do for himself, and which no one else can do for him. He doesn't see something merely because someone else tells him that he should — something has to click inside him. This I think is what happens in a broader class of situations than the particular logical situation which we are considering. Whenever we have an ostensible proof there has to be a flash of private recognition in everyone for whom the purported proof is really a proof. The Q.E.D. at the end of a proposition in geometry is for me sterile and empty unless I have the vivifying experience. I can imagine nothing more stultifying or deadening than to have to wade through a scientific argument accepting the say-so of the author that he is presenting me with proof. I suspect, however, that many people have to do just this, but they never get anywhere and for them I am truly sorry.

Because the role of proof bulks so large in mathematics and in those physical sciences built on a mathematical foundation I have frequently argued that science is essentially private rather than public, although the contrary view, that science is by its nature public, is almost universally held, and indeed sometimes is incorporated into the definition of science. In this connection I think it is significant that so far as I know there is no discussion from a technical formal standpoint of the nature of proof. I shall not attempt to argue the matter further here — it will for the present be sufficient if the reader can recognize that there is a private element when he is in the presence of proof, whether or not he wants to call this private happening "scientific".

It must not be thought that the private flash of recognition of proof provides any magical touchstone by which certainty can be attained. The flash may deceive me, and I may wake up in the morning realizing that I have been mistaken and did not see everything of relevance in the situation. This, however, is a hazard which cannot be avoided in any human enterprise. Even all of us together may be mistaken, as has happened more than once.

In seeing how it is that a syllogism may make true statements we do not have to remain content with the mere sterile statement that this is the way experience is, but we can see a little deeper into the nature of situations in which we feel the compulsion of truth. In this connection the use of the conventional circle diagram is informative. Such diagrams are adequate to handle the logical situations that are treatable by the methods of the calculus of classes, which covers many important cases, and in addition are adequate to handle many of the situations in the calculus of propositions. Here a member of a class is represented by a point within a finite, usually two dimensional circular region, which defines the class. Different classes correspond to different circles; these may intersect in various ways and the corresponding areas may overlap. A point within a region of overlap is thereby characterized as a member of two classes. Any statement in the calculus of classes may be transposed into a statement about the manner of overlapping of the various regions into which the various circles subdivide the total significant area, which represents the universe of discourse. The truth of any statement about the relations of the classes is at once verified intuitively by mere inspection of the corresponding diagram and seeing that the asserted state of affairs is actually so.

Our conviction of the validity of the logical process becomes so vivid when thus translated into a circle diagram that we may say that we have thereby "explained" how it is that the syllogism has validity and makes connection with truth. But at the same time a little reflection shows that there are certain assumptions concealed in the use of the diagram. In the first place, the diagram represents a static situation — the points represent fixed elements which are identifiable and remain always the same, and the classes are represented by fixed curves. The conclusion represents a relation between the subareas of the diagram which is entirely static in character. The logical process represented by the diagram is, on the other hand, an activity which takes place in time and in which the order in time is essential. The conclusions *follow* from the premises — we are told or state the premises first and then draw the conclusion. If we were told the conclusion first we could not infer the truth or falsity of either premise. The diagram therefore does not reproduce all aspects of the mental process which we perform when we reason syllogistically. However, the fact that we have not thereby sacrificed our ability to represent the "truth" aspects of the situation would suggest that our failure to reproduce all recognizable aspects of the process as we actually perform it is not very important in this connection. This indeed appears to be the case, and we can rephrase the syllogism in static terms as follows: Whenever we have a situation in which every member of the class *a* is a member of the class *b*, and at the same time every member of the class *c* is a member of the class *a*, it will occur that at the same time every member of the class *c* is also a member of the class *b*. There is here no trace of a temporal order of performing operations. The syllogism is to this extent not concerned with such temporal aspects of logical activity and disregards them, even if no activity can be completely divorced from temporal aspects.

The fact that the circle diagram does not reproduce the aspects of a syllogism as an activity in time thus constitutes no restriction in the usual context. In using the diagram we are abstracting from the temporal aspects as activity and concentrating on the static features.

Surely something is implied here in the assumption that this is possible. To see what it is, write out our syllogism in its most abstract form: all c is a, all a is b, therefore all c is b. Here each symbol occurs twice; each time that it occurs it stands for the "same" thing — otherwise it could not be represented by a single point in the diagram irrespective of whether we are dealing with its first or second appearance in the syllogism. The elements of the syllogism must have identity and remain always the same. In this respect they are like the "things" of ordinary experience. I think it is only when the elements of the syllogism have this common sense property of "thinghood" that we have the feeling of compulsion, or can say that we "see" that the syllogism is presenting us with a correct conclusion. We "see" it because past experience, both of ourselves as individuals and of the race has built this reaction into our nervous systems.

The syllogism as a formal verbal structure thus demands that we be able to say the same thing twice. But we can never say anything *exactly* the same twice, for we as living, or indeed as material, creatures are involved in the inexorable irreversible process of the entire universe. The "sameness" on repetition can therefore be only an approximate sameness, and logic cannot be completely sharp. How good an approximation to sameness must we have? It is easy to set up examples in which the demand for sameness is obviously not satisfied. If, for example, I let a stand for "what I last said," it seldom, or, strictly, never, can have the same significance twice. There are many ways of constructing expressions the denotation of which changes with every successive use. It is not always easy to recognize these, and some of the classical paradoxes in logic present themselves when such expressions are unwittingly introduced. Is there any criterion for deciding whether a proposed element for a syllogistic argument has sufficient identity and permanence to justify such use? I myself am of the somewhat cynical opinion that there is no independent criterion, but that we are here in the presence of an essentially circular situation. An element is sufficiently like a "thing" to permit its use in the syllogism if, when used in the syllogism, it does not lead to contradiction. This does not mean that in practise we cannot make the decision with assurance and success in most of the cases that present themselves.

The necessity for permanence in the terms of a logical analysis suggests the following partial characterization of logic. "Logic presents us with a skeletonized type of behavior suitable to be used in the presence of the permanent or the recurrent."

So much for our explanation of how it is that the formal processes of the syllogism have validity and yield true results under the very general conditions which correspond to class inclusion. In any specific concrete case, however, and this is usually what we are interested in, we have to consider more than the general notion of class inclusion, and have to decide whether in this special case it is true or not that the class inclusion is as stated. For instance, we have to decide whether it is true as a matter of fact that all men are mortal. To establish such a fact some method of verification is called for, not a logical method at all, but some special concrete method depending on the particular statement before us. Now I believe that in practise we often do not trouble to make the specific verification at all, but the feeling of compulsion and necessity in the conclusion persists provided only that we believe that the premise is true, without actually checking its truth or indeed examining whether it is possible to check its truth. The result is that we end by constructing syllogisms like this: "All just acts are good; the execution of murderers is just; therefore the execution of murderers is good." Here there are no generally accepted operations permitting the verification of either premise, so that even the meaning of the premises is in doubt, yet for many people the conclusion has all the compulsion of a proposition in elementary arithmetic. The feeling of compulsion results in acceptance of the conclusion, which issues almost inevitably in social action, often with far-reaching consequences.

In its social context and usage the aura of compulsion which surrounds a logical conclusion is one of its most important aspects. From some points of view it is even more important than the aspect of truth. For it is obviously of prime importance for the smooth functioning of a society that there be some method by which the members of the society can come to an agreement about what they will do. Given the logical process, which is of such a nature that any person of normal intelligence can perform it, and given the feeling of compulsion which accompanies the conclusion of the process, we obviously have a basis for concerted action. We also have a basis for rational argument and appeal by which agreement may be secured when emotional interests clash. The truth of the conclusion is usually of minor importance compared with the importance of consensus. In fact, the concept of truth often does not apply at all in social situations. How, for example, shall one go to work to verify the truth of the statement "the execution of murderers is good"?

We have seen that the static aspect of a logical process is not the only aspect, although in many contexts it is the most important aspect, as in the circle diagrams of the calculus of classes. From the broader point of view of logic as human activity other aspects must be considered. We have seen that in general an activity is not fully specified unless time, place, and performer are specified. Applied to the activities of logic, as typified by the conventional syllogism, I think it would be generally accepted that the place of the activity is irrelevant. The absolute time would also be irrelevant, but not the order in time, as suggested by the fact that the conclusion follows the premises. The person of the performer is, however, far from irrelevant, particularly when the person who states the premise or verifies it is not the same as the person who draws the conclusion. When we consider that the different parts of the syllogism may have been contributed by different persons I think we can see that the syllogism may play a considerably richer role than could be anticipated from the stark statement that the syllogism is nothing but a concealed tautology. The syllogism as thus conceived from the point of view of the performer becomes a method of exchange between different persons, and thereby acquires social value in addition to its compulsive quality. The tautological character of our stock syllogism about Socrates is obvious if I am the sole performer. For if I am to be sure that all men are mortal I must have observed all men to verify that they are mortal, and in so doing I observed in particular the mortality of Socrates. In stating my conclusion that Socrates is mortal I am merely saying again something that I already knew. But if it was not I who verified that all men are mortal, but John Henry, who made the verification and then told me what he had done, then when I draw the conclusion that Socrates is mortal I am not just uncovering something which was implicit in my own experience, for I could not have drawn the conclusion without the cooperation of John Henry. So far as I am concerned the situation is far from tautological. I think this is typical; in many cases we take the major premise on the say-so of someone else, and in drawing our conclusion we are capitalizing someone else's experience. In society this makes for economy of effort and so has value both for the individual and for society. A somewhat similar situation arises when the parts of the syllogism may have been the work of the same person, but when his use of the syllogism is spread over an interval of time. Here the syllogism may function as a filing system by which a large amount of information is compressed into compact form available for future quick reference. Thus I may have observed all men, including Socrates, and found that they were mortal, and summarized my researches in the statement "all men are mortal", which I then filed away in my mind for future use. Later, when I may have forgotten all the details of my former research, I may want to find a rational basis for charging Socrates for an annuity which I am selling him, and my assurance that Socrates is mortal, which I get from my mental file, guides me in setting my price. The syllogism thus has economic value for me in this situation. The unlettered American Indian, however, confronted by the same situation, would doubtless meet it by recalling that he had once verified that Socrates in particular was mortal.

It would be possible to make a systematic formal analysis of the syllogism from the point of view of who performs the operations implied in premises and conclusion and from the point of view of the relative times at which the various operations are performed. I started such an analysis at one time, but did not find it sufficiently likely to be rewarding and dropped it. Perhaps someone else may have a fresh point of view and may want to go on with it.

We have seen that consideration of performer and time mitigates the curse of tautology. There is at least one other mitigation. Consider our stock major premise: "All men are mortal". The truth of this we have verified by observing all men, including Socrates incidentally, and it is thus that the tautology has got into the conclusion. But it seems to me that in practise this procedure does not correspond to the tacit implications. I believe that in daily life the statement "All men are mortal" would carry the implication that there is some independent general principle in virtue of which all men are mortal, such perhaps as the physiological fact that the crucial cells in a human biological system are the seat of nonreversible degenerative processes which will eventually terminate in the dissolution of the cell. Such a principle would ensure the validity of the premise without necessitating verification by exhaustive examination of every special case. With this background the syllogism is saying "Socrates, being a man, is subject to the operation of the principle, and therefore is mortal". That is, concealed here is an assumption about the validity of induction, which in turn assumes the possibility of finding general principles from which one can draw valid conclusions without the necessity of examining all the particulars.

We now consider another aspect of this activity, logic, namely, the matter of scientific theories. A scientific theory is often said to involve a set of assumptions or postulates or constructs to start with, which are then combined according to the processes of logic to result in certain statements which have the property of being true when applied to the situations of experience. It is coming to be accepted more and more that the starting point may be quite arbitrary so far as any factual reference is concerned, a point of view much insisted on by Dirac, so that the characterization "true" may be meaningless when applied to it, provided only that the application of the logical processes yields a result which may be applied by interpretation to actual physical situations and in so doing yield true statements. The question for us here is: if the starting point may be quite arbitrary why may not the process by which the final true statements are "deduced" also be quite arbitrary? Why the insistence that the method of passing from the postulates to the conclusion be a logical process? I think one answer is to be found in the feeling of compulsion which we have seen to be associated with the logical process. Man is incorrigibly a logical animal — given a starting point on which he *could* perform the operations of logic he *will* perform them anyhow, whether or no. So we had better let him. The situation is like that of the man who said to his dog: "Towser, lie down. Well, if you won't lie down, sit up then. I *will* be obeyed."

A more general question suggested by these considerations is whether there are any processes more general than those of logic for arriving at true conclusions. We can, if we like, side-step the issue and make it a verbal matter by defining logic as that science which draws true conclusions from true premises. Even this would be unsatisfactory if one concedes that the starting point may be arbitrary, so that the concept of truth is not applicable to it. There is also another verbal matter here. In actual practice the processes of deduction used by the theoretical physicist are the processes of mathematics. Now there are mathematicians who recognize a difference between the structure of logic and of mathematics and who would, therefore, probably not be willing to say that the theorist arrives at his conclusions by the methods of logic. For such a mathematician we can readily make a verbal concession and simply say that the scientific theorist arrives at his conclusions by methods either of logic or of mathematics. There is just as much compulsion in the processes of the mathematician, for him who understands them, as in the processes of logic, so that we have not lost anything by making our concession.

With regard to the arbitrariness of the starting point of a physical theory, I think that in practice most of us prefer, whenever we can, not to start with something completely arbitrary and formal, but prefer to start with something of which we can ask "Is it true?" For instance, in electrodynamics we start with Maxwell's field equations. Some people may perhaps take these in the spirit of the postulates of a completely abstract mathematics, but I think most physicists would take these as something of which it makes sense to ask "Are they true?" and would engage to set up experiments to answer this question, experiments which would be quite performable on the scale of the long waves of radio communication, passing by imperceptible degrees to experiments performable only conceptually at optical wave lengths.

If we accept this limitation, the scope of our inquiry is limited and we have to ask: "Are there any other methods than those of logic for passing from true statements to true statements?" assuming that we are unwilling to make it purely a matter of definition by including under logic any methods as yet undiscovered which satisfy the criterion. I do not believe that the question has ever been subjected to systematic examination. From the point of view of complete generality we can see that there must be at least one other method because we have exhibited such a method, namely the consultation of tables exhaustively cataloging all concrete cases. This particular method will doubtless be judged to be a triviality and we would like to know whether there is any more general possibility. Any answer to this question will obviously involve an examination of the nature of "formal" processes in general. Now in structures erected by formal processes we encounter something closely analogous to the "truth" of concrete experience. We demand in our formal structures self-consistency or freedom from inner contradiction. Notice that the demand for self-consistency has no application to logical systems as simple as the simple syllogism; it is only when the system becomes complicated enough to permit getting to the same terminus by more than one route that the demand arises. The reason for the demand for self-consistency is obviously rooted in our intention of making application to concrete cases. In practice we cannot have a thing true and at the same time not true. From the point of view of *pure* formalism the requirement is not necessary — here it is only necessary that at every step of the formal process the next step, when taken, lead to an unambiguous result. We are not involving ourselves in an impossible situation in saying that the performance of the sequence "a" of operations led to the result "x" and the performance of the sequence "b" led to the result "non-x" so long as the result "x" has no other significance than to characterize the sequence of operations. It is only in view of possible applications that such a situation becomes intolerable.

There is evidently a very close involvement of "truth" with "self-consistency", but the two are by no means coextensive. Self-consistency in a formal structure is a necessary condition that it should be interpretable into concrete terms to which the notion of truth applies, but it is not a sufficient condition. Furthermore, the two things, truth and self-consistency, are by no means isomorphic. Experience is never self-contradictory — we cannot at the same time have a state of affairs and not have it — if there is any statement that we can make about the world of experience it is this. This statement is essentially the law of the excluded middle, which thus appears as a tautological definition of what we mean by "not". On the other hand we can never be sure that a formal structure is free from concealed contradiction which some day may be discovered — Gödel's theorem shows this. In constructing physical theories we cannot help giving hostages to fortune.

Finally, we have to ask to what extent a *purely* formal structure or a formal operation is at all possible. The answer to this has already been implied — we are presently driven to leave the formal level of operations no matter what we do. The reason is that all these operations are operations by us, with our nervous system, into which have been built such properties as ability to identify and to recognize recurrence, without which no formal enterprise is possible.

MEANING OF "ALL", "ANY", "EVERY"

Let us now consider several more specialized topics connected with logic. There are certain simple words which frequently occur in any logical argument and which are recognized as characteristic of logic. Such words are "if", "and", "or", "not". The meaning of such words is usually taken as intuitively known and they are therefore treated as unanalyzed in any logical enterprise. This does not mean, however, that they are incapable of analysis or that we should not try to analyze them. I have already suggested that since logic is palpably a verbal enterprise the referents of these characteristically logical words are to be found in certain typical verbal situations which frequently recur in any logical analysis. Thus, the meaning of "if" is to be found in the way we want to talk about certain verbal situations that frequently occur when we get ready to carry out programs of action.

I cannot attempt here to make a systematic analysis from this point of view of all the short logical words. There are, however, three of such widespread use in the situations of daily life, as well as in the situations of logic, that some consideration of them is almost necessary. These are "any", "all", and "every". Under what circumstances do we use these words? The situation is comparatively simple when we deal with finite groups of objects, but even here there are shades of meaning which are usually ignored. Consider a basket full of apples. We may apply "all" to the apples in this basket with different implications depending on whether we think of the apples together, in their group capacity, or separately, as individuals. We may say "All the apples in the basket weigh ten pounds", meaning that all the apples taken together weigh ten pounds, or we may say "All the apples in the basket weigh eight ounces," meaning that each and every individual apple weighs eight ounces. In such cases we can usually judge by the context which is the sense intended. In some cases there may be a fusion of the two meanings. When we say "All the apples in the basket are red", we may have in mind that from a distance the basket presents a uniformly red appearance, or we may mean that each and every individual apple is red. The connotations are somewhat different when we are dealing with a continuum instead of a collection of discrete objects. We say "All the water in the pail weighs ten pounds" with no implications about the weight of smaller subdivisions or the density. We cannot speak of the weight of "any" water in the pail, but we can say "All the water in the pail is wet" and can also say "Any water in the pail is wet". It may be that we have a basis here for a tenable distinction between "extensive" and "intensive" properties, a distinction which has always seemed to me difficult and uncertain. Weight is an extensive property — wetness an intensive property.

It thus appears that in many situations, but by no means all, statements in which "all" appears are transformable into statements in which "all" is replaced by "any" or "every". What is involved here operationally? Suppose that I have performed the operations which enable me to say "All the apples in the basket are red"; then I can immediately also say "Any (or every) apple in the basket is red" without performing any additional operation. Notice, however, that this statement could not be made unless the apples had the identity and the permanence of the objects of ordinary experience. The words "all", "any", and "every" have meaning only in a context of such common experience. Can the situation be inverted? Are there situations in which I can make statements about "any" apple in the basket without at the same time being able to make a corresponding statement about "every" apple or "all" the apples? When can I make a statement about "any" apple anyway? I may draw any apple and I then may observe that the apple so drawn is red, but this would not enable me to say with the usual connotation that "Any apple is red". I could say "Any apple is red" only if every time that I drew an apple I found that it was red. The connotation here points toward the future, and implies an expectation. I would not be justified in saying that any apple in the basket is red if my only experience had been that every time that I had in the past drawn an apple I had found that it was red. I can make statements about any apple based on experiences with individual apples only on a probability basis. The more times I draw "any" apple and verify that it is red the greater the probability that I may truthfully say "Any apple is red". We here encounter the question of to what extent numerical measures can be attached to inductive procedures in concrete situations, that is, a numerical measure of the justifiability of projecting into the future the regularities of the past. We avoid this question here; it is difficult and controversial. It would appear from the example above that we can have certainty in making a statement about any apple only when we are in a position to have certainty in a statement about all apples or every apple. The certainty is then a tautological certainty, concealed in the meaning of "any" and "all".

"Any" carries certain implications by itself, apart from any association with "all". We may say "Select any apple in the basket". What this means is that the selection is to be controlled by no rule that can be formulated in advance. Obviously, after the event, the description of the event may be transformed into a rule by which the selection might have been made. If it happens that I select the third apple from the lower right-hand corner, then a rule according to which the apple might have been selected is: "Choose the third apple from the lower right-hand corner". But this sort of postdiction does not count and does not prevent our selection from having been of "any" apple. It is obvious that a statement about "any" object or event made on the basis of direct experience and not on the basis of a tautological coupling of experience with "all" can have the significance merely of statements about particular historical happenings. Such statements acquire a broader significance only in a context of repetition under as nearly as possible identical conditions. In the case of finite aggregates, therefore, there are some statements about "any" which can be made only on the basis of statements about "all".

We are here in the presence of one of those very difficult words with no fixed meaning. I may say "draw any apple from the basket". I draw any apple and find that it is red. But then I may *not* say "Any apple in the basket is red". The meaning of "any" on the first occurrence is different from the meaning on the second occurrence, and the meaning on the second occurrence has changed in virtue of the mere fact that it has occurred before. There are contexts in which "any" is intrinsically incapable of meaning the same thing twice in succession.

Although paradoxical and puzzling, we have learned how to handle these situations consistently and satisfactorily enough so long as we are dealing with finite collections of discrete things. When we pass to continuous or "infinite" aggregates, the difficulties become more formidable. Some of the distinctions which arise here pass into the idiomatic usage of the language and we handle them intuitively. We speak of "all" the water in the pail; we speak of "any" water in the pail only in certain contexts which we can recognize, and we never speak of "every" water in the pail. In other situations the relative usage of "any" and "every" is different. We can say "Any number is either odd or even" and we can also say "Every number is either odd or even". As a matter of fact we can also say "All numbers are either odd or even".

When it comes to situations like those presented by the numbers it seems to me that the operational significance of "all" is recognizably different from that when we are dealing with a basket of apples. "All" numbers do not occur in a totality which can be handled together as a single self-contained unit. Our immediate experience is only with "any" number, that is, a number selected at random (by no rule formulatable in advance), and our statements about all numbers are transformed into statements about any number. The order of operations becomes inverted. With the basket of apples we had direct experience with all the apples, and only then were we able to pass to statements about any apple, whereas with numbers we can have direct experience only with any number, from which we pass by tautological transformation to statements about all numbers. "All" as a term applied to numbers has its primary meaning through this tautological connection with "any"; the primary meaning as in the case of the basket of apples has disappeared.

Nevertheless, people continue to talk about all the numbers with the connotations of the basket. It is in this context that the transfinite numbers appear. I shall not attempt again to formulate my objections to this, but I persist in my heresy.[3]

In many cases we are apparently able to deal directly with "all", not on a piecemeal basis. Thus we can empty all the apples in the basket onto the table and see at a glance that they are all red, without verifying it separately for each individual. It is a problem to find what is implied in an analysis into parts in those situations where we can perceive the whole as a unit.

The situation with regard to infinity is not always like that presented by the numbers. Thus we talk about *all* the points on a line between the origin and 1, for example, and make statements about all these points (such, for example, as the statement that all the points between 0 and 1 are also between −1 and 2), without ever the necessity of recognizing the existence of individual points or using the word "any". This situation requires further examination — a point is a curious thing and I do not believe that its nature is appreciated, even by many mathematicians. A line is not composed of points in any real sense. The above statement about all the points of the line between 0 and 1 is a paraphrase for "the entire line between 0 and 1". We do not construct the line out of points, but, given the line, we may construct points on it. "All the points on the line" has the same sort of meaning that the "entire line" has. It is exceedingly difficult here to free ourselves from thinking of geometry in terms of a ghostly physical background, something of which Euclid was guilty in his proofs by superposition, for one cannot think of moving geometrical figures about in order to superpose them without a physical background. The physical background may get into the line-point situation through the picture of a line as something generated by the motion of a point. The line, then, having been swept out by the moving point is composed of the ghosts of the point. This is illegitimate thinking. We cannot have motion without having something to move, and we cannot have something move unless it is identifiable, and this involves an element from physical experience. We *create* the points on a line just as we create the numbers, and we identify the points by the numerical values of the coordinates. The point *is* the number, or, more generally, a point is an aggregate of three numbers. Given the numbers, everything that can be said mathematically follows. And the point was not "there" before the numbers were given or determined.

Other implications of the distinction between "any" and "all" will be considered in the next chapter.

The fact that we say "all" and do "any" is an example of one of the things on the scale of everyday life which appears not to have been properly appreciated — the sort of thing mentioned in the introduction.

ON COUNTING

There are two aspects to counting — we can count things (counting used transitively) or we can just count (intransitive). The latter we do when we just recite in succession the integers. We have a rule for proceeding from one count or number to the next one — the rule is non-self-terminating — we can never count so long or so far but that the rule tells us what to call the next count. As we recite the succession of numbers we can pair off the successive steps in our recitation with other sorts of thing ("thing" is used here with no material implication). Thus we can recite the numbers as we walk and so count our steps. Or we can count our heart beats or the waves breaking on the shore. That is, we can count happenings or activities provided they are sufficiently punctuated by features to enable us to break them up into discrete episodes. Not only can we pair off the steps in our recitation of the numbers with discrete happenings as they occur, but we can also pair off the steps with discrete objects in our surroundings, as, for example, by touching an object at each successive step of our recitation. This sort of counting has no significance, however, unless we add another feature which so far as I know is always taken for granted in analyses of the counting procedure. Without this feature the counting operation on objects is of no importance whatever — I could keep on counting forever the coins in my pocket. But if the objects which I pair with the steps of my recitation have sufficient discreteness so that I can recognize them as different individuals, and if I take pains never to pair my recitation twice with the same object, then the counting operation at once takes on a new significance which entitles it to be regarded as one of the great human inventions. A new concept emerges, namely the total number of objects in a collection. The "collection" has its meaning in some other operation than that of counting, as the collection of apples in a basket or of people in a house. The number of objects in such a collection is the number which I recite as I make the count on the last object, after which there are no more objects which I have not already counted. The usefulness of knowing the number of objects in a collection hardly needs to be labored — if I know how many people will sit down to dinner I can tell whether I shall probably have enough food for them, and so forth.

Nature does not count nor do integers occur in nature. Man made them all, integers and all the rest, Kroneker to the contrary notwithstanding.

The point above I have never seen emphasized, namely that the concept of counting applied to objects involves both the operation of the recitative and also the possession of such properties by the objects under enumeration that one can know that the same object is not being counted twice. It may well be profitable to examine in detail the methods by which one can be sure that one is not counting the same object twice and to find the minimum sort of property of the object which makes this possible. I shall come back to this. First I want to examine a property of the counting operation which is at the basis of the extension of the counting concept to "infinite" collections. It is possible to count two finite collections at the same time, as by taking the apples out of two baskets simultaneously with my two hands, reciting as I do so. Or this could be extended to more than two by having a number of assistants each remove an apple from his particular basket in step with my recitation of the numbers. In case the last apple is removed simultaneous from the two (or more) baskets the number of apples in the two (or more) baskets was the same, and this is true irrespective of what the particular number is. In such a case the reciting of the numbers can be dispensed with if one wants only to know whether the numbers in the baskets are the same or not,

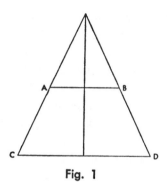

Fig. 1

and it is sufficient merely to pair off the contents of the baskets without reciting. This affords the possibility of generalizing one aspect of the counting operation by saying that the number in two collections is the same if the collections can be paired against each other without residue. This aspect of the counting operation can now be applied to situations in which the original concept of counting is not applicable at all. For instance, it is applied to "infinite" collections, as the points on a finite segment of line. For example, the points of the lines *AB* and *CD* (Fig. 1) may be uniquely, exhaustively and reciprocally paired with each other by the construction indicated. This possibility is the basis for saying that the "number" of points in the line *CD* is the same as the number of points in *AB*. By thus extending the meaning we put ourselves in the position of saying that two numbers are equal although we cannot say what either number is. Thus is the basis laid for many of the paradoxes of the infinite and the whole subject of transfinite numbers. The reason that mathematicians extend the concept of counting in this way is that it puts them in a position to do so many interesting things.

It must be recognized, however, that the original picture has materially changed on going to the geometric situation above, and this that we now call counting is not the same as what we called counting in the first place. We now have a "number" not obtainable by counting. The whole business of reciting is gone. What sort of a thing is it anyway that we now say is a number? What is a point? Does it have identity like the objects of everyday life, and is there some way we can mark a point after we have counted it to be sure that we do not count it again? The frame of mind here seems pretty close to that of the Greeks who saw a line as composed of points. But in what sense is a line composed of points? We certainly do not put the points together and obtain the line. And what is a line? Do we generate it or is it just there? And can we move it about carrying its points with it? It seems to be assumed in the superposition proofs of Euclidean geometry that we can do this. But cannot we equally well generate a line by shifting a segment along into successive positions parallel to itself or by stretching the segment? In the latter case it might make sense to say that the whole line has as many points as the segment, but in the first case, not. Points may be "specified" and different sorts of procedure may be used for the specification. We may specify a point on a line by giving the number which measures the distance from an arbitrary point on it chosen as the origin, or we may specify a point as lying at the intersection of two lines. When we have specified the point by the intersection we may ask what is its distance from the arbitrary origin. That is, it makes sense to ask whether the points specified by two different procedures are the "same" point or not. How do we go to work to answer such a question? Certainly not by painting the point red which we have determined by an intersection and then observing whether the point obtained by measuring off a given distance from the origin is the same red point or not.

Why may we not have two different points satisfying the same specifications? Simply because a point is not this sort of thing — it *is* the specifications. The meaning of the statement that two formally different specifications give the same point is concealed in the axioms underlying the geometric system. As, for example, the point specified by the intersection of the bisectors of the angles A and B of the plane triangle ABC is the same as that specified by the intersection of the bisectors of the angles B and C. Points are not *there;* we *make* them when we give their specifications. If we are going to talk about the number of points, their number is the number of ways we can independently specify them, the operational meaning of "independently" being implied in the axiom system. In the example above this implies that the two methods of specifying the points in terms of the angle bisectors are not independent methods, which we indeed know to be the case.

There is a curious self-reflexive paradox about this business of counting. We have spoken of intransitive counting — just counting without counting anything. But from one point of view it is impossible to count without counting something. Even if we do not purposely pair our counting recitative with things, we are automatically counting the steps in our counting procedure. What sort of thing is this "step" that we count willy-nilly? It is obviously not like the objects of common sense experience — the thing that we count was not there before we counted it, but we create it as we go along. It is the acts of creation that we count. We count the total number of creative steps, but it makes no sense to ask whether we may not have made a mistake in our counting and counted the same step twice. The same step does not recur, but every time we take it, it is new and different. It would seem impossible that all the implications of the ordinary process should apply here.

The situation thus presented by counting something that we create as we go along has features in common with our operation of comparing the relative number of points in two line segments of finite length. Here the "points" which we count were not "there" before we began the counting process, but we create them by the process by which we correlate the points in one segment with those in the other. It has always seemed to me highly misleading to assimilate this sort of "counting" with the counting of common sense objects.

Return now to a consideration of how we avoid counting the same object twice. We may, for example, arrange the objects in a row, and count as we walk along the row from one to the next. This is a good method if the objects remain stationary during the counting process and do not run around. We can tell whether the objects remain still as we count them by watching them; in fact we can allow them to move about a little as we count except that they must not move too much. We can exploit any other specifiable arrangement as well as arrangement in a row to make possible the counting operation; our progress through the arrangement as we count can be described in terms of the specification. If the objects do not maintain a sufficiently fixed arrangement we may try to capture them instantaneously by photography. We can now count the number of objects in the photograph by checking each object as we count it to be sure that we have got them all and have not counted any twice. But how are we to be sure that the photograph got all the objects, and that some of them were not hiding around a corner? If the photographic technique is not applicable and the objects have sufficient individuality so that they are recognizably different, then we may simply remember the objects as we count them and thus ensure against counting any twice. But in such a situation it is difficult to be sure that we have counted all the objects — about the best we can do is to keep on watching for a long time to be sure that we never see an object which we have not already counted. This sort of thing can obviously become unsatisfactory.

There is another sort of procedure, applied to the counting of sheep or it is said formerly to the counting of an army. The sheep are originally all in one pen which is connected with another pen by a passageway so narrow as to permit the passage of only one sheep at a time. The sheep are all driven from the one pen through the passageway into the other pen, and counted one by one as they file through the passageway. So long as the walls of the pens remain impervious and lambs are not born in the second pen and we can be sure that there are no wolves in sheep's clothing this is a satisfactory procedure. That is, the procedure is satisfactory in general if we can be sure that what we are counting has, like sheep, certain of the properties of what we call objects. I suspect that it would be extraordinarily difficult to make a list of necessary and sufficient properties to ensure this. I suspect we would find it difficult to avoid a circular proceeding and include as one of the properties that, when subjected to a counting procedure as above, we obtain consistent results. I do not know how much interest there would be in trying to find a minimum list of properties which would ensure consistent results under our conventional counting procedures. It is, I think, obvious that the properties which we ordinarily associate with the concept of "object" are from this point of view redundant. Modern communication theory suggests that in some circumstances there may be an advantage in such redundancy.

What does it mean to say that two repetitions of the counting procedure are the same? Obviously they cannot be the same in all respects. Or what do we do to ensure that we have not made a mistake in our recitation? One method would be to recite out loud and have our neighbor confirm that we have done it right. This is a better approximation that trying to check it ourselves, but there is nothing fundamental about it, and it only shoves the locus of self-doubt further into the background.

To what extent are the various counting procedures which we have been considering applicable to electrons? Obviously the extent is rather slight. Electrons may not be continuously observed; they may be created or annihilated, and there are no walls impervious to them. We cannot count the number of electrons *now* inside a given enclosure, nor can we say how many electrons there were inside the enclosure at some definite time in the past. It is to be examined to what extent other techniques could take the place of the counting technique. Can we, for example, determine the total electrostatic charge in an enclosure at any definite epoch? Although we cannot count the number of electrons now in an enclosure, we can count the number of electron flights from one enclosure to another through a passageway. What is the significance of the count we make in this way? Can we check the count to be sure that we are not mistaken, or indeed, does the concept of "error" apply to it at all? We can check the count to the extent that we can make a permanent record of the clicks in a Geiger counter, or what not, that marked the passage of the electrons. But how shall we be sure that one of the clicks was not due to a stray cosmic ray or other adventitious happening? In fact, this sort of consideration is very much to the fore as shown, for example, by the experimental evidence for the antiproton. Apparently the only way to rule out such possibilities is by repetition and statistical analysis. There seems to be no method, perhaps even in principle, to tell whether any particular record of the passage of an electron was spurious or not.

PROBABILITY IN GENERAL

There is a close relation between aspects of logic and probability. Thus in our discussion of the meaning of the logical terms "any" and "all" we have seen that the operations by which one passes from a statement in terms of "any" to a statement in terms of "all" often involve an element of probability, more especially in connection with assemblages of many members. And it is well recognized that the statements of inductive, as distinguished from deductive, logic have to be made on a probability basis. Beyond this, the methods of probability have come to play such a fundamental role in modern physical theory that a consideration of the subject for its own sake requires no apology.

I shall not attempt here any systematic argument, but shall first state somewhat categorically my present position with regard to probability. Very broadly, I think that the various difficulties and infelicities in the probability situation which give concern to so many people and which are the occasion of so much disagreement are not different in kind from the difficulties which we always encounter when we try to make rationally satisfying contact with the world around us; it is only that the difficulties are greater and hence more evident.

The first such infelicity is the impossibility of finding the sharpness in the fundamental concepts that many desire. That there is a fundamental lack of sharpness I think everyone can discover for himself by trying to carry through a rigorous analysis of the probability situation, or he can take as presumptive evidence for this the fact that even yet there is no consensus in this field in spite of long years of effort by men of the highest competence.

In all the welter of usage and meaning for the word "probability" I think it is profitable to single out two types of usage and center our discussion around them. The two kinds of probability which I shall thus distinguish are similar to, but recognizably different from, the two kinds of probability of Carnap.[4] There is in the first place the probability of common sense and daily life — the sort of probability which we use in arguing to ourselves about the best course of future action in situations where we feel doubtful. The other probability is the probability of the mathematical discipline. The probability of common sense runs the entire gamut of sharpness and articulateness. At one end it has almost mathematical sharpness, and we often use numbers in describing it, as when we deal with situations involving relative frequencies or "favorable" and "unfavorable" cases. At the other end we encounter great vagueness, as when we seek the relative probability of different theories, or as in such expressions as "It will probably rain tomorrow". It is, I think, characteristic of many of these common sense uses of probability that there is an associated serial order in the sense that we can say "This probability is greater or less than that probability". This implication can, I think, often be discovered even where there is no explicit statement of greater or less. Thus when we say that it is probable that it will rain tomorrow we are at the same time saying that it is more probable that it will rain than that it will not. This possibility, of arranging probabilities in a greater-less-than relation is, I think, what we are usually interested in in the common sense usages, even in those cases in which an approximate numerical assignment is possible. Now the existence of a greater-less-than relation always invites the attempt to convert it into a more precise serial relation characterized by numbers. This sort of thing has been carried through in other fields, as when the psychologist found how to make intensity of sensation numerically measurable when all he had to start with was a serial relation of more-or-less intense. One would anticipate the possibility of at least partial success in converting the common sense notion of probability to numbers, but I do not believe that any attempt is satisfactory from all points of view, and I do not believe that success is necessary for most of our purposes. This applies, in particular, to Carnap's "degree of confirmation".

The most important common factor in the various common sense probabilities seems to me to be the element of "expectation". I believe I can always find the element of expectation in any situation in which I try to guide action by probability considerations, and it is the element of expectation that gives some of its characteristic properties to this sort of probability. This enables us to recognize a purely formal sense in which it is meaningful to speak of the probability of concrete individual events, even those which have already happened and of which we have full knowledge. Here is technically a change from my previous position. I have previously said that the concept of probability is not applicable to the concrete individual event because after the event has occurred there is nothing that one can do to show, for example, that the probability of throwing an ace with a die was "actually" one-sixth, as one said before the throw was made. I would now say that it is at least meaningful to assign a probability to a concrete individual throw after it has been made, in the sense that it is possible to set up a universal procedure, applicable in particular to the individual throw, which yields a definite result. This procedure is one which is applicable whether the event is one which has already happened or is considered merely as a possibility in prospect. The procedure is merely to assign by definition the probability of one-sixth to every throw in the whole class of throws of a die, "actual" or "potential". We now have our answer automatically for every throw, regardless of whether the throw is an actual one which has yielded an ace, or whether it is potential in the future. Although this procedure is possible in the sense that it can lead to no logical inconsistency and is always applicable, it is nevertheless, in the context in which probability implies expectation, of so little interest to us that as a matter of fact we seldom apply the procedure. For when we have the full knowledge of the actual throw our interest in the expectation aspect evaporates; we stop talking about probability and turn to other matters. Of course, even after the throw has actually been made and before we know what it is, we still continue to think of the probability of an ace on that throw as one-sixth.

The distinction between the point of view that says that the concept of probability is applicable to no *single* concrete situation and the point of view that says that it *is* possible to assign a meaning to the probability of a single event, even after it has happened and the outcome is known, requires further examination. The first point of view envisages the following sort of situation. Given a die lying stationary on the table with the ace uppermost. Then I think no one would say that the probability of this situation was one-sixth. The probability of one-sixth is not a "property" of the situation, determinable, given only the situation, by performable operations. On the other hand, given a falling body, then it is determinable by operations involving only the body that its velocity of fall is, for example, 10 feet per second. In this sense the velocity of 10 feet per second is a "property" of the body. No one, speaking from the point of view of common sense, would talk about "probability" as applicable to the die resting on the table top unless he knew something of the history that led up to the situation. He would want to be assured, for example, that some one had not deliberately placed the die on the table with the ace uppermost, and he would want to know that something had previously occurred roughly equivalent to shaking the die at random in a dice box and letting it fall haphazard on the table. Given a properly random history, the holder of the first point of view above would be willing to say "The probability of an ace was one-sixth before the throw", but he would not willingly talk about the probability of the consummated event. The holder of the second point of view, however, might justify speaking of the present probability by saying "An event is an event, whether in anticipation or in retrospect. If its probability was one-sixth before it happened, it is still one-sixth after it has happened". I believe that it is possible to talk in this way without self-contradiction, and that if one does choose this way of talking one may meaningfully speak of the probability of an event being an "objective" property of the event "as such". But I believe this way of talking is not compatible with the point of view of probability which regards the expectation aspect as fundamental, and I shall try not to talk this way here.

It is easy to recognize the lack of sharpness in the analysis of the last paragraph. By demanding that it was the event by itself, "as-such," that was to have the probability we were effectively isolating the event. Now we have always recognized that the operation of isolation is one which is almost indispensable in the common sense handling of the world around us, but at the same time it is an operation which is never sharply performable, for everything has a fringe of involvement with its surroundings. If the fringe is not too much involved we may disregard it and profitably speak of the thing by itself. But if the involvement is too great we cannot isolate. It seems to me that in probability situations the involvement with expectation and knowledge and ignorance are too intimate to be disregarded, with the result that we cannot find the "objectivity" in the probability of an individual event that we would like. "Probability" as a property of an anticipated event is even more emphatically something that we say the event has than are the more specific conventional properties. The background of repetition and rehearsal necessary to give significance to what we do and say are even more indispensable. The concepts of probability are applicable only in a context of repetition. This is the situation, only more so, which we also find in daily life. Our life is composed of a sequence of individual events which are unique and occur only once. Yet we could not deal with them or even describe them without repetition and rehearsal. From this point of view there is an *ensemble* aspect to all our conscious experience. But nevertheless nothing is so obvious as that we can and must deal with the expected single individual situation. We live our lives only once, and the particular concrete happenings which constitute it are of the most vital concern to us. We do as a matter of fact attempt to deal with these happenings in anticipation. We cannot do this without forming expectations, which involve the concepts of probability.

The matter may be looked at from another point of view. What we are effectively doing in asking for some proof that the probability of the individual throw, after it has been made, was "really" one-sixth is to demand that there be some alternative method of getting to our terminus, such that we can apply the alternative method and thus check our statement. If there is no second method, then we are dealing with a convention, and are not saying anything when we say that the probability was one-sixth. Such seems to be the situation here; no second operation, independent of the remembered expectation, has been found applicable to the individual event after it has happened which yields one-sixth for the throw of an ace. Hence we may equally well describe the situation by saying that the probability of an individual event after it has happened is a pure convention. In general, pure conventions are sterile and uninteresting — such seems particularly the case here, although there is no logical inconsistency.

There is another matter connected with the application of probability considerations to actual situations which has features in common with the question of the "objectivity" of the probability of an event after it has happened. In statistical analysis use is often made of sequences of "random" numbers, and lists of such random numbers are published in books. Now there is a sense in which no set of actually exhibited numbers can be random. The meaning of "random" appears to be somewhat vague, but I think most people would accept as a necessary condition that if the sequence of numbers is random it exhibit no formulatable regularity. But any set of numbers in print exhibits a regularity, a regularity which can be specified by referring to the printed example itself. One might be inclined, therefore, to ascribe the randomness to the *process* by which the set of numbers was generated rather than to the actually generated set. But this only postpones the difficulty. For the actual set was generated by some actual concrete process. We might give a general specification of the process as one of a class in such a way that we cannot predict in advance how the individual process is going to turn out, but once the process has been performed and the set of numbers generated, the process becomes specific, with no element of indeterminism and no possibility of randomness. Randomness is a loose concept — it is useful in a context of certain purposes and intended use. We will say that a set of numbers is random if it exhibits no regularities of the kind which we intend to regard as significant in the use we propose to make of the numbers. The proposed use is usually conventionalized to such an extent that concrete criteria can be set up which the numbers must satisfy if they are to be accepted as random. But these criteria are not well defined and would seem to be limitless in number. Thus in any long sequence we may demand that each of the digits, 0 to 9, occur on the average only one-tenth of the time, with a deviation of no more than some specific amount, which has to be set somewhat arbitrarily. This will give 10 conditions. Next we can demand that every two-digit number occur on the average only one-hundredth of the time; this will give 100 conditions. Next we demand that every three-digit number occur on the average only one-thousandth of the time. This gives 1000 conditions. The imposition of continually more complicated conditions can obviously proceed without limit. One would guess that no actual set of numbers could possibly satisfy more of these conditions than there are numbers in the set. The situation therefore cannot be made precise — we stop when we are tired or when we think that we have made our conditions good enough.

So far our detailed discussion has been concerned with the probability of common sense. This is intimately associated with expectation. It is characterized by serial order. At one end of the range it is fuzzy and at the other end it acquires such a degree of sharpness that for practical purposes we may think of it in numerical terms. This sort of probability cannot be made completely "objective", but is nevertheless applicable to anticipated individual events. We now consider the other sort of probability, the probability of the mathematical discipline. This is a purely formal discipline, in which probabilities are manipulated according to definite rules. The probabilities so manipulated are numbers, which are "given" and accepted as such with no concern for the process by which the given numbers were generated. The resulting discipline has all the sharpness of mathematics. The general subject matter of the discipline is the calculation of the probability of events compounded in various ways out of the events for which the probabilities are given. The discipline originated in the attempt to meet certain situations of experience, in particular, to devise rational strategies in gambling games; the language of the discipline has never been able to shake off all trace of its origin. For instance, we speak of the probability of compound "events" and find it difficult not to read into the "event" irrelevant connotations from the events of daily life. As practitioners of this discipline we almost never operate exclusively on the purely formal level, but nearly always have one eye cocked on the practical applications which we intend to make. The sorts of situation to which we can most obviously make application are those situations in which the process for generating the numbers which are to be taken as given is simplest and sharpest. Now these situations are first and most importantly situations in which we deal with relative frequencies, which are usually to be obtained by the simple process of counting. In fact such situations are so overwhelmingly preponderant that application of the mathematical discipline has come to be regarded by many as almost synonymous with accepting the "frequentist" definition of probability. An enormous amount of effort has been spent in trying to sharpen the connection between the frequentist view of probability as something applicable in concrete physical situations and the formal mathematical discipline. I do not believe that any of these attempts have been completely successful, but I have always been able to find some specific difficulty in any specific proposal or analysis. As already said I do not believe that the difficulty here is different in kind from that attending the attempt to make rigorous connection between mathematics and actual experience in other fields; it is merely more patent and obtrusive. What we are essentially trying to do is to set up a mathematical model for the experiential situation, and no such model is ever perfect.

The difficulty in application manifests itself at both ends of the process — in obtaining from experience the numbers which are to function as the given of the mathematical analysis and in applying to experience the results of the mathematical calculations. In obtaining from experience the numbers one tacitly demands that the experiential numbers have the same properties as the numbers of the mathematical analysis, and it is in giving proof that the experiential numbers do as a matter of fact have these properties that difficulty arises. For mathematics demands that the numbers for compound events be derivable in certain ways from the simple events, and in giving empirical proof of this it is necessary to compound the events, which demands repeating the simple events, whereas in situations subject to probability analysis simple events do not repeat. The empirical check can be given only to a degree of approximation. Or in the still simpler situation of trying to establish experimentally that the chance of a single throw of an ace by a die is one-sixth we are reduced to counting the relative number of aces in a long succession of throws, and we know perfectly well that we seldom obtain the same number of aces in two successions of the same total number. The question then arises of how good an approximation we shall be satisfied with, and no sharp answer can be given because the mathematical theory assures us that no matter how crude the approximation we are willing to accept we shall eventually find instances in which even that approximation is not met. Considerations of this sort thwart, I believe, efforts such as those of Nagel [5] to describe a practical procedure with arbitrarily set tolerances of acceptable approximation. Instances will arise in which the throwing of a perfectly fair die will fall outside our toleration limits.

Mention of the word "fair" brings up other considerations. There has to be some method for showing that the die is fair or something equivalent, and this method is only approximate and logically entangled with the very probability concept whose legitimateness we are trying to prove. Attempts to make the frequency definition of probability rigorous by introducing the idea of a limiting process meet a similar difficulty in practise — the limit in the mathematical sense corresponds to no performable physical operation, and any attempt to give a "practical" specification in terms of a finite tolerance runs into the difficulty that there is a specifiable chance that no matter how long the series any preassigned tolerance will be exceeded by any amount that we please.

If one desires, one can secure mathematical sharpness in any concrete case simply by counting. If there are 30 white balls in an urn and 30 black balls, then one may take the number ½ for the chance of drawing a black ball as the "given" for the mathematical analysis. One thus secures precision in the mathematical analysis, and a formally sharp correlation with the experiential situation, but at the price of uncertainty in transferring any result of the analysis back to the experiential situation. For to make such a transfer one must be sure that the chance of drawing a black ball is "really" one-half. This assurance we have seen cannot be given by any actual succession of drawings. We may seek to give other sorts of assurance — to do this we would have to know that the balls are alike in all respects which might have an effect on the drawing (for instance they have to be of the same size and equally round). In demanding that the black and white balls be alike in all respects that can have an effect on the drawing we are in effect saying that the color can have no effect. This amounts to isolating the color from other properties; but we have seen that isolation is an idealization. Furthermore, we have to be sure that initially the balls were arranged at random in the urn, in particular being equally distributed from top to bottom. Now again, "random" is a concept which cannot be exactly established for any finite distribution, and in fact considerations already given indicate that the concept of random is not applicable to any actually given distribution.

These considerations do not exhaust the difficulties in making contact between the mathematical discipline and the experimental situation, but I believe enough has been said. The difficulties most often arise in trying to make connection with the frequentist point of view for the simple reason that it is that point of view which most often leads to numbers. Here we recognize a frequentist aspect of the probability of common sense, because in estimating common sense probabilities we count relative frequencies or estimate the relative number of favorable instances in the old original fashion of Laplace.

I have seen no attempt to set up a correspondence between the experimental and the mathematical situations which can be accepted as cogent or free from some infelicity like those suggested above. Furthermore, I believe it is impossible to set up such a correspondence. Always, it seems to me, in any probability analysis which deals with numbers we jump a logically unbridgeable chasm when we pass from the experiential to the mathematical or back, and I believe that all the men of high ability who have been trying so hard to bridge this chasm during the last couple of hundred years are engaged on an intrinsically hopeless quest. If the many able men saw a little more clearly that one can never make sharp contact between mathematics and experience in any situation whatever, I think they would not be so persistent and obstinate in their attempt to push through this point of view with regard to probability in particular.

INDUCTION

So much for general considerations. Now turn to some more specialized points. There is a close connection between probability and induction. The connection at once appears, because whenever we induce a law of nature from an examination of a number of special cases we can never say that we have *certainly* found a law, but can only say that the law which we propose has greater or less probability. This is particularly evident when we reflect that we are never able to examine all the pertinent cases, but have to draw our inductive conclusions on admittedly insufficient evidence. This is the modern formulation, such, for example, as that of Carnap in his endeavor to establish a rigorous inductive logic, founded on the notion of "degree of confirmation", alongside the traditional deductive logic. The older formulation was different in spirit — here it was regarded as the problem of induction to explain how it was that we are able to arrive at general laws from an examination of special cases, or, otherwise expressed, the problem of induction was to justify logically the inference of universal laws from limited experience. Or, more briefly, the problem was to see how induction could give "truth".

At least two attitudes are possible toward the older problem of induction. One attitude, the one which I find most congenial, is merely to say that it is no problem at all, but merely a pseudo-problem. There *can* be no *logical* justification of induction. All that we have here is a pragmatic matter — our proposed laws are only concealed programs for action drawn up in the light of past experience and they are to be judged by their success in application. Another attitude is that there is no real problem here but only a triviality. We are likely to take this attitude if we have vividly in mind the detailed operations by which we draw our inductive conclusions. It seems to me that we always draw such conclusions by projecting into the future the regularities of the past. If now we ask what is the nature of this logic by which we wish to justify our inductive procedure I think we can find no other answer than that logic is a projection into the future of certain kinds of regularity in past experience. So that, if we ask how induction, which is a projection of the regularities of the past, can be logically justified, the answer is that of course it is justified because that is also what logic is. This, of course, is a triviality.

From either point of view it seems to me that a great deal of the discussion of induction with the older connotations has been fruitless and unnecessary. This does not apply to such recent attempts as that of Carnap to found an inductive logic. Such an inductive logic is to a large extent a formal matter. It is to a certain extent a verbal matter whether the epithet "logic" should be applied here at all. There are formal correspondences between the sentential structure of the deductive and inductive disciplines which may doubtless be made the justification for describing them both as "logics". Whether Carnap ascribes any deeper significance to this formal verbal correspondence is not clear. He does clearly recognize and explicitly state a vital distinction between the two disciplines in that in deductive logic one may pass by inference from the truth of the premises to the truth of the conclusion, while in inductive logic "from the statement that the evidence (premise) is true nothing can be inferred". From my point of view this admission by Carnap is equivalent to letting the cat out of the bag. I cannot see why in the light of this he is interested in splitting hairs as fine as he does.

It seems to me that the problem of inductive logic can be seen in a broader light than just from the angle of probability. I would want to include in the inductive procedure any sort of groping search for regularities not yet discovered, and, after the discovery of the regularities, their formulation into a "law" which can be made the basis of a program of action. I would want to say that Kepler's discovery that the motions of the planets can be described in terms of ellipses with one focus at the sun and Newton's recognition that an inverse square law of gravitation would account for the ellipses, both involve inductive procedures. The mere fact that one can say of both these discoveries that what they found was "probably" true seems to me more or less incidental and beside the point.

In general, then, the inductive procedure seems to involve the recognition of regularities, their formulation, and their projection into the future. There is no ultimate justification for the procedure except that in the past it has worked, and we can see no other plausible procedure, particularly if we see all human activity against its background of the human nervous system. Now this business of formulating regularities is one that admits of no uniqueness. Every physicist knows that an infinite number of descriptions are possible of any finite situation. The whole past experience of the race involves only a finite number of observations. Past experience can be reproduced by any scheme of equations with as many undetermined coefficients as there are past observations. But the type of equation is completely undetermined by this requirement, and there are an infinity of types. Each different type will probably extrapolate differently into the future. Unique projection of the past into the future is thus not possible. The projection which we actually make involves other considerations. It is a matter of supreme importance to make this projection in the way most reasonable or most probable, and most feasible.

We descry here fundamental infelicities which we deal with as best we can by the device of operating on different levels. It seems to me, as already said, that the absolutely prior commitment of every human being who recognizes the necessity for adapting himself to his environment is to accept the future when it comes, no matter what it may bring or how it may clash with his preconceptions. It is this resolution to accept the future that gives meaning, on this level, to the statement "The future *may* break completely with the past". Or, another way of saying it: "We *may* not be able to project the regularities of the past into the future". It seems to me that we cannot at the same time say this and demand justification for projecting the regularities of the past, as we admittedly do. At this level we cannot justify projection. But on another level we may seek justification, the level on which we ignore the uncertainty of the future and say that the only conceivable rationally or logically justifiable method of dealing with the future is by projecting the past. Whether we are here really saying what we appear to be saying is not quite evident. For me, examination of other conceivable methods of dealing with the future does not disclose methods which I would be willing to call rational or logical, but I have an uneasy suspicion that all I am accomplishing by such an examination is to uncover the tautological implications in "rational" and "logical".

It must be recognized that there *are* other methods of dealing with the future than by projecting the past. Eating hashish is one, or opening the pages of the Bible at random, or paying attention to dreams. I reject the first two methods for reasons based largely on personal experience, reasons which observation shows are not universally accepted. I also usually reject the third method, but not always, as when I find the solution to a problem of apparatus design in a dream. This last suggests a possibility for which no present technique seems available but which could conceivably be developed. It may be that we could in some way turn the unconscious processes in our brains loose, in the same way that we give Dobbin the reins and let him bring us home when we are lost on a dark night. It would be nice to find a way to exploit the unconscious wisdom of our nervous systems, for they have a wisdom as surely as do our bodies, in the pregnant phrase of Walter Cannon. However, if after adequate checking we ever find such a method I think we would still want to say that our nervous systems were able to act wisely because they were continuing to act in the ways they had learned in the past, that is, by projecting into the future the regularities of the past.

Beyond the level on which we say that the only logical method of anticipating the future is to project the past, there is the level of the everyday practice of logic. Here our confidence in logic arises from our examination into the details of how logic works in practical applications. On this level we recognize that the elements of a logical analysis must have some of the properties of the "things" of experience, in particular, permanence and identifiability. On this level there is no sharp dividing line between inductive and deductive logic. For both logics demand identifiability and repeatability, which themselves are not sharp concepts and demand a projection of the past. Furthermore, as usually practiced, the premises of our deductions are obtained by inductive methods. When we say that all men are mortal we very seldom have behind us a verification by observation of all men, but the statement usually implies an inductive generalization of some sort.

PROBABILITY AS AN UNANALYZABLE

The view that the probability which we apply in concrete situations contains an essential element of expectation is very distasteful to some persons. They do not like to admit to scientific usage anything with so strong a "subjective" flavor. Here it seems to be the tacit demand that only those concepts should be used in a scientific context which are "objective" or "public" in character. But if we take seriously the insight that we can never get away from ourselves, we have to recognize that no concept or method of handling the world around us can be entirely free from some subjective element. Furthermore, there is nothing to prevent a subjective method from being public, provided that it is the same kind of subjectivity for every member of the public. The question then may arise of how much subjective element we are willing to tolerate. The answer, it seems to me, can be given only by an examination of the special cases as they arise to find whether our success is jeopardized by the presence of the subjective element. With regard to probability, the question is: have we unduly restricted ourselves by recognizing an element of expectation in our concept of probability? If there are such situations, I have not come across them. It seems to me that we can always recognize the factor of expectation in all the situations of daily life which common sense treats from the probability point of view, or in the refined situations of quantum mechanics in which the psi function determines a probability, or in those situations of stochastic analysis in which the numerical aspect of the frequency point of view receives articulate and full expression. Nowhere can I see that we have handicapped ourselves by admitting the factor of expectation. Neither do I see what more we can ask of a theory or a calculation than that it tell us what to expect. On the other hand, it seems to me that the desire for complete objectivity sometimes drives its proponents to extreme lengths. Complete objectivity is perhaps most insisted on by the frequentists. Most of them admit, nevertheless, that their probability is applicable to no single concrete case, but is logically applicable only to collectives. They will further admit, when pushed, that a collective never occurs in practice, for any purported actual collective is a single concrete aggregate of higher order. The collective is an idealization which, furthermore, is of such a nature that there is no method by which we can tell how closely we are approaching the ideal in any concrete case. But it is said, nevertheless, that the concept of probability is applicable only to collectives, and, going still further, some say that science in general and measurement in particular *can* have meaning only when applied to collectives. It seems to me that we have to demand a "probability" that comes a little closer to what we actually do. By associating probability with expectation it seems to me that we have provided this contact.

Not all the advocates of complete objectivity deal with this on the basis just outlined. Thus Professor Margenau[6] would, I think, adopt the frequentist position and at the same time maintain that probability is completely objective, and therefore *can* be determined in any concrete case. His exact position is, however, not very clear to me because sometimes he appears to be saying that probability has meaning only from the point of view of a collective. It does not seem to me that Professor Margenau has been successful, for detailed examination of what he does in any specific case where he wishes to assign a numerical probability to a concrete event discloses a jumping back and forth across the logically unbridgeable chasm between mathematical and common-sense probability.

The "expectation" which we have made so fundamental to probability analysis is a human activity, and as such bestows some of its own particular characteristics on anything with which it is associated. The context in which we talk of expectation usually implies some degree of ignorance. We are ignorant of the future par excellence, and use of the word expectation usually has some future reference. In its most neutral usage it may imply little more than simple futurity, as when we say "I expect the sun will rise tomorrow". But we are more likely to use it when the future is more uncertain. Thus we are more likely to say "I expect it will rain tomorrow" than to say "I expect the sun will rise tomorrow". We may use it with reference to the past if that past is not fully known to us, but only then with reference to an expectation of what we shall in the future find to have been the facts about the past. We would never say on Wednesday, knowing it to be Wednesday, "I expect yesterday was Tuesday". It follows that our expectations change abruptly when the knowledge on which our expectations are based changes. This results in some of the apparently paradoxical situations of wave mechanics in which a probability changes abruptly after an act of measurement. I think the paradox disappears if one is reconciled to accept the partly subjective character of the probability.

Many people, of whom Einstein was one, feel a deep-seated uneasiness in the presence of all probability methods. They feel that in accepting these methods they have to that extent renounced the possibility of "understanding" the situation. This is to a certain extent true, because probability methods were devised specifically to apply to those situations in which our knowledge is not complete and in which we are not in complete control. Because such people are not willing to renounce the possibility of an eventual understanding, they are not willing to believe that "probability" can be the expression of any deep property of the world around us, but can only mark a temporary and heuristic stage in our analysis. We can indeed understand why probability methods are successful in many of the situations of daily life as an expression of our failure to control adequately. The fall of a coin when tossed is doubtless adequately controlled by the laws of classical mechanics, and if all the details of the toss could be specified we would doubtless be able to predict whether it will be heads or tails. But the precision of knowledge to make this prediction is so high, and the alternation from heads to tails occurs for small changes in the initial conditions so hopelessly beyond the present possibility of control or measurement, that a statement of "pure chance" is the most adequate statement that we can make in the circumstances, although are dealing with an ostensibly completely deterministic mechanism. It is a mechanism analogous to this that Einstein and those who think like him hope to discover sometime beneath the at present apparently unresolvable situations in wave mechanics.

One might perhaps hope to find some experimental procedure by which this point of view could be tested. I do not think, however, that this is possible. I think there is no conceivable experimental test in the universe of presently known facts by which operational meaning could be given to a distinction between a probability essentially fundamental and unanalyzable, and a probability resulting from our inability to control theoretically deterministic details. The only present operational meaning to the distinction is to be found in what we say. Any distinction based on instrumental operations in the laboratory can have meaning only in terms of our programs for the future, and must wait for the discovery of at present new and unspecifiable kinds of physical fact for validation.

One can, nevertheless, have a great deal of sympathy with the point of view that is unwilling to accept probability as an unanalyzable basis of the world, for it does seem that a world "governed" by *pure* chance is indeed completely inconceivable. Such a world would have no continuity of form which would enable me to think about it or even to describe it. Like as not I might at the next instant turn into my dog Towser and Towser might turn into my Ford. In all the situations in which we successfully use probability methods the factor of pure chance is applicable to only a restricted aspect of the situation — all other aspects remain subject to law and the conventional regularities. When I say that the tossing of a coin is subject to chance, the coin itself is not subject to chance, nor am I who toss it, but both remain permanent and absolutely predictable in the context which justifies me in treating the result of the toss by probability methods. So it is in the situations of wave mechanics where we at present treat probability as an unanalyzable; the experimental set-up which gives operational meaning is described in the conventional macroscopic completely deterministic terms of everyday experience. The "law" of large numbers, which seems so completely incomprehensible in a world of pure chance, is a law in which everything except a single inconsiderable feature is controlled by deterministic law. I have a temperamental aversion to speaking of statistical or probability *laws* as some people do.

It seems to me that there is concealed here a difficulty, perhaps amounting to a logical inconsistency, in attempting to make probability fundamental in quantum theory. For the presuppositions of the concepts of probability imply, as just said, that all aspects of the system, except that one singled out for probability treatment, be classically deterministic, identifiable, and insolatable. Now this is exactly not the case in the quantum domain where we can no longer isolate and the system has to be treated as a whole. It looks almost as though we have here a cancellation of the effect of two errors. We can, for example, obtain correct results for the interference pattern of electrons by thinking of an electron as an identifiable object, which it is not, and by treating probability as fundamental and unanalyzable, which it is not.

In this connection the situation in the kinetic theory of gases is illuminating. The macroscopic properties of a gas, such as that expressed in Boyle's law, are deduced by probability methods starting from a completely deterministic base. Now if one follows the details of the deduction, such as in the original discussion by Boltzmann, for example, it will be seen that the assumption of "molecular chaos" has to be made, in virtue of which the average of the interchanges of energy or of direction of motion of the individual molecules during their individual encounters can be treated on a probability basis. It is often felt that we are here in the presence of a logical paradox, for how can a probability situation evolve from one completely deterministic? The justification for the assumption of molecular chaos is sometimes given as the "law of large numbers", which is said to be applicable when we are dealing with numbers so large that it would be hopeless to attempt to follow the details of the individual happenings. I think this rests on a misconception. In any concrete gaseous system the encounters between the molecules are idealistically controlled by the deterministic laws of Newtonian mechanics. The future evolution of the system in this context is completely deterministic and the concept of molecular chaos is not applicable. Molecular chaos gets into the picture, not through the details of the mutual collisions of the enormous number of molecules within the gas, but through the encounters of the molecules with the walls. The state of the walls has to be treated as one of molecular chaos, because the walls are coupled to the entire external universe. A deterministic treatment of any finite system is theoretically impossible when that system is coupled, like the gas, to an indefinite external system. We might hope to control the finite system, but we may not hope to control the external system to which it is coupled, for any attempt to control it results in a divergent process of ever-expanding contact with an ever-expanding external universe. In other words, probability gets into situations like those of the kinetic theory of gases because the operation of "isolation" is not applicable. In this context the logical paradox disappears.

The repugnance of so many to accepting probability as a fundamental unanalyzable property of the world usually arises in a context in which it is forgotten that we cannot get away from ourselves, and that the world is not to be dissociated from the knower of the world. It does not seem so repugnant to postulate that we shall always find it most advantageous to use probability methods in treating that part of the world at the frontiers of knowledge.

PROBABILITY AS A NUMBER

We finally consider a couple of more special topics. We have seen that the probability of common sense is often characterized by the possession of serial order. We ask ourselves how we would go to work to convert this serial order into a numerical order. At one end of the scale we already have approximate success in our identification of probability with relative frequency. How shall we go to work in general? We may seek an answer in analyzing how this has been done in other fields. Physics affords an example in the construction of a numerical temperature scale on the basis of the simple physiologcal recognition of hotter or colder, and psychology affords an example in the construction of a numerical scale for the intensity of a sensation (the topic of conversation in Fechner's law) on the basis of the minimum detectible difference of sensation. Is there anything analogous in the probability situation? We notice in the first place a couple of rather important differences. Although we have described our probability as having serial order, it is a serial order only within a narrow context. We might have undertaken to give meaning to our statement that it was more likely that Eisenhower would be re-elected than that McCarthy would be re-elected, but I think it would be more difficult to give meaning to a statement that it is more probable that Eisenhower will be re-elected than that it will rain tomorrow. That is, the full probability situation has a multidimensionality which is going to make difficult its representation by a single numerical sequence. The second point to notice is that in the two instances above where we have been able to convert a serial scale into a numerical scale there have been numerical features in the corresponding physical situation which we have been able to make the basis of the definition of the recurrence of the basic sensation. Thus in constructing the scale of temperature we have the position of a thread of mercury in a glass capillary, which enables us to say by definition that the same sensation recurs when the mercury returns to its position. Or if we are trying to lay a physical basis for the numerical intensities of sensation of sound we have the amplitude of vibration of air at the ear, in terms of which we can say that the sensation of intensity is the same whenever the amplitude has its prescribed value. Given this, the construction of the numerical scale is immediate, in terms, for instance, of the position of the mercury thread measured in centimeters. It is to be noticed that although we can in this way construct a numerical scale, it is not a unique scale — we might have used alcohol in the thermometer instead of mercury.

In those cases where we have had approximate success in correlating probabilities with numbers we have something analogous to this sort of physical correspondence. The number assignable to the probability of a toss of heads is loosely correlated with the relative frequency of heads in a long succession of throws. What makes the logical difficulty is that this physical basis is not exactly defined or reproducible. The general probability situation does not appear to me to have features which are the analogue of those features which, in other sorts of situations, have made possible the conversion of a serial scale into an exact numerical scale, and until someone has a bright new idea I do not see how such a conversion is possible in general. That is, I do not believe that the probability of common sense with all its implications is in general measurable, although it is certainly approximately measurable in frequency situations. Perhaps such a basis will some day be found. Perhaps some unnoticed common feature will be discovered in the reaction of all people to probability situations which can be made the basis of a numerical correlation. One is reminded of the discovery by S. S. Stevens[7] that people recognize a hitherto unnoticed "largeness" attribute of sound which is not the same as the attribute of "loudness".

APPLICATIONS OF PROBABILITY ANALYSIS

There are at least two different sorts of application which we can make of a probability analysis to practical situations. There are in the first place the positive applications. Here we deal with situations in which we have no adequate causal control, it may be either because we do not know what might be the nature of the causative agencies, or it may be because we cannot know the causative agencies with sufficient precision to yield a definite prediction. In such situations we capitalize our causal ignorance or inability to control — we say that such an event is a chance event, we estimate what the chances are on the basis of our causal impotence, and we apply the results of our estimate to directing our course of action. We do this in the spirit of a best bet, because we can think of nothing better to do in the circumstances. There are many instances of the successful use of such a procedure, ranging from the life-expectation tables of the life insurance companies to statistical mechanics and the kinetic theory of gases. If our expectations are not acceptably fulfilled in practice we cast about to find some element of regularity which we neglected in our analysis and which would modify our assumption of complete ignorance or impotence. Often we can find such a factor, as when the insurance companies correlate an unexpectedly large insurance loss during some one year with the occurrence of an unusual hurricane. However, unless we are able to exhibit some specific feature in which our analysis went wrong, we can never be sure that the failure of the event to come up to our expectations was not due merely to a fluctuation such as is to be expected in any probability sequence.

In the second place, there are the negative applications of probability analysis. Here we calculate our expectations on a probability basis, find that our expectations are *not* met in practice, and draw what conclusions we can from our failure. The question here for us is: what sort of conclusions can we draw from our failure? We can of course draw the general conclusion that something went wrong with our analysis, but we would like to put our finger on the specific respect in which it went wrong and to modify our expectations accordingly. Unless we can find something specific, about the only thing we can do in practice is not to bet in those situations in which we find that our previous bets have consistently failed. But suppose that we think we can account for our failure; how shall we prove to ourselves that we have found the true explanation of why our expectations went wrong? We can do no better here than we ever can when called on to justify an explanation. The least we can do is to show that we have hold of something which is not just something which we say, but which is something susceptible to some sort of control and prediction. This demands the possibility of repetition, and is pretty nearly equivalent to saying that we cannot explain the failure of our expectations unless we can find some causal regularities which we had previously overlooked. If we are fortunate the failure may stimulate us to find the factor which we have overlooked.

These considerations have an immediate application to the situation present by ESP (extra-sensory perception). Here phenomena occur definitely not in line with expectations formed in accordance with the conventionally accepted view of the nature of our environment or of our relations to each other, such phenomena as too large scores in guessing cards. The advocates of ESP then draw the conclusion that the failure of our expectations has a single specific explanation, namely a hitherto unrecognized ability of human "minds" to communicate directly with each other or with inanimate objects. Here it seems to me the advocates of ESP are on logically untenable ground. It may perhaps be granted that given the assumed novel powers of the human mind the unexpected results could be accounted for, but this is logically a quite different matter from turning the argument backward and proving that this is the actual explanation. It is not even pertinent to argue that there is no other conceivable explanation — such an argument does little more than to capitalize our inability to conceive of another explanation. To prove that unknown or unconventional powers of the mind are actually involved would require the exhibition of regularities and consistencies of the same sort that we always demand when convincing ourselves that some experience of ours is real and not a hallucination. This demands, in general, regularities of the kind that we find in the presence of causality. Although every effort has been made to find them, such regularities are persistently absent in the situations of ESP. It does not seem to be generally recognized that the application of probability analysis to ESP is not of the first, positive, kind which has been amply justified in practice, but is of the quite different second, negative, kind which attempts to capitalize a failure.

In general, if some situation is not as one would expect according to probability considerations, one is only at the beginning, and still has before one the exacting task of finding specifically why one's expectations failed. Failure of expectation can at most legitimately serve as an incentive to further research — by itself it can prove nothing.

There is one feature about the conventional ESP tests with the special pack of cards which I am surprised no one has apparently thought to exploit. Why is it that most apparently rational human beings will respond positively to the demand that they "guess" what a card is of which they can have no possible knowledge in any accepted sense? What sort of a game is it that we thus play with ourselves when we guess, and what is the significance of the fact that so many of us can play the game? It seems to me that a clever advocate might make as much out of the mere fact that we respond to the injunction to "guess" as he might out of the occurrence of scores higher than the probability expectation.

V

SOME ASPECTS OF THE PHYSICAL SCIENCES

There is no point in trying to define what is or what should be included in "physical science". Today we have a more or less definite body of practice and a more or less tacit agreement whether any specific discipline or activity shall be called a physical science or not. Inspection of the specific examples of what are called physical sciences discloses certain features common to them all.

It is a truism that we cannot have science without a scientist — in fact, one not too flippant a definition of science is: "Science is what scientists do". Nevertheless, in the physical sciences the scientist usually remains in the background. Paradoxically, this minimizing of the role of the scientist can be described in terms of what the scientist does. The scientist, as he functions in the laboratory, is usually not conscious of himself nor is he explicitly present in the report which he makes of his findings. In fact, one of the ostensible ideals of such a science as physics or chemistry is to report the facts in such an impersonal way that any other scientist could put himself into a position to make a similar report. The physicist or chemist takes himself for granted — he accepts the findings of his senses at their face value and is not bothered by such questions as the nature of knowledge or by a self-doubt which would continually question his own sanity. Here is a feature which in common usage pretty much distinguishes all "science", namely, science as such appears not to raise the issue of self-doubt. This applies not only to the so-called physical sciences, but also to biology or the life sciences, and to the mental sciences, at least so far as mental science is typified by experimental psychology in the laboratory. This means in particular that no scientist, as scientist, is concerned with his own motives, although there can be no question that the scientific edifice as a whole is affected by the motives of those who construct it. By the same token, the scientist as such, as proved by an examination of the nature of the articles in the scientific technical journals, is not concerned with the social impact of his activity, although in his capacity as citizen he cannot help recognizing that there is a social impact and he may try to do something about it. To attempt to broaden the concept of science to include social responsibility, as appears to be the popular temper at present, can result only in confusion. It is not necessary, for one thing, because the scientist as citizen can always be got hold of by society by methods which it already has. It is better to keep the two concepts separate.

The ideal of science as at present understood is thus an impersonal one. One of the methods of achieving impersonality is by consensus. If all competent reporters agree in their reports it would seem to be highly probable that the personal elements have been eliminated from the report — at least those personal elements depending on personal idiosyncracy or error. This accounts for the high value placed on consensus in all scientific enterprise. In fact, some people go so far as to *define* science as the consensus of all competent observers. This it seems to me goes too far and misplaces the emphasis. For in the first place, the significance of consensus is limited. "Competent persons" at any epoch means those who at that epoch have been subjected to a definite preconditioning, so that consensus merely means that persons who have been subjected to this preconditioning react in a certain way. It does not preclude the possibility that all competent persons are reacting incorrectly because of some feature in contemporary culture, and there are examples, as Weierstrass in mathematics, where consensus was ultimately shown to have been wrong. In any event the "correct" or ultimately accepted "scientific" point of view takes its origin with some individual. Neither, in the second place, is consensus free from a more insidious possibility. For all the competent persons have nervous systems organized in the same way (in other words they are "normal") and consensus could show only that a nervous structure of a specific kind reacts in a certain way under certain stimuli. Consensus does not enable the human race to get away from itself, and for that reason consensus appears of less significance that is usually esteemed.

Physical science as it is understood and practiced today involves in the first place measurement, which involves the use of numbers. A consequence is that mathematics is used in correlating the results of measurement; the possibility of using mathematics is one of the characteristics of most physical sciences. Then there is the use of experiment, which may be more or less extensive depending on the subject matter. Experiment as distinguished from measurement plays only a small part in astronomy, which for that reason would perhaps not be called a physical science by some people. Experiment, or plain observation either, does not get very far without the use of instruments. All these factors present questions for consideration. In this chapter we shall consider some aspects of the questions presented by measurement, experiment, and instruments, all of them taken as impersonally as possible. This does not mean that I cannot or should not say "I make the experiment". The "I" which is necessary to make the report reproduce as closely as possible what actually happens may be an entirely neutral "I" so far as the inclusion of any so-called private factors goes. That is, every observer will be able to make his own "I" report in identical words.

This chapter will not exclude some aspects of biology or psychology, since in both of these we may make measurements with physical instruments. The discussion in the following makes no pretense to systematic completeness — I shall primarily attempt to gather some considerations to which I have paid little attention in my other writings.

THE ROLE OF EXPERIMENT

The indispensable role of experiment in modern science is universally recognized — in fact it is often said that experiment distinguishes modern science from its forerunners and is the one thing which has made possible its rapid progress. One talks of the "invention" of the experimental method. In general, experiment would seem to involve a study of phenomena which occur under artificially varied and controlled conditions. We distinguish between the experimental and the observational sciences — the latter are sciences in which it is difficult to control or vary the conditions, as, astronomy or geology. Doubtless every science would like to be fully experimental if it could find how to manage it; this is becoming more and more possible, as in biology, which in the beginning was almost exclusively observational, but which has now become largely experimental.

Two aspects of experiment can be recognized, corresponding to the two kinds of challenge which the world presents to the scientist. In the first place, there is the challenge to the scientist as explorer to discover previously unknown or unsuspected phenomena and thus to enter domains where no man has previously trod. There is in the second place the challenge to the scientist to understand the world about him, both the old world with which he has long been familiar and the new world which he is entering as explorer. Experiment is a most powerful tool in meeting either challenge. It is true that new factual worlds may be entered by means which we would not usually call experimental, as when a botanist makes a collecting expedition to a country not previously visited. But more usually it is experiment itself that creates the previously unknown world. The world of modern chemistry, for example, is a world which for the most part has no existence outside the context of the conditions artificially created by the chemist. Still more, the world of the nuclear physicist is a world which exists mainly in the context of his new instruments and artificially created conditions.

On the other hand, the importance of the role of experiment in facilitating understanding can hardly be overestimated. By the controlled experiment we can pick a situation to pieces and analyze it by devising our experiments to vary one factor at a time, and thus reduce to order situations which otherwise might be so complicated as to be wholly untractable. In fact, the importance of the role of experiment in giving understanding is so great that I believe many writers overemphasize this aspect, and in so doing present an unbalanced picture. For example, Hutten, in his recent book, *The Language of Physics*,[1] states or implies that experiment is always made in connection with some hypothesis, usually for the purpose of testing it, so that experiment, according to this view, is impossible without some preliminary theoretical attitude toward the situation. Perhaps, by the exercise of sufficient virtuosity, it may be always possible to find some trace of a theoretical attitude, but the theoretical implication on occasion becomes almost vanishingly small. In my own work on the various physical effects of pressure, for example, the interest so far as I was concerned, was almost entirely in discovering what new things there were in fields hitherto unexplored. Of course, I never made an experiment without having some kind of expectation how it would turn out, but the interest of the experiment was not at all to verify the expectation. On a more exalted level, I would be willing to wager that Rutherford got more kick out of his discovery of the mere fact that the nitrogen nucleus would come to pieces than he did out of his fitting of this new fact into a general theoretical picture of the nature of the nucleus.

One universal feature of experimenting is to be emphasized, whether the experiment is designed to give better theoretical understanding or to give new facts. Experiment is significant and interesting only insofar as it refers to repeatable situations — we would not be interested in finding that in a particular experiment water freezes at 75° C under 20,000 atmospheres unless it always freezes under these conditions. The situation need not, however, be repeatable in full detail, provided only that there are statistical regularities, as in the situations in quantum physics. And here, it is the statistical regularities which are of interest and which are established by experiment, rather than the individual details. Strictly speaking, the scientist in experimenting is concerned with classes of objects or situations rather than with individuals. This is so well understood that it usually need not be said.

ON INSTRUMENTS IN GENERAL

It is often said that man is a tool-using and tool-making animal; some of these tools we refer to as instruments. We shall not try here to distinguish tools from instruments or even to define closely what a tool is — if we did we would have to meet such situations as having to decide whether a savage who had let his thumbnail grow abnormally long in order to open clam shells the better was using a tool or not.

There are, however, certain restrictions which we usually tacitly impose on any gadget before we call it an instrument. An instrument is usually supposed to respond to local conditions which prevail at the moment of operation of the instrument. This tacit implication may perhaps be a result of the structure of our thinking mechanism, which seems to attach a special significance to conditions here and now.

Here we have a special kind of "isolation". The physicist does not talk of "reality" if he can help it, but it seems to me that he attaches a significance to the readings of his instruments analogous to the significance which the philosopher attaches to "reality".

In addition to the requirement of here and now, we usually like to have our instruments simple — either in actuality like a meter stick or in principle like a clock. However, it is obvious that there is no sharp criterion of simplicity in an instrument, and in fact when we attempt to devise instruments which will respond automatically to some of the simplest physical concepts, such as mass, we shall see later that we are driven to great complication. In principle there is no reason why an instrument should not contain a built-in computing machine, or perhaps even a hired computer enclosed in a box. Nor is there any fundamental reason why an instrument should not give a response integrated over conditions in past time.

The picture of the nature of the world which we have evolved is heavily colored by our experience with tools or instruments. We supplement and extend the evidence presented to us by our senses by the use of instruments, so that the very meaning of some of our most important concepts can be defined only in terms of operations with instruments. Optical instruments enable us to extend the visual world of our sense of sight. The extension may be of varying degrees of potency. Just by getting into a better light we can often see detail that we had not seen before. Or our neighbor may have better eyesight than we and tell us of the existence of objects beyond our own immediate perception. The exceptionally keen sighted individual has always been prized. When such an individual tells us that a courier is approaching on the distance plain we have, in the past, usually been able to verify his statement by waiting for the courier to get nearer. Or, by going nearer ourselves, we can perceive detail imperceptible from a distance. In some such way the concept of the "existence" of objects beyond the reach of sense apprehension may have arisen. This concept was fortified by the invention of new kinds of optical instrument. For instance, a drop of water constitutes a crude magnifying glass with which the individual fibers can be seen in a twisted thread, fibers too fine to be seen now with the naked eye, but which we know are nevertheless there because we put them there when we twisted the thread. Here we have a check on the "reality" of the trans-sensual object by two methods of getting to the terminus. Such experiences constitute the justification for the extension of the concept of a real world beyond the reach of unaided vision. Other checks of such extension are possible with such mechanical devices as the micrometer of the machinist. The micrometer enables us to extend the tactual world of ordinary experience; when we do so we find the same sorts of correlation between tactual and optical experience which we find in the everyday range. Or we can extend the acoustical world with instruments which are mostly a recent development, but which can be traced back in principle to the first savage who held a sea shell to his ear. Again we find that the extended acoustical experience is not different in kind from that familiar to us through our unaided hearing.

The extension of the world of experience which may be justifiably made with such instrumental auxiliaries is always a limited extension, and it should not be assumed without critical examination that such an extension can be carried indefinitely far. There is, on the other hand, no obvious natural or sharp limitation to such an extension, so that we are likely to end by uncritically ignoring the possibility that there may be any limit at all. It is in this context that we produce such intellectual monstrosities as the humunculus which contains within itself the microscopic replica of the man into which it develops and all the potential descendants of the man, who are present, fully formed in minutest detail, in his germ cells. This sort of picture has, of course, now become forever impossible in the light of our knowledge of the atomic structure of matter. However, something very much like this survived in physics at least as late as the electron theory of Lorentz, in which the electron was divided into mathematically infinitesimal elements of volume, each one of which experiences a force of the same nature as that experienced by the small parts of the electrical systems of everyday life. The vision that it may be conceptually illegitimate to extend indefinitely the world revealed to us by instrumentation is one that we owe to recent quantum theory. We now perceive this clearly enough, but there is no such clear apprehension of what is to be done about it. Recent discussions of the possibility of minimum lengths and minimum times, or of natural units of length or time, are an indication of an awareness of the situation, but it does not seem to me that any of the suggestions made up to now has very much physical appeal.

MEASUREMENT AND MEASURING INSTRUMENTS

The question how far the world of sense as extended by instruments is similar to the world of unaided sense will demand precise measurement for a satisfactory answer. Only thus, for example, can it be answered whether the geometry of the subvisual world is Euclidean as is the geometry of the world of ordinary experience. This introduces the topic of measurement and measuring instruments. Consider first the subject of measurement. There have been many systematic and elaborate analyses of the subject of measurement: those of Norman Campbell, Harold Jeffreys and S. S. Stevens[2] may be specially mentioned.

Measurement, in its most general aspect, may be taken to be description by the use of numbers. We may describe objects or we may describe events, or, in general, situations. The criterion of successful description of an object or an event is that we shall be able to reproduce it, or at least to recognize it when it recurs. The criterion that we have successfully reproduced or recognized is often intuitive, but in more difficult cases the criterion may be that performance of the operation of measuremnet on the purported reproduction yields the same number as the original measurement.

We encounter here the possibility that the process of measurement may feed on itself — the invention or discovery of new methods of measurement results in new features to be described if our description is to be complete. An example to be discussed more fully later is the invention by Galileo of "instantaneous" velocity.

The description afforded by the number given by a particular measurement may be, and usually is, only a description of some aspect of the total object or event. For instance, we have adequately described the velocity aspect of a body said to be moving with a velocity of 10 feet per second if we can produce at will a body on which a velocity measurement gives 10 feet per second. We are not required to reproduce the *same* body, black or red or round or what not, moving with velocity 10.

The process of assigning numbers, that is, measuring, is done according to certain rules which naturally have to presuppose some sort of relation between the operations and the subject operated on. This means that certain types of measurement can be made only on bodies with certain kinds of property. Further, the rules of operation usually involve the use of instruments, which must be constructed according to specifications and manipulated in ways allowed by the material of which the instrument is constructed. Measuring instruments are usually subject to certain very broad limitations. Ideally, measuring instruments are transportable or at worst can be set up on demand in any arbitrary locality. They should be capable of repeated use, and the result of any specific measurement should not be affected by past measurements. In certain very important types of case the instrument itself has properties similar to the properties of the object of measurement. Perhaps the most obvious example is length — the instrument for measuring length is the meter stick, which itself has length and can be measured.

The numbers which are the result of descriptive measurement are themselves, regarded as pure numbers, subject to all the operations of mathematics. The operations of physical measurement by which the numbers are obtained often permit combinations which run parallel to and are isomorphous with the permissible mathematical operations on numbers. For instance, the operation of measuring length with a meter stick is to move the stick along on the object, placing it end to end. The physical operation of placing the stick end to end is isomorphic with the arithmetic operation of adding a number to itself. It follows that the length of a compound object, made up of two simple objects placed end to end, is the arithmetic sum of the two lengths taken separately. Or, the length of the compound object is the same whatever the order of the simple lengths in the combination. Further, because the meter stick itself is subject to length measurement and could be compounded out of, for example, ten sticks each one-tenth of the length, we have the possibility of changing the size of the fundamental unit used in the definition of length. In so changing the size of the fundamental units the arithmetic rules for multiplication and division hold — a measuring unit one-tenth the length gives a measure number ten times as large.

The advantages of an isomorphism between the physical operations and the operations of arithmetic are so great that nearly all the schemes of measurement in scientific use are selected to have this property. In fact, some people restrict by definition application of the term "measurement" to such situations. It is only such situations that permit dimensional analysis. An example in which there is not isomorphism, and no physical operation corresponding to the arithmetic operation of addition, is afforded by the Mohr scale of hardness, used by the mineralogist. Whether one wants to call a determination of hardness on the Mohr scale a "measurement" of hardness is mostly a verbal matter. It satisfies our fundamental requirement because, given the Mohr hardness, we can produce a mineral with the same hardness, and in that sense our description is adequate.

There is another verbal aspect to this matter of measurement that is not so obvious, nor are the effects so easily dealt with. We naturally ask *what* it is that we measure when we make a measurement. The answer often comes of itself — with a meter stick we measure lengths. But what is this "length" which we thus measure? Is it a thing independent of this particular thing that we do, so that it would make sense to ask "Can you *really* find the length by counting the number of times you lay on a meter stick?" Is length anything more than what we measure when we make a length measurement according to prescription? In calling it a "what" at all are we in the presence of anything more than a verbal ellipsis for shortening our description of what we do, an ellipsis which is useful and works because we encounter the situation so often that no one is confused? Such ellipsis seems particularly congenial to the Indo-European languages with their propensity for inventing reified objects for their verbs.

We are here again in the presence of the tendency of our thinking to isolate and pick out a single feature of the situation for emphasis. But meticulous attention to what happens would demand, as always, that we reproduce the whole situation as closely as we can. It seems to me that a very simple way of doing this is not to talk about measuring a "length", but instead to talk about making a "length-measurement". Or, better still, talk about "length-measuring", the "length" here being an adverb. The "what" that we measure when we measure a length is an aspect of an object. The length of an object is a number, related by the process of measurement to the length aspect of the object — or, more simply, a number obtained by performing the operations of length measurement on the object.

The situation is comparatively simple with regard to length, and we need not be too pedantic about our exact language. But in other situations it is not so simple, and the consequences are more serious. Such a situation is, I believe, presented by time. What is this "time" that we purport to measure? It is obvious that we are not dealing with an aspect of an object or of any sort of "thing", but are instead dealing with an aspect of events. For the purposes of getting started we may say that we measure time with clocks. Clocks are defined as instruments built according to Newtonian mechanics and in terms of which Newtonian mechanics is valid for the moving objects of everyday experience. The time of physics is essentially the time of clocks, which again is the time of the equations of physics. The physicist when asked to define time might reply "I use the word 'time' when I am dealing with those temporal aspects of situations which can be described by measurements with clocks." The numbers obtained with clocks can, of course, be used mathematically just as can any other numbers. If this use is to be significant there must be corresponding physical operations for "times". In particular, events can be juxtaposed, as when one event succeeds another, and the time of the two events together is the sum of the times of the two events separately. Or the times can be measured in shorter or longer units, so that the time of an event measured in hours is one-sixtieth of the time measured in minutes. It appears, then, that there are physical operations isomorphic with the operations of arithmetic.

But it is to be noticed that the numbers obtained by operations with clocks are not capable of describing all aspects of experience which common sense lumps under the term "temporal". The time of experience is irreversible and unrecoverable — we cannot reproduce the hour of yesterday for re-examination today, even if the clocks give us the same readings. We cannot move our times about and place them end to end as we can our objects when we measure their lengths. It would seem that clock time, or the time of our equations, is concerned only with that temporal aspect of experience which would be more accurately described as time *intervals*. Time intervals in this sense can be displaced, juxtaposed, and subdivided into smaller intervals in a way not possible for the fuller thing we would like to call "time". We will return later to examine other aspects of time.

We now turn to a consideration of some of the aspects of the instruments with which we usually make our measurements. Instruments may be of varying degrees of refinement or accuracy. If the instrument is for measuring length, for example, it may have finer or coarser graduations. Other things being equal, we say that an instrument with finer graduations gives a more accurate measurement of length than one with coarser graduations. What is implied in this requires examination. In the first instance it may mean merely that we can perhaps get one more significant figure in our result with the more finely graduated instrument, and that these results have a greater self-consistency. For example, if our measuring stick is graduated only to centimeters, and we estimate tenths of a centimeter in reporting our readings, then we might report the length of some object as 100.5 or 100.6 or 100.7 centimeters according to successive measurements. But if the measuring stick is graduated to millimeters, then we may report the result of successive measurements of the same object as 100.55, 100.56, or 100.57 centimeters. Still further refinements, as, by adding a microscope with a micrometer eyepiece, allow us to push still further into the decimals the part of the number which is subject to fluctuation on repetition. There is obviously a reciprocal tie-in here with the concept of rigid body. I do not know whether it is possible to make a logically satisfactory separation of the concept of rigid body from the concept of length as something capable of indefinitely precise measurement. In practice we deal with the situation by the method of successive approximations.

Any actual instrument has imperfections which it is usually possible to minimize by one method or another. Thus the graduations may be faint or blurred, and we can sharpen them. Or the material of the scale may be stretchable, and we can make it stiffer. Or the material may be subject to variation of temperature, and we can use a material with lower coefficient of expansion. A measurement made with an instrument which has been refined in one of these ways is a "better" measurement than one made with an unrefined instrument. It is better because it has less "error". We may idealize, and imagine the perfect instrument which has incorporated all possible refinements. A measurement with such an instrument would be "correct" if we could only find some way of eliminating the indefiniteness arising from the finite size of the finest graduations. The fluctuating measurements furnished by any actual instrument are ascribed to error. This is a justifiable form of description of the results with the coarser instruments. But what about the concept of error when applied to the limiting case of the perfect instrument? The assumption in the background would seem to be that a perfect instrument would yield results which would not fluctuate except for our difficulty in estimating the fractions of the finest graduations, so that such an instrument would give the "correct" or "true" length, forms of expression which frequently occur. But our experience with quantum phenomena shows us that we have concealed here an assumption about the behavior of matter which is not justified. For there is no actual object which does not fluctuate in length, and therefore no scale, no matter how rigid the material, which does not itself fluctuate in length. What, then, is this idealized thing which we have invented and call the "true" length of an object, which contains no error? It obviously corresponds to nothing in experience — at least experience as we ordinarily describe it.

The concept of "true length" would seem to be a survival from pre-quantum days, and is perhaps a projection of the fact that we have always been able to improve our best instrument. Or, it may be that the tie-in is with mathematical theory. The result of measurement is a number of some sort — even when we know that the number we obtain by measurement is uncertain we have to say or write it as definitely something or other. Even when we bracket our measurements within limits of error we have to write the limit as some definite number. As soon as we have made a theory, we substitute the numbers which we have obtained by measurement into the equations of the theory. The theory may be one in which we have great confidence because it has worked in a great variety of situations. Nevertheless, it seldom happens that the two sides of any equation of ours exactly balance when we substitute measured numbers into the two sides. We again idealize and say that the "true" lengths or masses or what-not are numbers that would make the two sides exactly balance. It is our belief, or, better, it is in accordance with our program to assume, that the two "true" parameters, namely those obtained by indefinitely increasing the accuracy of our measuring instruments and those which make our equations exactly balance, would be the same.

But of course there never can be experimental proof of this. It would look as though we had defined a concept in terms of its properties — the discovery of quantum effects again emphasizes the danger of doing this. But, in fact, quantum theory itself seems to use the concept of "true" length in dealing with so-called pure cases.

Does the following sort of situation ever occur? Given some object. I measure its length with my best scale and obtain a number which I recognize is subject to some uncertainty, which at most is not more than two or three times the value of the smallest graduation. Then can I ever say that the length of the object is *certainly* greater than some number corresponding to, say, five graduations smaller than the lower limit of my measurement, and similarly that it is *certainly* smaller than some number equal to the upper bound of my measurements? Or, put much more crudely, can I ever say that the length of some object is *certainly* between 1 and 2 feet? The answer to this question would seem to involve what we want to mean by certainty. I do not see how self-doubt can ever be eliminated. Nor the kind of uncertainty that arises from our recognition that we can have no assurance that nature has been continuously regular in the past, but that there may have been singular points in space and time where the regular causal sequence was suspended. But the following sort of uncertainty I think we can rule out, namely the mathematical uncertainty arising from a literal acceptance of the Gaussian theory of error, with its thesis that there is *some* probability, no matter how small, that in any particular instance or succession of particular instances there may have been a chance conspiracy of errors resulting in a total error of any magnitude whatever. This sort of extreme has no basis whatever in immediate experience, any more than Bertrand Russell's freezing of water on the fire, which is much the same sort of thing. Anything that might lead to this sort of conclusion has never been observed, if for no other reason than the finite length of human history. The limitations imposed by finite human experience do not often have to be taken into account, but here at least is a case in point.

THE INSTRUMENTALLY EXTENDED WORLD

After this very incomplete examination of some of the characteristics of any measurements that can be made with instruments, let us examine to what extent the instrumentally extended world is similar to the world of direct sense perception. The situation with regard to length is fairly straightforward, and I have examined it at some length in *The Logic of Modern Physics*. The most important property of the space of ordinary perception is its Euclidean character. This property continues a long way toward the very small, perhaps even as far as the dimensions of the nucleus, 10^{-13} centimeters in diameter. Of course the operational meaning of microscopic length continually changes, and eventually the only meaning is that certain equations are satisfied when complicated functions of macroscopically measured quantities are substituted into them. Beyond the dimensions of the nucleus the resemblance to the geometric world of experience gets vaguer and vaguer, until with the minimum lengths of Heisenberg of 10^{-23} cm or the characteristic lengths of Eddington of 10^{-43} cm all immediate physical significance would seem to be lost.

When it comes to time, the instrumentally extended time loses contact with the time of perception much earlier. Instrumentally extended time behaves like the time of perception so long as the time of perception is also the time of mechanics, that is, for intervals as short as 10^{-8} seconds, or perhaps even shorter. In this range we can construct crystal clocks whose vibrations satisfy the ordinary mechanical equations of elasticity theory, and which have an accuracy greater than that of most timepieces. The accuracy of atomic clocks, in which the time is the time of the equations of electrodynamics, is even greater.

The question whether small-scale instrumental time is the same sort of thing as large-scale instrumental time is in some respects equivalent to asking whether there are clocks for small-scale time. Now the question of what is a clock for even large-scale time is not altogether simple. In the first instance the time of ordinary experience is a nebulous sort of thing, characterized only by the relations "earlier than" and "later than", but without any obvious basis for making it more precisely numerical. The situation is much the same as it is with regard to temperature. Here we start with a physiological temperature, characterized only by the relations hotter than and colder than, and eventually are able to turn this into something more precise by coupling temperature to other sorts of phenomena which are capable of exact numerical specification. For temperature the additional requirement is provided by the second law of thermodynamics —

temperature is presently defined so that the second law holds in terms of it. The definition is not a mere convention as it would be if the second law were formulated with respect to a unique set of phenomena (for example, the thermal phenomena in gaseous hydrogen), but the character of convention is eliminated by the fact that the second law is universal for all substances. In the same way with time and clocks, Newtonian mechanics holds for time measured with a "clock", the clock being, I think, otherwise undefined. If one wants a formal definition the scheme has to be inverted and a clock defined as such an instrument that Newtonian mechanics holds when time is measured with it. Again, because of the universal validity of Newtonian mechanics, we are not dealing with a pure convention — a clock constructed to make Newtonian mechanics hold for one particular system would at the same time make it hold for all mechanical systems.

At first glance it would seem that we are here defining a physical concept in terms of its properties, something forbidden operationally, but closer examination will show that this is only apparent. For the prescription, "Construct the clock so that Newtonian mechanics holds", can be turned into a specific prescription with each step uniquely determined. For instance, the clock may be a body falling from rest, the indicated time to be determined by the position of the falling body on a scale. The scale is then to be graduated to give the time calculated by the ordinary laws for a falling body, that is, graduated so that $s = \frac{1}{2}gt^2$, where s is the distance of fall in centimeters. With a clock so constructed *any* mechanical phenomenon may be measured, and *all* will be found to satisfy the Newtonian equations.

It would seem that the same sort of attack must be made on the problem of short times. Can an instrument be made which will give numbers to short intervals of time in such a way that Newtonian mechanics holds in these short intervals? We have seen that the answer would certainly seem to be yes for times as short as 10^{-8} seconds. But for much shorter times one will probably have to change the definition of clock from "an instrument determined by Newtonian mechanics" to "an instrument determined by classical electrodynamics". We have such an instrument in the so-called atomic clocks. The consistency of short-wave phenomena down to wave lengths at least as short as 1 centimeter is another indication of the large-scale significance of times extended to at least the order of 10^{-10}. To give meaning to times still shorter one will probably be driven to lean on the indirect results of theory and be satisfied if one can develop a consistent theory of atomic and nuclear action that reproduces experiment. The time so accessible cannot well be less than the time required by light to travel across the diameter of the nucleus, or say times of the order of 10^{-23} seconds. As long as theory is successful we probably will be justified in continuing to handle time in the same way as we do the time of ordinary experience, which means using it formally in the same way in our equations. But what about times very much shorter? What about Eddington, who had a natural unit of time of 1.3×10^{-43} seconds and a unit of length of 4×10^{-33} centimeters, and who declares with regard to the unit of length, "But it is evident that this length must be the key to some essential structure". And what about Heisenberg who talks about a minimum length and a discrete structure of space?

In any event it would seem that the question of the nature of time in the small cannot be separated from other sorts of thing — perhaps most generally, for very short times, the structure of the mathematical equations. This is, however, not different from what we find on the scale of everyday life — there is no such thing as time in and for itself — it gets its meaning and its measurability in conjunction with other things.

Among the properties of mechanically extended time are transitivity and additivity. That is, if event A is earlier than B and B is earlier than C, then A is earlier than C. Or, the time interval from A to B plus that from B to C is equal to that from A to C. In the world of direct perception this sort of thing by no means corresponds to direct experience when we deal with short times, but we are stopped by the "psychological present". Within this we have such phenomena as A being simultaneous with B and B simultaneous with C but A not simultaneous with C. It is typical of the intellectual temper of the times that we have no hesitation in giving priority to the time of instrumental extension and in seeking for an explanation of the phenomena of the psychological present within the framework suggested by our instrumentation. There is one respect, however, in which I am unable to divorce myself from the involvement of my concept of time with my introspectional experience. For me it is meaningless to talk of time going backward, although it is possible to set up a formal description of circumstances under which other people say that they would speak of time going backward.

There has been considerable discussion recently of time flowing backward (Margenau, Feynman, Reichenbach, Grünbaum).[3] The meaning of a backward flow may be made a matter of pure definition, if one cares to, but such discussions seem to me to overlook the fact that the clock time of physics is concerned with only part of the temporal aspects of experience. It seems to me that the full time of experience has to be treated as an unanalyzable — our descriptions are in terms of it and there is nothing which we can recognize as more fundamental or which is capable of replacing it. What possible sort of experience can we formulate which we would describe as meaning that time had reversed its flow and was going backward? Would we not say that it was our clocks which were going backward in time, or that events were occurring again in the inverse order in time? If we are asked to explain why it is that time flows forward, and if we accept the view that "explanation" consists in reducing a situation to elements with which we are so familiar that we accept them without question, and if we take seriously the thesis that time is unanalyzable, then we must say that no explanation is possible of the forward flight of time because *there is nothing to explain.* To say that time flows forward is, in this context, a convention. This time of direct experience may be called psychological or introspectional time. As it emerges in consciousness it can only be accepted. It is essentially private, yet we all can talk together about it, just as we can talk together about our toothaches. It seems to me that the persistent endeavor of many people to ascribe a meaning to the backward flow of introspectional time, and their no less persistent failure, is a striking example of the nearly universal urge to get away from ourselves and of the impossibility of doing it. The "time" of the physicists above, for which it makes sense of sorts to flow backward, is a different sort of thing.

These remarks all apply to local time as distinguished from the extended time of general relativity theory. In the fuller context of extended time many other questions arise — some of these have been touched on in my *Logic of Modern Physics.*

Our world is essentially the world of our perceptions, and the nature of this world is indelibly colored by the nature of the psychological present. But this psychological present is essentially different from the present of an idealized extension of our world of instruments. The psychological present is a smeared-out totality in which we grasp whole visual fields in a single glance as units, and *see* objects moving at a single instant of time, whereas instrumentally we find structure in this temporal amorphousness of a fineness of scale presumably limited only by the frequencies of the atoms of our nervous systems. These frequencies are of the order of 10^{13} per second, so that if we take the duration of the psychological present as of the order of 0.01 second, we have here the possibility of instrumental detail nearly a million million times finer than that accessible to direct perception. There is room here for all the complexities of conscious experience, and for complexities not yet suspected. On a scale of this fineness the coherent wholes of conscious perception will get broken down into a succession of discretenesses, just as happens on a television screen. In fact, a due consideration of the implications of the movie or television screen might well have revolutionary repurcussions on our outlook on the world around us. Even without the suggestion of the movie and television, a sufficiently acute analysis of our ordinary perceptions might have prepared us for this, because we can sometimes see that the apparently homogeneous scene which we take in at a glance is built up by the rapid shifting of attention from detail to detail.

The suggestion is not infrequently made by reputable physicists, Heisenberg, for example, that space and time may be discontinuous. This is usually taken to imply the existence of a minimum length and a minimum interval of time. Closely related to this is the view that there may be natural standards of length and time to be found in the direction of the very small, as, for example, by L. L. Whyte.[4] Such natural standards, when found, would play something of the role of minimum lengths or times. The question for us is: what is the meaning of all this, and, in particular, if there are such things, how shall we recognize them experimentally?

Consider the discontinuities first. Under what experimental conditions would we want to speak of a discontinuous space? Now the concept of space is not to be disassociated from the positional aspects of the bodies which occupy it — in fact it may be defined in terms of those positional aspects. Discontinuous space therefore means something about our experience with bodies that occupy space. Imagine an apparatus as follows: a length-measuring apparatus, which consists of an optical projecting system by which any arbitrary body to be measured can be projected, enormously magnified, on a screen with a scale. The length of the body is then calculated from the position of the images of its end points and the optical magnification. If it should turn out that the manifold of numbers which we get in this way for the length of all possible objects under all possible circumstances was a discrete set with missing ranges of numbers, then we would probably want to say that space is discontinuous. Furthermore, we would probably want to say that the minimum differences between the numbers in our discrete manifold, if there is such, is the minimum length. But what a strange situation, and how shall we rationalize it? Shall we say that it is a matter of experiment that the end points of a body, or its other points too, for that matter, can occupy only certain discrete positions? And can we avoid asking *where* these discrete positions are, or what it is that determines that we have one particular set of discrete positions and not another, displaced with respect to it by half the minimum distance, say? The set of discrete positions must obviously be the same in all reference systems, and what does this mean except that the old absolute frame of reference has come back, with a fantastically fine granular structure and with the traditional difficulties of the classical ether enormously magnified? How shall we describe the motion of a body in such a system? Its points must jump from one position to the next — what determines when they shall jump, or when shall we say that they have jumped? The difficulties here appear enormous, but perhaps they are not insuperable.

The upshot would seem to be that if one wants to connote by space merely an aspect of the complex of all experimental happenings, then one can specify conditions which one would describe as discontinuous space, at least without running into self-contradiction. But if one wants to include in the concept of space the mental operations by which one correlates or thinks about the experimental findings, then discontinuous space does involve self-contradictory operations, that is, so long as we correlate the manifold of real numbers to the points of a line. So long as we tie together the concept of space and the fact that we can always think of a number between any two given numbers, no matter how close, we cannot admit a discontinuous space, simply because it is unthinkable.

How now with discontinuous time? The discontinuity of time is evidently connected with the measurement of time. Time is measured with clocks. If the intervals of time which we obtained with clocks, that is, the numbers which we obtained from our readings of the position of the hands of a clock, formed a discontinuous manifold, then we might conceivably want to say that time is discontinuous. But is this what we would probably say? If we assume that space is already discontinuous we know that the hands of the clock can occupy only certain discrete positions. Would we say that time is discontinuous or that the appearance of discontinuity is due to the discontinuity of space? We would doubtless want to speak of a discontinuity of time if the discrete jump in the values of time corresponded to the jump of the hands of the clock over an interval of space much larger than the minimum interval. Such a state of affairs would obviously land us in great difficulties when we tried to use clocks with hands moving with smaller and smaller velocities. There are other conceptual difficulties in trying to imagine what a situation would be like that would make us want to say that time is discontinuous. Although the velocity of light is the upper limit to the propagation of signals or other causal effects, there is no upper limit to other possible velocities. A searchlight on the sun sweeps the orbit of Neptune with a velocity greater than the velocity of light by as much as we please. Now imagine a clock in which the hand is such a sweeping ray of light. The time of this clock is the time of arrival of the sweeping ray at the graduations along the circumference. These graduations may be separated by the minimum distance, if there is such. But there would seem to be no lower limit to the time interval between the possible arrival of the sweeping ray at one graduation and its arrival at the next graduation. For this reason I find it much more difficult to imagine circumstances under which I would want to say that time is discontinuous than circumstances for a discontinuous space. And whatever the structure of physical space turns out to be, it would appear to me that mathematics, particularly elementary mathematics, will probably continue to treat space as continuous. The length of the diagonal of a square will probably continue to be written as $\sqrt{2}$ times the side, in spite of the fact that this is inconsistent with a minimum length. The complications arising from not writing it in this way would appear to be too formidable.

If it should turn out that physically there is a discontinuous space and time, that is, a granular structure for space and time, then minimum lengths and times are logically determined incidentally as the differences between the neighboring discrete numbers that express the granularity. It is also logically possible that the differences of these numbers should not be constant, but they might vary with position and epoch. As a matter of fact, however, when the physicist talks about minimum lengths and minimum times he usually means something logically different. Such minima may be defined in terms of various combinations of atomic and other constants which have the requisite dimensions. Several different suggestions of this sort have been made by various authors — the significance of such suggestions is to be found only in a theoretical context and I shall not attempt to go into the matter further here. It is to be remarked in general, however, that the numerical magnitude of such natural minimum lengths or times, which can also serve as natural standards of length or time, is of a higher order than the minimums set by any possible discrete structure of space or time.

Not only do we use instruments to give us fineness of detail inaccessible to direct sense perception, but we also use them to extend qualitatively the range of our senses into regions where our senses no longer operate, as when we detect and measure radiation phenomena at wave lengths beyond the sensitivity of our eyes, or acoustical phenomena above the range of our hearing. More than this, we use instruments to make ourselves aware of the existence of phenomena to which our senses are totally unresponsive, as, for example, the phenomena of magnetism. In fact, there are so many phenomena beyond the range of our senses or to which our senses are totally insensitive that the world of modern physics has become predominantly the world of instruments. We have to ask ourselves how seriously we shall take the indications of our instruments. What sort of significance shall we ascribe to them? And what sort of a world can the world of instruments be, anyhow?

It can be said in the first place that the brute material of the physicist is the data of his instruments to an almost exclusive extent. The task of the physicist might be defined, in the first place, to acquire factual mastery of the data given by all possible instruments under all possible conditions, including here sometimes data given directly by the unaided senses, and then to correlate this material so far as possible into a conceptual whole. In carrying out this task the physicist will have to think about the nature of his instrumental data — it is questions concerned with this that I want to examine now. What sort of information is an instrument capable of giving us? To what extent is what the instrument gives us colored by the instrument itself, or is the instrument capable of revealing to us something "independent of the instrument"? We would not have asked this last question before the advent of quantum theory. We now know that this is a very important question indeed for a certain range of phenomena, and that in this range instrument-of-observation and object-of-observation cannot be separated from each other. On the scale of ordinary sense perception, however, where we have the possibility of getting to the same terminus by the use of several senses, the question loses its importance, and we can usually think of the object as something in itself, unaffected by the instrument, the only function of the instrument being to reveal the object to us.

To forget the instrument through which our knowledge comes constitutes an enormous simplification, a simplification without which one may well question whether men could, up to the present, have been able to cope intellectually with their surroundings at all. In most practical situations such neglect of the instrument is highly justified. The point I wish to make here, however, is that even on the scale of everyday life there are some situations in which this divorce of object from instrument is illegitimate, so that the concept of object, in and for itself, becomes meaningless.

THE FIELD CONCEPT

An example is afforded by the "field" of modern physics, in particular, the field of electrodynamics. The field has for the physicist a definite "reality", because if he goes to the point where there is a purported field with an appropriate instrument the instrument will give a reading of what the field is. The field, as thus instrumentally defined and measured, is absolutely fundamental to the whole structure of electrodynamics, and has received the most sweeping confirmation possible by practical application in every conceivable sort of situation.

The modern physicist, however, thinks of the field in a context even broader than this, and in particular thinks of the field as expressing action through a medium by the handing on of action through contiguous parts, in contrast to direct action at a distance, a concept to which many physicists have a violent allergy. There are two points to be made in connection with the field and its instrumental involvement. The first is that there is no instrumental method of distinguishing between action at a distance and action through a medium, because the same instrument which would reveal the action through a medium, if that hypothesis is true, would also respond to action at a distance, if that hypothesis is true. This point I have elaborated in my London lectures,[5] and I need not go into it further here. The second point, which I wish to elaborate here, has to do with the question of to what extent the instrument is capable of revealing a state of affairs independent of the presence of the instrument, whether action at a distance or through a medium. The mathematical situation with regard to this question has been understood for a long time, but I do not believe that the significance of it has been properly appreciated. Suppose that we are concerned with an electrostatic field and our instrument consists of a test charge and a device for measuring the force on it. We set ourselves the problem of accounting in detail for the response which the test charge of our measuring instrument makes to the presence of the field. The Maxwell field equations yield the answer if we accept the point of view of a medium. The test charge experiences a net force because of the action of the "Maxwell stresses", which push with greater intensity on one side of the test charge than on the other. The reason that they act with different intensities on the two sides is the asymmetry introduced by the charge itself — on the one side, the field of the charge by itself has the same direction as the original field, and on the other side the directions are opposite. The test charge by its presence modifies the field, and the charge responds, not to the field that was present before it was introduced, but to the modifications in the original field introduced by itself. Detailed working out of the mathematics shows that the difference between the Maxwell stresses on the two sides of the test charge gives a net result numerically equal to the product of the charge and the field before the introduction of the charge. This result could probably not have been intuitively anticipated, but it was no accident, because the Maxwell stresses were explicitly constructed so that it should hold. One may contemplate with admiration the fact that a single simple analytical expression for the Maxwell stresses gives, for all possible distributions of charge, a modification in the field such that the modification measures "what was there" before the modification occurred, but the fact remains that there is no instrumental method of giving meaning to "field-in-the-absence-of-the-instrument-of-measurement". Neither is there any instrumental method of answering the question whether the test charge "really" modifies the original field, or whether the Maxwell stresses are "physically real". When we attempt to answer these questions by instrumental procedures we become involved in an infinite regress. Our meanings must be sought entirely on the paper-and-pencil level, in the symbols of our mathematics, that is, in the realm of things we say. And the only meaning we can give to the question of the truth of our mathematics is the indirect meaning given by examining whether the mathematics checks with experiment wherever it is capable of making contact with experiment. Of course, we have always been able to make this indirect check.

The conclusion of the last paragraph that the test charge cannot tell us "what was there before the charge was introduced" holds also if we approach the question from the point of view of action at a distance. On this hypothesis, before the charge was introduced there was nothing at the point, and action at a distance on nothing yields nothing. The test charge experiences a force only because it is there.

In the case of gravitation there is one consideration that makes the action at a distance point of view perhaps more natural physically than action through a field. It was one of the great mathematical discoveries of Newton that a gravitating sphere of any size acts at external points as though its entire mass were concentrated at the geometric center. In deriving this result it was assumed that the action of the distant elements is unaffected by the nearer elements. That is, the mathematics recognizes no such thing as a gravitational shielding. If the mathematical result applies, as it does, there can be no instrumental method of demonstrating gravitational shielding. But it is natural to expect physically that if gravitational action is propagated through the contiguous elements of a medium there should be something of the nature of gravitational shielding. Now there seems to be no observational evidence from astronomy of shielding, but I suspect that the accuracy of these observations is not so great as for many other astronomical phenomena. It would be interesting to have a discussion of the accuracy with which the astronomical evidence compels the conclusions that the gravitational effect of different masses is additive, which is equivalent to no gravitational shielding.

The fact that modern electrodynamic analysis is so successful in meeting the situations of practise suggests that the role played by the field concept is that of an intellectual dummy, which cancels out of the final result, in the same way that the variable of integration cancels from a definite integral.

In discussing operations, we have repeatedly emphasized that if our operations are to be of significance in a scientific context they must be capable of emerging eventually onto the instrumental level, and not remain indefinitely on the verbal level. The fact that here we have not been able to give complete instrumental meaning to the concepts of field or of action at a distance leads me to suspect that in any theoretical correlation of instrumental results we will never be able to make the instrumental emergence complete, but there always will remain some verbal or "paper-and-pencil" component.

AUTOMATIC INSTRUMENTS

Going back to the question of what it is that our measurements with instruments give us, we have seen that the concept of the "true" length of an object, which it has in its own right, irrespective of what we do, is an invention that does not exactly correspond to what happens. The reason that the invention fails to correspond exactly to what happens is that we made an abstraction by neglecting the role of the instrument (or the method) by which we measure length. We have met this sort of situation before: quantum theory has been insisting on its importance. This means that if we want to reproduce fully what happens we should never think of the microscopic world without thinking of microscopes, or never think of the universe of galaxies without thinking of telescopes. All the more should we never think of the interior of the nucleus of an atom without also thinking of cyclotrons or betatrons. The physicist is well on his way to learning the latter lesson in the sense, at least, that few physicists can now think of a betatron without thinking of a million dollars.

The ultimate instrument is ourselves. This means that not only should we never think of the microscopic world without thinking of microscopes, but we should never think of the microscopic world without thinking of ourselves using the microscope. In general, we should never think of the world around us without also thinking of the nervous machinery in our heads by which we acquire knowledge of the world. To discover the best way of holding ourselves to this awareness constitutes what seems to me to be perhaps our most pressing intellectual problem.

Most of the parameters with which the physicist describes the world about him, although involving measurements with instruments, are not given directly by the instruments, but involve more or less complicated calculations by him from the data provided by the instruments. "Mass", "momentum", "energy" do not occur naked in the world around us, but occur only in conjunction with a nervous system and with activity in that nervous system of unfathomed complexity. It does not make sense to ask what mass, and so forth, might be like if there were no human nervous system, but it does make sense to ask how the activity of the nervous system, when it delivers a number which represents the mass, say, of a concrete object, differs from its activity in delivering a number representing the kinetic energy of the same object. We certainly cannot answer such questions at present. Neither, at present, do these seem to be profitable questions, for we would not know what to do with the answers if we had them. We can see, however, that if we had the answers, the center of gravity of the total complexity of such a concept as "mass" would lie almost entirely in the nervous system. Now it seems to me that there is a possibility of shifting the center of gravity of this complexity toward the physical side by the construction of new types of physical instrument. If we could construct automatic instruments which, when directly coupled to the body about which we wish information, indicate automatically on a dial the mass or energy or what-not of the body, then we could *define* mass or energy in terms of the readings of these instruments. We could thereby reduce the cooperation of our nervous systems (which of course we can never entirely get rid of) to the use which they make of the readings presented by the instruments.

Whether this motivation appears cogent or not, I think that in the design of instruments which automatically indicate this or that physical parameter when coupled to the object to be measured one has a line of attack which might conceivably yield fresh insights. The study of such automatic instruments obviously might be elaborated in great detail for all the physical parameters and properties of bodies, such as length, velocity, acceleration, mass, momentum, energy, temperature, viscosity, electric conductivity — in fact, any of the quantities treated in works on physics susceptible of measurement. All I shall attempt here is to suggest some of the considerations which might arise in trying to carry through such a program. In the first place, the instruments will be of varying degrees of complexity. Perhaps the simplest would be the length measurer. For this we could use a spring caliper, which we would snap over the body, the length of which would be automatically indicated by the position of a pointer on a scale. Even with an instrument as simple as this there are conflicting requirements which demand some sort of compromise in the design. The calipers, by their tension, should exert no appreciable deforming force on the body being measured; this demands a light spring to provide the tension between the jaws of the calipers. On the other hand, we want the indication of the instrument to be instantaneous so that we can follow a length changing with time, and this requires a stiff spring. The compromise we make between these two requirements will probably change according to the intended range of use.

After the length measurer, perhaps the next simplest type is the velocity measurer. Here we run into a new situation, in that a self-contained instrument coupled to the object of measurement is not possible, but the instrument has to be coupled to two objects, the object of measurement and another with respect to which the velocity is being measured. But since velocity is a relative concept anyway, this appears to be as it should. We may take as a typical velocity measurer some sort of spring governor arrangement mounted on the object and with a point of contact with the body of reference, as in the speedometer of an automobile, the reference body being the ground with which contact is maintained through the wheels. But here a new situation presents itself because we can no longer secure quick response to changing velocity by changing the tension of the spring of the governor balls, this tension being already determined by the requirements of the steady operation of the governor. Speed of response must be secured by some more questionable and more complicated adjustment. That is, we can see that the question "Is the velocity of a body an instantaneous property of the body?" requires serious consideration and that it is even conceivable that such a question might prove meaningless in this instrumental context (that is, the context in which the velocity is *defined* as the reading of the "velocity instrument").

Assuming, however, that it is possible to construct a velocity measurer that has a sufficiently instantaneous response to changes of velocity, we see that both length and velocity measurers are continuous reading instruments.

Consider next an instrument for automatically recording the mass of a body when coupled to it. I have not been able to think of any automatic mass measurer which is not very much more complicated than the comparatively simple length and mass measurers. This would suggest that there are concealed physical complexities which we ordinarily overlook in the context of our conventional verbal analysis, an analysis in which it is just as easy to say "mass" as it is to say "length". The best that I have been able to do in the way of a mass measurer is a sort of shaker, consisting of a heavy mass against which rests a spring which can be set into vibration of known frequency. The free end of the vibrating spring is pressed against the body whose mass is to be determined. The body is thereby set into vibration the amplitude of which is to be automatically measured by a suitable device mounted in the mass measurer, and which is then to be converted into mass by the appropriate calculations, the calculating machinery being supposed built into the mass measurer. It is evident that with an instrument as complicated as this a host of new questions present themselves. Such an instrument cannot, for example, be a continuous reading instrument, for it can indicate only the average mass over an interval embracing a number of the periods of the spring. Does this indicate that it has no meaning to ask what is the instantaneous mass of an object? It is also obvious that the instrumental difficulties are going to be much greater the smaller the object whose mass we attempt to determine with such an automatic instrument. This suggests that the Newtonian massive particle may be an improper conceptual simplification.

In extending the use of instruments of any sort to small objects we will evidently presently run into limitations of various sorts — these limitations will become operative for the more complicated instruments sooner than for the simple instruments. Accompanying the modified functioning of the instruments as we proceed toward the small there will be modifications in the corresponding concepts. It does not appear that these modifications and limitations have very direct or obvious connection with the sort of modification demanded by quantum theory and the indetermination principle. This suggests the possibility of new sorts of complexity in the structure of the physical world not yet envisaged.

It will doubtless be objected that an analysis of this sort of the world as it appears to automatic instruments is too complicated to handle. It may be answered that this complexity is as nothing compared with the complexity of the full picture when we take into account the functioning of the nervous system. It would appear that the world is really of a frightful complexity. We ordinarily disregard it, and in fact do not see it, because so much of the complexity is buried, like the submerged part of an iceberg, in the structure of our nervous systems.

The theoretical physicist, whether we consider him as he operates at present with the findings of our present conventional instruments, or whether we envisage him in a possible future with the findings of the new types of instrument suggested above at his command, cannot help interjecting something more into the situation than that given by the instruments alone. In particular, he can hardly help using mathematics. Now the concepts of mathematics, such as the concept of continuity or the distinction between the rational and the transcendental numbers, correspond to nothing that instruments are capable of giving. This means that the correspondence between what I have called "paper-and-pencil" operations and instrumental operations cannot be precise. Very often the distinction between the concepts corresponding to the two sorts of operation may be qualitative in character, not merely a matter of some refinement as above. For instance, the energy of thermodynamics is in the paper-and-pencil domain a point function, uniquely determined by the state variables of the body. On the other hand, in the instrumental domain, energy is a "point-couple", having meaning only when two point states, an initial state and a final state, are given. We pass from the instrumental to the paper-and-pencil energy by interjecting into the situation an arbitrary origin of energy. The paper-and-pencil concept thus involves here more than the instrumental concept. An example in which the paper-and-pencil concept involves less than the instrumental concept is afforded by the heat flux at a point of a body. Instrumentally, heat flux is unique, whereas the corresponding paper-and-pencil heat flux which we use in our equations is undetermined by the addition of any divergenceless vector whatever.

INSTANTANEOUS VELOCITY

Historically the concept of instantaneous velocity for bodies moving with variable velocity was one of great difficulty. The simpler concept of unaccelerated velocity was itself difficult for one who had inherited the Greek habit of thinking of space as composed of points of zero extension and of time as compounded of instants of zero duration. However, the fact that bodies do move was directly manifest to the senses, even at an instant, because the fact that a body is moving can be perceived as a direct datum of consciousness in times no longer than the psychological present. Velocity as a fact had to be accepted and dealt with as best one could. I suspect that a large part of the difficulty of the Greek philosophers in dealing with velocity was due to the literalness with which they took all the implications of their verbal machinery. A verbal outlook on the world, which was particularly congenial to the philosophic propensities of the Greeks, emphasizes the static aspects of the world, corresponding to words with fixed meanings. For the point of view which regards an analysis of the world in terms of happenings as the most fruitful, the problem is the exact opposite, namely, to reduce the apparently static to the moving, rather than to reduce the apparently moving to the static.

Whatever the difficulties may have been with simple uniform velocity, a variable velocity was felt to be a different sort of creature. What could a velocity at a single instant of time possibly mean when the only method for measuring velocities appeared to demand observations at two different times, and when the mathematical methods and concepts of the differential calculus had not yet been developed? It was apparently Galileo who had the essential insight here, and this made possible his treatment of falling bodies. One can see by looking, or by measuring average velocities over fixed distances, that the velocity of a falling body is increasing. Galileo described this state of affairs by associating a number, the instantaneous velocity, with the falling body at every instant. His insight consisted in seeing that there must be such a number. He convinced himself of it by arguments essentially from continuity — by considering a body moving at first with some constant velocity and then later with a greater constant velocity, and asking how the body could have got from one condition to the other without passing through intermediate states each characterized by successively increasing velocities. A mathematician would say that Galileo saw that at every moment of the motion of a particle an instantaneous velocity *exists;* a physicist would say that he saw that a moving particle at every instant *has* a velocity.

If a moving particle has at every instant a velocity, then a complete description of the instantaneous state of any physical system demands that not only the positions, but also the velocities, be specified. If this is so, then there should be some sort of measurement that one can make instantaneously on a system, *not* a measurement of the position of its particles. The Greeks did not envisage this. Galileo's mechanics enabled him to discover what these additional possibilities of measurement were. One possible method might involve a determination of momentum by measuring the force on a spring balance that would reduce the particle to rest in unit time. More modern and more truly instantaneous methods might employ the Doppler effect of sound or light reflected from the moving object. A method more in keeping with Galileo's own experiments of getting the velocity of a ball rolling down an incline would be, at the required instant, to rotate the incline about the instantaneous position of the ball up into the horizontal. The ball would then roll along the horizontal with constant velocity, which could be determined by methods already mastered.

The fact that Galileo recognized that a body "has" a velocity at every instant and that there are methods for measuring it meant that he had invented a new parameter which must be determined if the description of the body is to be complete. This illustrates the fact already mentioned that the process of measurement sometimes feeds on itself.

The importance of the invention of the concept of velocity lies in the fact that by its use the world of experience acquires order and predictability. With no concept of velocity at all the world must have appeared completely chaotic, identical present positions (identity being defined as possession of the same space coordinates by all the particles) developing into the most unpredictably diverse configurations. With the addition of velocity as a new parameter, we can predict where the particle will be in the future if we know its present position and velocity. In this context, velocity is essentially a "predicting parameter". It was a discovery that prediction is possible and that there is a predicting parameter, no less than was the method of measuring velocity a discovery. In the case of constant velocities the range of prediction thereby opened was unlimited; if the velocity is variable, demanding a determination of the instantaneous velocity, the range of prediction is narrower, the precise restriction of acceptable range depending on the rate of variation. This latter concept had to wait for the development of the concepts of the calculus before it could be handled to give widely usable results, and it involves the higher time derivatives.

ON VELOCITY IN GENERAL AND THE VELOCITY OF LIGHT

Whenever we have a position which changes continuously with time we also have a velocity. If we wish we can give a numerical value to this velocity by defining it as change of position per unit time. But the position has to be position of something. Neither can we just have velocity, but the velocity has to be velocity of something. The something that the velocity is of is the same as the something which the position is of. What are the limitations on this "something"? It would seem that a great deal of latitude is possible — we may have a velocity of a material particle, or we may have a velocity of a phase of a wave in a continuous medium. In all cases, as a minimum, it would seem to be necessary to have some recognizable feature to associate with the changing position. In many situations susceptible of visual description the recognizable feature is something that we can recognize by sight, and we can *see* the motion. The concept of recognizability here seems to be broader than the concept of identifiability — we can recognize the moving particle and the particle also has identity, but we can also recognize the moving trough of a wave. I think we would be unwilling to say that the moving trough preserves its "identity", although we might be willing to say that the moving trough preserves identity of form. What it is that gives the recognizability to the moving position is capable of great variability, with the result that the velocity which we can coordinate with a given physical situation is not unique.

For instance, if we have a moving water wave in a beam of parallel light, then the recognizable region is the region from which light is reflected, and if we arrange matters suitably this region may be made the bottom of the trough and the velocity becomes the phase velocity of the wave. But if we slowly tilt the beam of light, the recognizable region, which continues to be the region from which light is reflected to our eye, no longer remains at the bottom of the trough, and the velocity which we find under these circumstances is no longer the phase velocity.

The recognizability may be conferred by some feature in the physical situation, as above, or it may be conferred mathematically by demanding that satisfaction of some mathematically formulated condition constitute the feature that bestows recognizability. The physical condition can usually be formulated in mathematical terms, but on the other hand the mathematical condition is capable of such great generality that all contact with the physical situation may be lost. It is only velocities that have some physical tie-in that are of interest to us here.

One of the most important physical situations in which we apply the concept of velocity is with regard to light. In what sense may we speak of the velocity of light? Before we can answer this we would like to know what light "is". To answer this question we adopt our general tactics of side-stepping, when we can, any question of what something or other "is", and rephrase the question "Under what circumstances do I use the word 'light'?" If we can answer this I think we have all the physicist can use. I have already, in some of my other writings,[6] devoted considerable attention to an analysis of the nature of light, so that no attempt at a complete analysis will be made here. In general, it appears that we use the word light only in connection with "things lighted". We never encounter light as a thing in itself, either in the form of an emanation from the eyes of the seer, as Aristotle had it, or as a corpuscular emanation from the luminous source, as Newton had it, or as a wave in an electromagnetic field, as modern physics has it, for that matter. It is always "things lighted". When we speak of the linear propagation of a ray of light we are merely describing the relative geometric configuration of things lighted by the ray.

Now in what sense can we speak of a velocity of this "light", trying to bring the velocity of light under our general scheme of a time change of position of something recognizable? On the scale of ordinary macroscopic experience this is easy to do, with the help of partially transparent screens, which let through most of the light but reflect a sufficient portion to become visible when interposed in the path of the ray. If we interpose a series of such screens in the path of a ray, we can see the illuminated region progressing from one screen to another with a definite velocity when we turn on the ray. This velocity we call the velocity of light. We can use this velocity consistently in describing various sorts of phenomena. Thus if the row of screens is at some distance and at right angles to a line from our eyes to the row of screens, we directly see the illuminated region travel along the row with a velocity of 3×10^{10} centimeters per second. Or if the row of screens and the ray are in a line reaching from our eyes we see the illuminated region traveling from us with a velocity of one-half the former velocity, if the ray is traveling away from us, or, if the ray is toward us, the illuminated region appears to us simultaneously on all the screens. The dependence of apparent velocity on the direction of the ray in these last two situations is naturally described as a result of the velocity of light itself from the illuminated region. Or, finally, we can shine a ray of light on a distant mirror, whereupon we perceive the reflection at a time later by a sufficient interval for the light to go and come from the mirror with a velocity of 3×10^{10}, just as if it were a material projectile. In all cases we can calculate the temporal relations between the illuminations of objects as if light were a material thing like a projectile with the definite velocity of 3×10^{10} centimeters per second. However, in no case do we make experimental contact with the projectile apart from the objects on which it impinges. Further, the following sort of experiment we could not do: we could not put a screen in the path of a ray of light and move it with the velocity of light (forgetting for the moment relativity difficulties) and expect to see an *illuminated* screen moving with the velocity of light. Such a screen would not be illuminated at all. "Light" is not a "thing" — if we move alongside it with its own velocity there is nothing there.

So much for light on the ordinary macroscopic scale — it has certain aspects which can be treated with the ordinary concept of velocity. However, when we reduce the intensity of light to such an extent that we are dealing with individual photons, partial reflection at a screen is no longer possible and there is no possibility of seeing a moving illuminated region. With the single photon the act of detection totally destroys what we are trying to detect. We are left only with discrete events — an act of initiation at some locality, which consists in the emission of a photon and which may be given independent instrumental significance in a momentum recoil of the emitting object, and the consummation of the act of emission (at least in closed systems) by the reception of a photon somewhere else, which again has independent instrumental significance through an increment of momentum. The consummation event is retarded in time over the initiation event by an amount calculable in terms of the macroscopic picture and a projectile light velocity, but there can be no instrumental answer to the question whether the photon "really" traveled like a projectile through the intermediate space.

In spite of our dictum that the meanings of all our "microscopic" experiences must ultimately be found on the macroscopic level, I think the physicist would be inclined to ascribe greater significance to the behavior of light at limitingly small intensities than to its behavior at the intensities of ordinary visual perception. He should, therefore, it seems to me, ascribe a special significance to the fact that there is no direct proof of the possession by the photon of projectilelike properties.

It is obvious enough that light and its velocity plays a very special role, but it is perhaps not entirely easy to formulate what this role is. It is, of course, fundamental to relativity theory. Such results of relativity theory as the impossibility of imparting a velocity greater than that of light to material bodies are universally accepted and seem to be universally confirmed. Nevertheless I think there are still some considerations here to which we may devote a little attention. For instance, the fact that the velocity of light is an upper limit for the velocity of material bodies is sometimes loosely paraphrased in the statement that velocities greater than the velocity of light are impossible. But a little thought will show that this is an improper formulation, and that velocities, in our generalized sense of the change with time of the position of something recognizable, can be produced of any magnitude whatever. The searchlight sweeping the sky, already mentioned in the discussion of clocks, is an example. Not only is there no limit to the velocity with which I may see the illuminated patch on the clouds moving through the sky, but there is no limit to the velocity as directly measured with clocks in the path of the traveling patch of illumination, as by clocks in two airplanes in the path of the beam. Usually some attempt is made to point out a fundamental distinction between this sort of velocity and the velocity of light. Thus it is sometimes said that no "causal" effect can be transmitted faster than light, or that "information" cannot be transmitted faster than light. The implication here is that if we have "information" we can in some way turn it to causal use. However, the ordinary notions of cause and of information are notoriously fuzzy, and I believe we may profitably stop to look a little further into this situation.

Imagine a long train of explosive of such a nature that the explosion at any point of it can be initiated only by the reception of radiant energy of an intrinsic energy greater than some threshold value. Imagine further a sweeping searchlight of cosmic rays on Sirius of greater than the threshold energy. Whenever this beam impinges on the train of explosive a wave of explosion travels along the train with a velocity unlimitedly greater than the velocity of light. We suppose, furthermore, that this particular beam of cosmic rays is the only one with the requisite energy, so that the explosion is initiated only on reception of the beam from Sirius. Now it may well be that I do not know of the beam from Sirius and have no instrument able to respond to photons of such short wave length. For me, all that I will know is that every now and then a wave of explosion is propagated along the train with superlight velocity. How far can such a situation be described in causal terms? We can at least predict in this situation, and there is usually supposed to be a connection between prediction and causality via determinism. I can predict, because whenever I observe the train of explosive exploding where I am I can predict that I shall presently receive a light signal from a distant part of the train announcing the explosion there. The time at which this distant explosion occurs is such that I could not possibly have received news of the distant explosion by the conventional method of light transmission in time to have made the prediction. For instance, later calculation might show that the distant explosion occurred one-half second after I made my prediction, whereas it requires one second for a light signal to reach me from the scene of the explosion. This sort of thing is conventionally supposed to be impossible. Is it legitimate to apply the notion of prediction to this situation? Is it or is it not appropriate to describe these things in causal terms? May I say that the explosion here causes the propagation of the explosion to a distance? May or may I not say that the occurrence of the explosion here "informs" me that it will presently occur at a distant place, but at an epoch too near for me to have caused it by any conventional causal apparatus? The concept of causality is often formulated in terms of invariable sequences of events. We have such sequences here, but are embarrassed whether we should use a causal description or not. It is evident, I think, that we are here in the presence of a largely verbal situation. In spite of the verbal difficulty, I think no physicist would have much doubt about what he could do in situations like this or what sort of measurements he could make with his instruments. This is not the first time that what we do is wiser than what we say.

I digress here to remark that I think this example throws a certain light on the causality situation in general. In the first place, it would appear that not all invariable coupling of events is a causal coupling and that predictability is not coextensive with causality. We do not ordinarily say that Monday is the cause of Tuesday. If A is to be the unique cause of B we would want to demand not only that B occur whenever A occurs and that it never occur when A does not occur, but also we would want to have sufficient control over A to be able to make A occur or not at will. There is no necessary anthropomorphic implication in this formulation in terms of "at will" — we could demand that we be able to make A occur or not in accordance with the tossing of a coin. In the example above, by hypothesis we have no control or knowledge of the sweeping beam from Sirius and so far as we are concerned the propagation of explosion along the train follows the explosion here in the same way that Tuesday follows Monday. We would not ordinarily describe this whole situation in causal terms, although it is perhaps debatable whether we would not attempt to describe one feature of it, the propagation of the explosion after its initiation here, in causal terms. But once let us acquire greater command of the situation, in particular, let us detect the beam from Sirius, and our description in causal terms is drastically altered. The propagation of the explosion now appears as a causal phenomenon. However, the cause of the apparent propagation is said to be the incidence of the beam from Sirius, not the occurrence of the explosion at earlier stages of the train. In thus ascribing a causal function to the beam from Sirius we are not deterred by not being able to control the incidence of the beam at will. It is enough if such control does not appear impossible "in principle".

It thus appears that the account we give of a situation in causal terms depends on the universe of allowable operations — our causal account is altered when our universe of operations is expanded to allow us to detect the high-frequency radiation from Sirius.

The situation presented by the superlight-velocity explosion has other aspects than the causal aspect. There is, for example, an aspect with regard to knowledge and information. We "know" that the explosion is taking place at a distance before news of it can be transmitted to us by light — in what sense can we talk of a propagation of knowledge here? Information and knowledge have close connections with each other and with causality. In virtue of having information we can make things happen which otherwise we could not. And if we have invariable sequences so that we can predict, we can arrange it so that certain things happen contingent on the other thing happening which we can predict. But in what sense can we say that our prediction on the basis of invariable past happening involves "knowledge" or "information"? Or, in what sense can we talk about a propagation of this knowledge or information? These things are obviously all related, but the relationship is fuzzy. In particular, I think that the "information" of ordinary conversation is obviously not coextensive with the "information" of technical information theory. The encoding of the information must be flexible enough to permit the information to be encoded and transmitted after the corresponding event has occurred, and be possible no matter what the nature of the event, over which by hypothesis we have no control. We would not ordinarily use the word information in connection with invariable events — we would not ordinarily say on Monday that we have information that tomorrow will be Tuesday. The situation here with regard to information is not dissimilar to that with regard to causality, where we have seen that if A is to be described as the cause of B we should be able to make A occur or not at will.

Returning now to our discussion of the nature of light, our inability to give instrumental meaning to light as a thing traveling in such a way that its independent existence can be demonstrated in flight between source and sink reminds one of, and is very similar to, our inability to give independent instrumental meaning to "field-at-a-point-in-empty-space" in such a way as to distinguish between action at a distance and action through a medium. In either case the difficulty is introduced by the instrument. We require to establish by instruments a state of affairs which by definition can exist only in the absence of the instrument. The distinctions which we are trying to establish cannot be instrumental distinctions, but are only "paper-and-pencil" distinctions — they are in the realm of what we say. The situation seems to be a pretty general one which presents itself whenever we try to deal with a physical situation with partial differential equations. The equations themselves can never adequately reproduce any physical situation, but always have to be supplemented by boundary conditions. The boundary conditions we have in our control, and they are *all* that we have in our control. One experimental situation is differentiated from another by its boundary conditions. We vary the initial conditions, that is, we make different experiments by varying the boundary conditions, and we measure the results of our experiment with instruments which are themselves simply part of the boundary conditions. We never make contact with the equations themselves through our instruments, but only by calculation and through the boundary conditions. So long as mathematical machinery remains as it is now — equations plus boundary conditions to describe a physical situation — so long will we be unable to answer such questions as "Does the field 'really' exist?" The only check and the only meaning we can give to our physical world is through the boundary conditions. We start with boundary conditions, which we impose, and we end with boundary conditions, which we measure. Our only demand is that we know how to correlate initial and final boundary conditions. At present we make the correlation through the intermediary of the differential equations. These equations cancel out from the final result and play only a dummy role. Why is it that our mathematics cannot pass directly from boundary condition to boundary condition? We can in the simpler situations but not in the more complicated ones.

SOME IMPLICATIONS OF QUANTUM THEORY

I have already discussed in previous writings various aspects of wave mechanics — here I shall single out for discussion a few topics which I have not discussed at any length before, and which suggest points of view the significance of which have been growing upon me and which are therefore basic to some of the insights which have provided the primary motivation for writing this book. For some of these insights, quantum theory plays the part only of a catalyst, and in some cases certain changes in present quantum practice and outlook suggest themselves. In the following I shall not narrowly restrict myself to following out the consequences of quantum theory in the field of quantum phenomena in the technical sense, but shall freely explore the wider implications, which I think are numerous and more important than the technical consequences. Some of these points have already been hinted in the introduction.

Perhaps first to be put is the realization, which has often been expressed by writers on quantum theory, that quantum theory is an activity by us, who are macroscopic creatures, and that the results of quantum theory have to be expressed in terms of manipulations by us of our macroscopic apparatus, and furthermore have to be expressed in our language and find their meaning on the level of our language. This insight is a special case of the insight that we can never get away from ourselves. Although quantum theorists recognize this and pay lip service to the insight, they often abandon the point of view when they get down to concrete applications. Thus it is often said that quantum theory shows that our ordinary concepts fail when they are pushed into the microscopic domain. I suspect that I often used to say this myself. DeBroglie is one of the writers who more articulately emphasize that the quantum domain is the domain of the very small — particularly in his book *Physics and Microphysics*. I have already emphasized that strictly there is no such thing as a "microscopic" world, but merely an altered world of macroscopic experience.

Another way of saying that our meanings must be found on the macroscopic level is to say that the operation of isolation fails when we attempt to apply it to the microscopic. We cannot think of the microscope in and for itself, but always we find it embedded in a macroscopic matrix. There is a sense in which all the revolutionary aspects of quantum theory can be subsumed under the single point of view that the operation of isolation always fails eventually.

The whole conceptual revolution forced by quantum theory is really a revolution on the common sense level of daily life — we have to find how to deal with the new things on this level. It is not going to be easy to do this in such a way that we will be able to think about the actual macroscopic world with the confidence and facility with which we now think about our constructed microscopic world, but I think the attempt has to be made. A promising first attack will be found in a recent book by William Bender entitled *An Introduction to Scale Coordinate Physics.*[7] Quantum theory provides us with no new intellectual tools — we have to get along with what we have always had. The fact that we are able to do this and adapt ourselves with considerable success to the new phenomena suggests that there were features in our thinking of which we were not aware, an insight already mentioned in the introduction.

Another insight with very wide implications is that the object of knowledge is not to be separated from the instrument of knowledge or the method by which knowledge is acquired. The Heisenberg principle of uncertainty is one of the expressions of a technical working out of the consequences. There is, however, a much cruder and fuzzier way of stating some of the consequences which I think removes the atmosphere of paradox from the situation and in fact puts quantum theory in a light which need not be unacceptable even to common sense. In considering the dual situation, object of knowledge and instrument of knowledge, two extreme cases are to be considered. At the one extreme we have the object of knowledge much larger than the instrument of knowledge, and at the other extreme we have the instrument of knowledge much larger than the object of knowledge. The first extreme corresponds to the situations of everyday life and the second extreme to quantum situations. Now we know in everyday life that a small instrument of knowledge can deal more effectively with a relatively large object than can a large instrument of knowledge deal with a relatively small object. We can get a relatively more accurate description of a field which we measure with a meter stick than we can of a drop of water which we attempt to measure with the same meter stick. Or we can give a more accurate description of the physiology of a horse after naked-eye inspection than we can of the physiology of a flea after similar naked-eye inspection. Remembering that we ourselves are the ultimate instruments, so that we have no control over their magnitude, I think it makes sense to anticipate that we should be able to deal more effectively with objects large relative to us than with relatively small objects. One of the features in the effectiveness of our dealing with the objects around us is the success with which we can predict their future behavior. It makes sense to me, therefore, to anticipate that we should find that we can predict the future behavior of large objects better than we can of small objects. Now this is a partial and qualitative statement of the content of the Heisenberg principle. To me this aspect of quantum theory makes sense, and I think it can be accepted without rebellion on the part of common sense.

Nevertheless, I believe that many will persist in rebellion. One is in rebellion if one continues to believe that small-scale events *must* be causally connected. Now the adoption of such an attitude may lead, as a practical matter, to the discovery of at present unknown and unsuspected phenomena which will restore the causal connection between small-scale events. But if a rebellious man does make such a discovery it must not be taken as justification of his rebellion. Such a discovery might also be made by a man who is willing to say "It may be that there is no causal connection", because such a man realizes as well as anyone else that there is no security against the discovery of at present unknown phenomena, and he may equally well be on the lookout for them. In science, as in a game of whist, the justification for a present move is not to be found in how the play turns out, but in what could have been known to the player when he made his play.

The whole issue of determinism naturally presents itself here. As usually discussed at present the picture of a deterministic universe is the picture presented by a universe controlled by the exact mathematic equations of Newtonian mechanics. This picture is usually contrasted with the picture presented by wave mechanics. But of course we had the concept of a deterministic universe long before we had Newtonian mechanics or the idea of mathematically exact laws. A deterministic universe was demanded by the religious and philosophic notion of an omnipotent and all-knowing God. This God knew the minutest details of the future, and of course if God knew what was going to happen it had to happen, and the future was therefore determined and unalterable by anything that anyone could do about it. It was a point of view implied, for example, in the biblical phrase "No sparrow falleth to the ground without the Father" and also, of course, in the Mohammedan idea of Kismet.

The classical conception of determinism is usually formulated in terms of Laplace's demon, a being sufficiently powerful to have simultaneous knowledge of the positions and velocities of all the particles in the universe. To such a being the future development of the universe, down to the minutest detail, is determinable and describable in advance, being controlled by the equations of Newtonian mechanics. Such a universe would be completely deterministic. In the early years of this century the physicist had come to think of the laws of electrodynamics as more fundamental than those of mechanics, so that he would not have formulated the principle of determinism in the same terms as did Laplace. His formulation might have been, "Given the *complete* present condition of the universe, then its future unfolding is completely determined by the equations of electrodynamics". The difference, compared with the Laplacean formulation, would be that a complete description of the present state of the universe demands a knowledge of the electromagnetic field at all points of empty space as well as the location and velocity of the charges. The alteration in the picture makes no difference for my present point. Both specifications demand a specification in terms of *all* the particles and *all* the points of space. I believe that under these conditions "all" is an illegitimate concept. The point at issue has been raised earlier in another context in our discussion of the logical meaning of "any" and "all". In the physical situation which here confronts us, as well as in nearly every other physical situation in which we are concerned with more than a few objects, we see that what we immediately experience and deal with is "any", not "all". "All" is our construction to enable us to correlate a complex experience of many "anys". We do "any" and say "all". When dealing with the universe we can, by suitable instrumentation, measure and give meaning to position and velocity of *any* particle. But to give meaning simultaneously to position and to velocity of *all* would demand instrumentation which would infinitely swamp its object. In the limited finite situations of ordinary life we may successfully pass from the "any" which we experience to the "all" which we postulate and talk about. For we can give approximate instrumental meaning to the condition of all the elementary parts in terms of measurements made with instruments reaching into the system from the outside and not interfering with the motion of the system. In terms of measurements with such instruments we can predict approximately what will occur in the system, pro-

vided that we can control or measure any other influence that gets
across the boundary from outside. If we are not in a position to describe what comes across the boundary, the system then becomes
deterministic only when it is isolated — that is, when nothing comes
across the boundary. Prediction, and therefore determinism, occurs
only on a limited scale when we have the two features of precise
describability and isolatability or control of what comes across the
boundaries. When we pass to the entire universe we lose both features. The instruments which give knowledge of the universe are
themselves part of the universe, and to describe them will demand
other instruments in infinite regress. The operation of isolating the
universe or of controlling what comes in from outside becomes meaningless. We have no reason to think that as we make the part of the
universe which we endeavor to annex to our deterministic system
larger the influence of what comes across the boundary does not
become larger and larger. (An aspect of this has been discussed in
connection with "molecular chaos" and the law of large numbers.)
In fact, it seems to represent a divergent factor. When we pass to the
entire universe the ordinary implications in "all" simply fade out.
There is no "all" in this context. Yet we continue to read into our "all"
the implications of ordinary experience and end with a picture of a
deterministic universe, which has no plausibility whatever in terms of
anything that happens to us and which has only a verbal meaning
and a metaphysical verbal meaning at that. There can be no question, however, but that the picture of a universe "really" deterministic, whether we can establish it in terms of experience or not, has
had the greatest effect on human conduct. This might be explicitly
documented by the history of Calvinism, for example.

When it comes to dealing with "all that there is" there are some
things which simply cannot be done. The situation here is somewhat
like the situation envisaged by Archimedes, only in reverse. Archimedes said that he could move the world if he were given a place to
stand. Here there is no place on which we can stand to give meaning
to "all the world".

We again encounter a failure of the operation of isolation. Determinism and causality have a meaning only in a context in which
we can isolate. In practise, isolation is a divergent process. Deter-

minism and causality have only rough and fuzzy meanings, and then only when applied to systems of small size.

So much for prequantum determinism as a doctrine universally applicable; we never had a right to such a doctrine and quantum mechanics therefore strictly can have nothing to say about it. But quantum theory does have something to say about the behavior of small systems which can be approximately isolated. What is usually meant by "small" system is one on the atomic scale. What it says about such systems is negative. It says that as a matter of fact we know of no way of predicting the future behavior of such isolated systems from the most complete measurements we can make on their present condition, so that in this sense small atomic systems are noncausal or indeterministic. In spite of this, however, such systems do show regularities of a sort when we deal with many similar systems, and their behavior usually tends to a type which can be described in terms of probabilities. An essential part of the mathematical arsenal of quantum theory consists of the mathematical theory of probability, which has become so integrally involved in the texture of the theory that it could not be abandoned without destroying the whole theoretical structure. Since this theoretical structure has had a spectacular success in meeting practically all the newly discovered experimental situations in the atomic domain, physicists are understandably loath to contemplate giving it up or submitting it to any serious modification. Nevertheless the matter is one of lively controversy. Part of this controversy, it seems to me, is primarily verbal, and it involves such questions as whether a system may properly be called deterministic if the individual events which characterize it do not develop in a causal manner in time, but if the probabilities which "control" the system themselves develop in time according to causal principles. Some people are satisfied to call this sort of thing "deterministic" — others do not like to. These issues are, I think, somewhat superficial. Pretty close to these are other deeper issues. It is, for example, often said that because of the fundamental role played by probability in quantum theory the only sort of knowledge we can have is probable knowledge. Along the same vein it is often said that the subject of scientific measurement is never an individual, but always has to be an ensemble.

To me it is simply bad description to say that the measurements of the scientist are ensemble measurements (see also Chapter III, page 64) — it certainly does not describe my own activities in the laboratory. It is true that the scientist likes to have some sort of check on the correctness of his measurements, and one of the most effective methods of giving the desired check is to repeat the measurement. But no repeated measurement thereby becomes an ensemble measurement. Ensembles are an abstraction basic to the mathematics of probability theory, and logically any probability analysis has to make reference to ensembles when it uses mathematics. But ensembles do not occur in the laboratory — here we always deal with the concrete and the individual. Even when we multiply our readings to secure greater accuracy we have not introduced an ensemble in the technical sense, but have a concrete situation on a higher level, it is true a situation composed of many subsituations each of them individual and concrete, but still a situation which as a whole and regarded as a unit retains its character of individuality and concreteness. Furthermore, repetition, even in the laboratory, is not a practice employed by any means universally, but whether we repeat the measurement or not depends on the purposes of the moment and the corresponding requisite accuracy. If we want to know whether a certain piece of metal will float or not when we throw it into water, and if we measure its density and obtain the number 12, we certainly will not repeat the measurement. In no case in the laboratory is repetition a perfectly simple matter — we have to have some way of being sure that we are really repeating and that some necessary variable has not altered without our knowledge. Furthermore, in most laboratory situations repetition is not as a matter of fact the most effective way of dealing with the possibility of error. We are more likely to vary the conditions deliberately by small amounts for our successive measurements, and obtain in this way a succession of readings which we can plot. We then draw a smooth curve through the plotted points and expect that the curve will have a greater accuracy than the individual readings.

There is, however, one situation in measurement on the laboratory scale which makes close connection with the view that scientific measurement is ultimately ensemble measurement. This arises when we wish to push our accuracy to the limit. An example will illustrate. Imagine a device, like the micropipette of the biologist, for injecting a very small amount of fluid. It is required to determine what this amount is, but the accuracy of measurement of the volume of a single injection is not satisfactory. We try to increase the accuracy by making a large number of injections, such as a hundred or a thousand, which we can count with perfect precision, catching all the injections in a single container, and determining the total volume. We divide this by a hundred or a thousand and purportedly have a number with a hundred or a thousand fold the accuracy of a single measurement. But have we "really" increased the precision by as much as appears? To prove this we would have to prove that the individual injections were constant to this limit of accuracy, and we have no instrumental method for doing this. Our question, taken at its face value, is meaningless. But we can nevertheless give an indirect meaning. If the individual injections are "really" constant, then individual exemplars will fluctuate about a mean in a manner given by the Gauss error function. Furthermore the averages of a great many runs of a hundred or a thousand will themselves fluctuate about a mean in a way given by probability theory. By studying such fluctuations we can obtain some indirect evidence whether the individual injections were "really" constant. Something like this may perhaps be the ultimate method of measurement. However, it is to be avoided when possible because it is excessively tedious. Furthermore, the resemblance to the ensemble situations of statistics is only superficial, because by definition an ensemble is composed of identical exemplars, and here there is no independent method of ensuring that this condition is satisfied.

Carrying still further the line of thought that claims that all scientific measurement is of ensembles it is often said, as remarked before, that all knowledge is only probable knowledge. Now if all that is meant by this is that we can never make measurements which do not have some error or that we can never make statements of which we are completely certain, I think that no one can object, even if one may be a little surprised that so much point is made of such a perfectly obvious statement. But I think there is usually an implication when it is stated that all knowledge is only probable knowledge to which one may legitimately object. This is the implication that somewhere there is such a thing as certain knowledge, only for some reason we are not able to attain to it. This is the sort of implication that we have so often seen is difficult to avoid because of the structure of our language — the unfortunate results of the implication can usually be avoided if the issue is brought out into the open.

Whatever the uncertainties and the probability of our ordinary knowledge there is no question that we have to use it as our tool in dealing with the concrete individual situations of daily life, which we often deal with on a simple "yes" or "no" basis.

The knowledge that I have been talking about is the knowledge of ordinary experience as I see it in consciousness. If we ever become sufficient masters of the microscopic physiology of brain functioning to describe in full detail what happens during mental activity it may well be that the activity which we call "knowing" may prove to have a strong component of probability in the sense that states of knowing which appear to conscious introspection to be the same may have a microscopic structure varying over a wide range fixed by probability considerations. We are at present discouragingly far from being able to give such an account of mental activity, but there is at least nothing logically contradictory in assuming that some day we will be able to do it. Even now it is obvious that the nervous system does not function in knowing without an enormous amount of preconditioning, which means an enormous amount of concealed structure. This structure need not be the same for different individuals, and the differences may have a probability distribution.

There are other situations in quantum theory which as ordinarily expressed involve paradox. One such is with regard to the electron, which paradoxically has no identity, so that we cannot follow a particular electron about in its adventures as we could a mote of dust suspended in the atmosphere. Here again the difficulty occurs only in a context in which we attempt to isolate the electron and think of it as something independent of the other circumstances which always occur when we experiment on it. Here the other circumstances are the rest of the physical apparatus used in experimenting with electrons. An electron is an aspect of a total situation, the major part of which is the rest of the apparatus. We should not talk about "electrons" as such, but rather say: "Under such and such conditions the apparatus *electrons*".

Interesting questions present themselves of what we should expect if we could make our physical manipulations fast enough to switch arbitrarily from a position apparatus to a momentum apparatus or vice versa after we have caught our electron. The experimental physicists tell me that the possibility of this sort of thing is in sight.

Consideration of the whole apparatus removes the paradox from another single electron situation. This is the situation presented by the interference pattern formed when electrons pass through a screen in which there are one or two apertures. The interference pattern in the one aperture situation is entirely different from that when there are two. The paradox presents itself when one looks at it from the point of view of individual electrons and attempts to understand how the electron, which has to pass through one or the other of the two slits, distinguishes the cases in which there is another aperture through which it might pass but doesn't, from the cases where there is no other aperture. The paradox is not lessened when one considers that the interference *pattern* is not relevant to the individual electron, but that the pattern appears only when there are many electrons, the pattern being a probability arrangement of the many. Nevertheless, each individual electron as it comes through one or the other aperture, must somehow "know" the pattern into which it is supposed to fall, for otherwise how could the pattern get built up from the individual acts? Here the paradox disappears when one ceases to think of the electron as an isolated something which interacts with the isolated screens, but instead thinks of the whole together, electron and screen, as one indivisible whole. The whole, when the screen contains two apertures, is different from the whole when the screen contains only one, so that there is no paradox in a different pattern in the two cases.

Some discussion is required of Bohr's principle of complementarity. This had its origin and achieves its most precise mathematical formulation in connection with the Heisenberg principle of uncertainty. In accordance with this principle it is not possible to make simultaneously position measurements and momentum measurements with indefinite precision, but increased precision in the one has to be purchased at the price of decreased precision in the other. This may be expressed by saying that the position aspect and the momentum aspect are "complementary" aspects.

It may be mentioned incidentally that the apparent paradox in this situation, which is strongly felt by many people, disappears when it is considered that the electron means nothing by itself, but only in a context with an apparatus. "Position" of an electron means a measurement obtained in a complex including a particular kind of apparatus, a "position apparatus". Similarly momentum of an electron has meaning only in a context including a "momentum apparatus". If we recognize that there is no a priori reason why the two sorts of apparatus should be the same, the paradox disappears from the statement that the electron cannot simultaneously have position and momentum.

The mathematical formalism may be extended to any situation in which we deal with conjugate variables, "conjugate" having a technical mathematical significance in the fact that the p and the q operators do not commute. Many people still restrict what they mean by the principle of complementarity to this special mathematical context. However, Bohr and increasingly a greater number of other people apparently see here a special case of a general principle of much wider application, the scope of application sometimes bordering perilously close on the metaphysical. Bohr has mentioned a possible application to biology which Schrödinger has seized on and elaborated. This is the view that it may be "in principle" impossible to describe fully a living system, because the instrument of description must probe so deeply into the organism that by so doing it destroys the life which it is seeking to analyze. The analogy with the position-momentum situation is obvious and it is tempting to seize on it as something significant. It seems to me, however, that it is much too early to ascribe any such sweeping significance to it. Biological techniques are continually being improved, with less and less interference with the functioning of the organism, and it is by no means evident that a description of molecular processes sufficiently detailed to enable us to understand what life involves must necessarily demand instrumental procedures which destroy the life and which are therefore self-defeating.

Bohr carries the point of view still further, and speaks of the impossibility of reconciling the simultaneous demands of justice and love in dealing with our fellows as an example of complementarity. Whether or not one wants to regard such an opposition as an example of a profound new principle, it would certainly be difficult to formulate any principle with so wide a scope with any approach to precision. I do not believe that experience with quantum theory was necessary to show that very often we run into the vague dualism or dichotomy brought to light here, but that this is a sort of thing which we have always had with us, and which has often been the subject of comment in other contexts. Almost invariably we push our analysis to a point where our tools of attack are no longer good and we have to shift to another line of attack. It is the sort of thing that we encounter when we say that we have to operate on different levels, or that all we are capable of is a spiraling approximation. It is built into the structure of language and communication. We know that there are situations which cannot be reproduced in language, but we nevertheless are constrained to say in language what it is that language cannot do. Always we run into these self-contradictions, and always we deal with them by shifting our point of view. This shift in the point of view is nothing more nor less than a shift to the "complementary" aspect of the situation, and wherever we have to make such shifts we will find an example of complementarity. Usually the shift in the point of view presently demands a shift from the shift; we thus encounter regresses or, otherwise expressed, chains of complementarity. When dealing with myself and my relations to society I have to shift continually back and forth between a public and a private language. Or, if we make our analysis of the everyday world into objects, we can only express what we mean by objects in terms of happenings. And we can only express what we mean by happenings in terms of objects. We cannot deal with the world except by isolating, and when we have isolated we are forced to talk about emergence in the context of the whole. "Emergence" and "isolation" are a complementary pair.

A far-reaching complementarity or dichotomy is the yes-no complementarity. It seems that rational thought is impossible without "not". When we get to the limit of language, all we can say is that the language which we have been using is *not* capable of doing what we wanted, but we cannot say, without passing to a metalanguage, what it was that we wanted. "Not" is a verbal flag that we fly to announce that we are going to change verbal cars. To ask whether the locus of this complementarity is predominantly in ourselves or in the external world is to ask a meaningless question.

Seldom if ever have I seen a discussion of the implications of quantum theory which seemed to me to carry the implications far enough. The insight that we have to encounter situations as wholes, that we cannot isolate, and that the object of knowledge is not to be separated from the instrument of knowledge doubtless carries us a long way. This insight is sometimes briefly expressed by saying that quantum theory has emphasized the importance of the observer. However, the observer of quantum theory is a highly conventionalized and stylized observer, typified by the measuring instrument. The concern of quantum theory with this observer has been to allow for the reaction between the measuring instrument and the object being measured. But for me the observer has to be much more than this, if we are to take into account the entire situation and not isolate parts of it. We must take into account not only the object of knowledge and the instrument of knowledge but also the "knower", without whom the knowledge is of no more significance than an undeciphered Etruscan inscription. The fact that manipulation with certain instruments gives the momentum of some object is of no significance until there is a knower to know that the measurement is of momentum and to use the measurement in the proper way. The physicist ordinarily takes the knower for granted, and in the context of his ordinary purposes he is amply justified in doing this. But in a wider context, and for the purpose of acquiring the widest possible understanding, one cannot forego asking what is this knower and his knowledge which the physicist takes for granted. The situation which thus presents itself is of the greatest vagueness and it is even not easy to see what the conditions are which an answer would have to satisfy if we were willing to accept it. But whatever the answer we finally give about the nature of the knower and his knowledge and their relations to the objects and instruments of knowledge, we shall have to give due recognition to the fact that knower and knowledge occur only in conjunction with a human nervous system. This nervous system is of a complexity so formidable that we are only beginning to have an inkling of how complex it may be. Furthermore, the conjunction of knower, knowledge, nervous system occurs only after the nervous system has been subjected to a most elaborate preconditioning. It seems to me that we cannot be permanently satisfied with an analysis which, as does quantum theory, hopes to reduce to understandability the ultimate structural units of the world, when that understandability itself demands the cooperation of superstructures of as yet unfathomed complexity, formed from these same structural units. Again we encounter a system dealing with itself. I suspect that we cannot hope to meet this situation by anything better than a process of successive approximation, which, if we are lucky, may approach some sort of limit. It does not appear at present that we have traveled far enough along the road even to be sure that the process will converge.

STATE OF THE SYSTEM

Cassirer in his book *Determinism and Indeterminism in Modern Physics*[8] makes the point that the most important mental revolution implicit in quantum theory is not in the abandonment of causality, but in the modification it demands in our concept of "state of the system". Now the concept state of the system is one which we have had with us for a long time. This concept was never precisely formulated, and there were always certain inconsistencies in the implications of the concept of which physicists were usually unconscious. The concept was to a large extent colored by the impact of Newtonian mechanics, and was closely connected with the concept of determinism. We have seen that with the rise of electrodynamics the situation was somewhat altered, but not in a very fundamental way. But there was another branch of physics, thermodynamics, which developed as a more or less self-contained discipline, without much cross-fertilization with mechanics and electrodynamics, in which the concept "state of the system" was also fundamental. The equation of state of a body was fundamental to the canonical treatment of the thermodynamics of reversible processes. The equation of state, together with the equations expressing the consequences of the first and second laws, uniquely determined the thermodynamic behavior of the body. The equation of state was given in terms of the "state variables", which were parameters such that the thermodynamic behavior was determined by them. These were variables, such as pressure and temperature, which were susceptible to unique instrumental measurement at any instant of time. The implications in the classical thermodynamic concept of state were thus the same as in the mechanical and electrodynamic concept — that "state", in general, is the aggregate of all the measurements that can be made *now* on the system, so that two systems are in the same state if all the measurements which we are now capable of making on them give the same result. The classical concept of state seldom, if ever, received so explicit a formulation as we have just given it, but this was nevertheless, I believe, implicit in the practice of prequantum physics. The "state of the system" formulated in this way may be regarded as a matter of pure definition. However, it receives physical significance in a deterministic context, in that, so far as the future of such systems is determined by their present, two systems initially in the same state remain the same throughout the future in the same environment. But now the satisfactory simplicity of this concept of "state" was shattered by the facts of irreversible thermodynamics. For most of the systems of daily life, such as any solid strained beyond its yield point, are capable of no reversible displacement whatever when this displacement is specified in terms of the conventional variables of state, but all displacements are irreversible. Such systems differ from the classical reversible systems in that the future development of systems initially in identically the same state, as determined by the conventional parameters, may be different under identical external conditions. The deterministic thesis may be maintained "in principle" by the device of introducing concealed parameters, such as the microscopic distortions of the individual crystal grains for the solid strained beyond its yield point. But these, from the point of view of thermodynamics, are completely fictional, for their existence is in no wise demonstrable by operations in the universe of discourse of thermodynamics. The thesis of determinism may, however, be retained in the universe of discourse of thermodynamics by generalizing the concept of state. Two systems may now be said to be in the same state if all measurements presently performable yield the same result and if in addition the past history back to some suitably chosen epoch in the past is also identical. The significance of such an extension of the concept of state appears in the experimental finding that all systems in the same state according to the extended definition also unroll in the same way in the future under identical conditions. In this sense a specification of the state gives a complete description of the system. It would appear, therefore, that the classical concept of state evolved and has meaning only in a context of determinism. The "state" of a plastically strained body is not given in terms only of present measurements, because its future is not determined in terms of such measurements, but the "state" is determined in terms of present measurements and past history because the future *is* determined by such a specification. The Laplacean concept, in which only present measurements without past history are determinative, is consistent with the generalized definition of state, being only a special case in which past history has no effect.

I digress for a moment to discuss the nature of the past history which must be specified to make the future behavior of irreversible classical systems deterministic. It is a matter of experiment that in all cases some episode can be found in the past history which can be taken as a fiducial point, so that it is sufficient to give history back to this epoch and not beyond it. In the case of the plastically strained metal it is sufficient to give history back to the occurrence of the metal in the liquid condition, in which all traces of any previous irreversible plastic straining are wiped out. Although experiments may not be repeated on a single individual piece of matter in virtue of irreversibility, it is possible to produce "identical replicas" of such an individual piece of metal and conduct an indefinite number of experiments on such replicas. The notion of "identical replicas" appears to be an important one, not only for dealing with irreversibility, but in other situations also.

Returning to the argument, the classical concept of state developed in a context of determinism, and has its utility against a deterministic background. We have now found that determinism does not occur in the quantum domain, but we nevertheless want to retain the concept of "state". How shall we modify the concept to be applicable in the new domain? It seems to me that the natural procedure is to retain as much of the old concept as we can. It would be natural, consistently with this demand, to define the present state of a system, as before, as the aggregate of all the measurements which can be made on the system at present, retaining the possibility, if it should prove advantageous later, that we may supplement present measurements by a specification of past history. But the "concept" of state, as distinguished from the "definition" of state, no longer carries the implication that the future is determined. In the quantum domain we now have the brute statement of fact that the present state of a system does not determine its future state because it is possible to have a number of systems all with the same present state, according to the definition, but different future states under identical external conditions. Here, the future state of the system is by definition the aggregate of all the measurements that can be made on the system at some future time. This is a perfectly straightforward statement. But it seems to me that the Heisenberg principle is often expressed in a way which implies retention of the classical concept of state with its deterministic implications. Thus it is often said that we cannot predict the future state of an electron because we are unable to measure the present position and velocity with the precision necessary to project the motion into the future. But this projection into the future is a deterministic projection in the context of the classical description in terms of both position and velocity, and it must now be given up. Our description of the situation must be in terms of operations which we can actually perform, not in terms of those which we could have performed if the classical description had remained valid. The question should be: "Is it possible to predict all the measurements that I shall be able to make on a system in the future, given all the measurements that can be made on it now?" The answer is a flat "No".

It is not easy for me to see why Cassirer regarded it as so intellectually revolutionary to give this sort of answer, nor why he regarded the modification in the meaning of "state of the system" required by quantum theory as so radical, unless he was trying to retain as an essential ingredient the deterministic implications in the classical concept. This, it seems to me, must be admitted to be impossible, because we are here in the presence of an intrinsic inconsistency.

We digress for a moment to comment on the fact that in the classical domain there is another field besides thermodynamics in which it might have appeared advantageous to modify the concept of "state" to include past history. An electrodynamic system is usually specified in terms of the present condition of the charges and the field at all points of space within the system. Such a specification suffices to determine future behavior if, in addition, the field on the boundary is specified at all future time. This is necessary because the influence of the external universe enters across the boundary, and this obviously also has to be specified. Now such a system, with its field assignable at pleasure (within restrictions) at every point, is a system with an infinite number of degrees of freedom. It was the infinite number of degrees of freedom which, in conjunction with the classical theorem of the equipartition of energy among the degrees of freedom, led to the "ultraviolet catastrophe" which was the occasion of the invention of quantum theory by Planck. But these infinite degrees of freedom are inaccessible instrumentally to the physicist, so that it is to be questioned how much "physical reality" they have, and in particular whether it is inevitable, even in a classical context, that all the energy should be drained off into the infinite number of concealed coordinates. Now if the ultraviolet catastrophe had been found as a matter of fact to occur, one would have independent evidence of the "reality" of these degrees of freedom. The fact that the catastrophe does not occur makes one wonder whether there is not some other method of determining the state of the system. Now there is, as a matter of fact, such an alternative method of describing the state of the system with all the classical deterministic implications. The future evolution of an electrodynamic system is completely determined, except for a small transient effect, by the equations of electrodynamics if one gives the present state of all the charges and the complete description of the field on the boundary through past and future time. We have here a line of attack on the radiation situation that might have been taken, but as a historical fact was not. I do not know what the result of such an attack would have been. It is conceivable to me that the ultraviolet catastrophe would not have occurred — it is at least obvious that the energy associated with the two-dimensional field of the boundary surface is of a different order of magnitude from the energy of the three-dimensional field in the interior of the system. On the other hand, it is quite conceivable that mathematically the two surface variables and the one-time variable required for the new specification of the state are equivalent in their effect to the three space variables required for the traditional specification. At any rate, it seems to me that the attack should have been made from the point of view of a surface and its history, which has full instrumental significance, rather than from the instrumentally meaningless specification in terms of fields throughout three-dimensional space, in terms of which the attack was actually made.

The ordinary principle of determinism may be broadly formulated somewhat as follows: "Whenever the present state of a system repeats, its future states also repeat if the system is placed in the same environment", with the understanding that "state of the system" means the aggregate of all the measurements which can be made on it now. Classical or Newtonian determinism is a special case in that it is postulated that present measurements need include only masses, positions, and velocities. What we mean by "same environment" is not often analyzed. We may take it to mean "everything that happens to the system which is imposed from outside". Precisely what "imposed from outside" means requires analysis. Electromagnetic theory sets up the thesis that "imposed from outside" can be specified in terms of measurements made with instruments stationed over a closed surface completely enclosing the system. This need not commit us to the point of view of action through a medium in preference to action at a distance. Strictly, these surface measurements must be supplemented by initial measurements of the field at all points in the space inside the closed surface within a short interval of time about the initial interval. Except for this small supplementary term, instrumental measurements on the boundary through all time subsequent to the initial interval suffice. If now we generalize "state of the system" to include all of its past history in addition to the measurements that can be made now, and if we leave the term "environment" somewhat vague without committing ourselves to accepting the electromagnetic definition, we can envisage a sort of super-principle of determinism, of which the conventional determinism is a special case, namely: "Whenever all present measurements, past history, and future environment of a system repeat, then all future measurements of the system repeat". Another way of saying it is: "Whenever all present measurements and future environment on identical replicas repeat, all future measurements repeat." We might call this super-principle the principle of essential correlation. It seems to me that this is about as broad a principle as we can conceive and hope to reduce the world about us to order and understandability. It provides about the minimum in the way of "isolatability" that will allow us to speak of parts of the world without speaking of the whole world. It is almost equivalent to the principle of sufficient reason. It is about the simplest principle that can guide the construction of a physical theory — it is about as noncommittal as possible and merely maintains that somewhere in the past we shall find the cause of the present and the future. If, however, we push the principle too far, we end by saying that the entire present is determined by the entire past, and if we reflect that the entire past is unique and may not be made to recur, we realize that we are peddling a mere truism. For in thus striving for the greatest possible generality we have deprived ourselves of the possibility of getting to the same terminus by two paths, and have put ourselves in a position where we can say nothing.

Quantum theory makes the flat statement that the principle of essential correlation or of sufficient reason does not hold "in the small".

If we probe still deeper we shall find further infelicities in the concept of "state of the system" as we had it, or even in our much generalized principle of essential correlation. The verbalization "state of the system" implies by its very form that there is a distinction between a system and its states. The implication is that we can start with a specific system, and that this system is then capable of various states, the interrelations of which may be made the subject of investigation. But what are the operations by which we determine what system it is, and how are these operations to be distinguished from the operations by which we determine its state? In specifying what we mean by state of the system we could hardly avoid saying that it was the aggregate of *all* the measurements or operations that could be presently made on the system, thereby tacitly including the operations which specify the nature of the system. Then, again, what is this "all" when we talk about all possible measurements? Does it include all the higher-order time derivatives? It took a Galileo to realize that the first time derivative had to be included in the parameters of state, and also to realize that this first time derivative was directly measurable in the present, without the necessity for observing the system at two successive instants. No doubt all the higher time-derivatives could also be directly measured at a single instant of time if we make our instrumentation ingenious enough. Where shall we stop — there are an infinite number of time-derivatives. Newtonian mechanics side-stepped this difficulty by connecting the second and higher time-derivatives with the forces between the parts of the system, which were supposed given in terms of the positions of the parts of the system and the way in which they interact on each other, that is, if we know the nature of the system. But, if we are not willing to commit ourselves to a Newtonian mechanics, by what method shall we find the nature of the system?

There are also difficulties outside the system. We had to formulate our principle of essential correlation in terms of equality of future behavior in *all* environments. How shall we be sure that we have investigated *all* environments? Before the discovery of magnetic forces we might have thought two environments identical which we now see to be different. How can we be sure that the same sort of thing will not happen again?

It seems to me that we can in no ultimate sense separate a system from its states or a system from its environment. Perhaps the best we can do is something like this: "Given an isolated enclosure and all the measurements that can be made inside the enclosure as a function of time, then these measurements will be found to be correlated into some sort of pattern". But this is so general and vague as to be self-defeating, and besides, the meaning of "isolated" cries for specification. It is, however, the sort of thing we always run into and is probably rooted in the nature of knowledge.

One of the commonest words in the field of nuclear physics is "particle". This may occur either in a primarily theoretical context, as when we are concerned with the wave-particle complementarity of the Heisenberg principle, or in a primarily experimental context, as when we talk about the various elementary particles, of which there are now fifteen or twenty. At the same time, there seems to be no very articulate analysis of what is meant by "particle". Is there something fundamental and inescapable in the concept of particle, or is particle merely a word that we use to indicate that we have come to the end of our theoretical analysis and also the end of our experiment? There seems to be in some quarters a tendency to regard the particle as pretty fundamental. One sometimes finds an expression of the conviction that the particle aspect of experience is more fundamental than the wave aspect, and that behind the waves we shall always find particles. An example is the following quotation from Max Born.[9] "We have no other language to describe what we do and what we see in experimenting than in terms of bodies and their movements. Schrödinger himself cannot avoid the particle language even when he tries to demonstrate the superiority of the wave language".

The idea of particle seems to imply a certain simplicity, but it is obvious that as a historical fact "particle" as used by the physicist covers a growingly complicated experimental situation. The particle of Newtonian mechanics was a fairly simple thing — a finite and constant and eternal mass associated with a moving point. The motion of this mass point was governed by the equations of mechanics, so that the motion could be found when the forces acting on the particle were known; this of course was an idealization from experience. At first its value was mostly in treating the situations of astronomy, in which the dimensions of the planets or other heavenly bodies are so small compared with their distances apart that their motions can be calculated within the precision of measurement by treating their masses as all concentrated at the centers of gravity. The validity of the idea of mass-points was presently accepted for itself and projected toward the very small, where it found itself in congenial ground already prepared by Lucretius with his atoms and by the innate urge of men to think in terms of atoms. Here it proved of value in attempts to explain the constitution and properties of matter in bulk, as, for example, in some of the speculations of Lord Kelvin, or the speculations of Newton himself in the *Opticks*. Even this early mass-point developed complications, and almost from the beginning was invested with the property of impenetrability or infinite hardness in addition to the possession of mass and position. When one stops to think of it, it is rather hard to imagine precisely what one can mean by talking about the impenetrability of two points. We certainly are willing to talk about the coincidence of two geometrical points and find no difficulty in imagining a moving point successively occupying the position of other points. Nor would there seem to be any conceptual difficulty in imagining the moving point to carry mass with it, nor in imagining that when two such points coincide the mass concentrated at that point is doubled. But what is the experiment by which one could decide whether such mass particles are "really" impenetrable or not? What is the experimental difference between two colliding particles behaving like two colliding billiard balls, when the colliding particle is reduced to rest and the other particle continues with the motion of the first, and an encounter in which the first particle merely moves through the other, continuing its original motion undisturbed on the far side? The latter picture is repugnant to our physical sense, but it is not thinking of the particle as characterized only by its position and mass which makes it repugnant. What makes it repugnant is our whole experience with everyday finite bodies, which do interact with each other when brought close enough together, and of which no two can be made to occupy the same space.

It probably does not disturb us very much to discover by considerations of this kind that we have smuggled into our concept of massive particle more than we had originally supposed. However, in the light of this discovery we may now ask ourselves questions which we would not previously have thought of propounding. One such question is: "Why is it that the particles are impenetrable?" Another question is "How many independent parameters may a particle have and still be a particle?" May it perhaps be that our massive particle has other independent attributes than position, mass, and impenetrability? What about "identity", or is it perhaps that impenetrability is merely another way of saying that the particle has identity? At any rate it is not easy to think of what one might mean by identity that does not imply impenetrability. How about velocity as another independent parameter? It would seem to be pretty incontestable that the objects of experience can have velocities independent of their position, and any idealization of the bodies of experience would certainly seem to have to admit this parameter also. It therefore seems almost inevitable that our "particle" must be capable of having velocity as well as mass and position. When we admit velocity we at the same time admit other parameters, such as momentum and kinetic energy. These new parameters are indispensable in describing the behavior of our particle when brought into reaction with other particles or objects but they are not independent parameters because they may be computed in terms of velocity and mass. We recognize, nevertheless, that with the possession of these various parameters our particle is getting more complicated than the simple thing with which we started. We cannot mull over this situation without presently wanting to ask questions of "how" or "why". Our feeling of compulsion to find an answer to such questions, or even our feeling of whether the questions have meaning, will doubtless depend on our background. A Greek like Zeno would have been genuinely perplexed to find a satisfactory answer to the question "How is it that a thing characterized by position can also have velocity?" The modern physicist, on the other hand, does not regard this as a pressing or important question. He accepts as a brute fact that ordinary bodies *have* velocities and, simultaneously, positions, and regards any difficulty of reconciling them as due to something in his thinking machinery, which he need not bother to straighten out for most of his purposes. The modern physicist would, however, be much more inclined to give serious consideration to the impenetrability of particles. Here is something for which he feels it makes sense to seek an explanation. His attempts at explanation do not prove very illuminating, however. Impenetrability might, for example, be explained in terms of the infinite forces brought into play when two particles are brought into close juxtaposition, but such infinite forces are themselves in need of explanation. If one attempts to explain them in ordinary terms, one is soon talking of infinite elastic constants of the material of the particle, which involves deformation of the particle and all such unwelcome logical consequences as the ultraviolet catastrophe which sparked the development of quantum theory.

The notions of particle and explanation thus seem in a sense incompatible. One can only postulate the possession of certain parameters by the particle. If one seeks to explain why the particle has these properties one is driven to the assumption of detail inconsistent with the notion of particle.

The question arises how far this process can be pushed. Is there no limit to the number of independent parameters which may be associated together such that we would be willing to call the association a particle? The way particles are proliferating in recent physics it looks as though the answer to this question is "no". Particles now have as independent parameters: mass, charge, angular momentum, magnetic moment, spin, statistics, mean lifetime, and nature of the disintegration products, but apparently not identity. The acceptance of many of these new particles is forced by experiment. What sort of experimental properties must there be for one to talk profitably about a particle? One talks about "elementary" particles as distinguished from just particles. Thus a neutron is usually referred to as a particle, but not as an elementary particle because it is, or may be, composed of a proton and an electron. But in what sense does the fact that on occasion we may find a neutron in our apparatus replaced by a proton and an electron compel us to say that the neutron is not an elementary particle, but compound? The question becomes more urgent now that we recognize that particles may be created or annihilated.

With expanding experimental knowledge the concept of particle thus becomes more fuzzy. In practice we are likely to use the word particle when we get to the end of our tether. Our experimental knowledge at the end of our range is understandably more meager than in fields where we have greater mastery. If it is meager enough, we have simply a collection of apparently unrelated facts, which we have to accept or postulate. If we permit ourselves to ask the "why" of these facts we thereby implicitly demand a mechanism or structure on which to hang our explanation, the mere existence of which would involve a lack of simplicity that would make our term "particle" inappropriate. But in using the term particle the physicist is making no dogmatic commitment to the thesis that no such structure will ever be found. The acceptance of particles is a perpetual challenge to the discovery of new experimental facts that will remove any particular particle from the category of particle altogether. But when we have removed our particle we shall probably find that others replace it — particles we shall always have at the edge of our competence.

In practice the meaning of particle has points in common with the old "atom". It denotes a concatenation of events which are so closely tied together that we have not yet found how to make them take place separately. The association of the idea of particle with point is not necessary — in fact we give numerical value to the diameter of an electron or proton. It is true that this diameter is somewhat nebulous; it may mark the order of magnitude of the distance from the associated mathematical point at which the forces begin to increase in a catastrophic surge, or it may mark the boundary of the region within which the charge must be concentrated in order to account for its mass, as in the Lorentz electron. The idea of mathematical point thus does not appear to be essential — only that of a physically unanalyzable region.

How does mathematics handle particles? There seems to be a tacit ideal here which is not attained in practice. We would like to have a system of equations, some of the solutions of which have point singularities with unique properties which can be set into correspondence with the physical properties of the corresponding particle. That is, the existence of the singular point and the particle should be forced by the equation. But this is not what we have, as can be seen by looking at the simple electrostatic case for an electron. The potential is subject to Laplace's equation. On the right-hand side of this equation occurs the charge density. If this is *given* we can find a solution of the equation which corresponds to any arbitrary distribution of charge density, and in particular we can find the solution corresponding to the concentration of a charge at a point, and this solution will have a singularity at the point in question. But this is not what we set out to do, which was to set up such an equation that we have no control over the charges demanded by it, but these are uniquely determined by the equation itself. As it is, we specify the charges (point singularities or not, as the case may be) from outside, and then the equation adapts itself to them. Obviously a mathematical scheme is incomplete as a description of nature which has to be supplemented at such a vital point. This I think is characteristic of the situation in general. We do not have equations, the singularities of which are forced by the equations themselves, but we have equations which respond by singularities in their solutions to other singularities which we impose from outside. In other words, given only Laplace's equation, there would be no way whatever of predicting the physical occurrence of electrons. So far as I can see, the same is true of Schrödinger's equation for wave mechanics.

The question requires further examination of what we can mean by asking whether a particle that is capable of disintegrating and giving rise to disintegration products is simple or compound. Is it meaningful to say that the disintegration products were already present in the original particle? What is the meaning of the concept of "creation" applied to such a situation? I think it is evident that there must be some sort of invariance in the situation to justify such a way of speaking. For instance, suppose that we have a particle X, which sometimes decomposes totally into A and B and sometimes into C and D. We suppose further that A, B, C, and D are simple in the sense that they cannot be made to decompose. Then I think we would not say that A and B were originally present in X unless we were willing to say that the fact that X decomposes in two ways shows that there were "really" two different kinds of X. But in the absence of independent evidence for other sorts of difference in the two X's before the decomposition, this is a sterile verbalism. If there is such evidence, the propriety of talking about two X's is unquestioned.

On the other hand, if X invariably decomposes into only A and B, we might very well be predisposed to say that A and B were already present in X. This way of talking would be fortified if it should turn out that the prehistory of X is such that X makes its appearance after the disappearance of A and B. Even in this strongest of all cases we might be required to prove that A and B were "really" present in X and were not "created" anew at the moment of disintegration. In the absence of other kinds of experimental evidence and in the absence of a definition of creation that distinguishes creation from a mere transformation, this distinction is largely verbal and there is not much point in trying to make it. In the absence of new sorts of experimental data it would seem that we are pretty much restricted to describing as well as we can the total experimental situation and letting it go at that.

Physically, and for the physicist, we would appear to be in the presence of a particle when there is no experimental evidence demanding internal structure. There is an unavoidable connection with theory here, because it is theory that demands the internal structure. Mathematically it does not seem that the mathematics (the equations) of itself proclaims when we are dealing with a particle, but a "text" has to be added, stating that this or that property of the mathematics means a particle. The simplest example is a point singularity, which the text proclaims to mean a particle. This is natural enough, but is it inevitable? Logically and humanly the concept of particle comes pretty close to containing a concealed contradiction. Logically, "particle" is a verbal flag to indicate that we have come to the end. We should react to this situation by simply shutting up, but humanly and verbally we are incapable of this, but can always ask for the explanation of the particle or for what is inside it (as did Lorentz). Is this another situation which Bohr would describe in terms of complementarity?

"Particle" seems to be in some ways a necessity of thought. I have seen no evidence that any physicist, or any one else for that matter, is capable of thinking of an ostensible continuum, as in the equations of hydrodynamics for example, without inventing particles in the continuum to which to tie his thought. "Particle" for the physicist plays a role similar to that of "point" for the geometer, and seems to be equally unavoidable. How shall one describe the significance of a situation like this?

There is a certain similarity between the physical situations in which we encounter particles and those in which we encounter probability. In both cases we have come to the end of the road — if we were to go inside the particle and allow it to have structure it would no longer be a particle, and if we allowed ourselves to speculate what the reason or the causes of the events may be which we treat by probability we have thereby removed them from the domain of probability. The end of the road at which we thus find ourselves is to a certain extent there because we have agreed that it shall be the end. We are saying more about ourselves and our ways of theorizing when we talk about particles and probability than we are about nature. Not that there may be good objective reasons for our agreeing to declare that we are at the end of the road. We have, for example, no definite experimental knowledge of any structure inside the electron and we therefore have experimental justification for declaring that the electron is a particle, at least for the present and from the point of view of a theory which will allow itself no paraphernalia which does not have some kind of involvement with experiment. For I believe that the remark of Hertz and Poincaré still holds to the effect that a system with any complicated behavior whatever, even a system that was apparently completely quantum mechanical, could be reproduced by systems satisfying classical mechanics only, provided that the mechanisms were sufficiently isolated and concealed from any possibility of discovery by an external agency. However, no one today would think of wasting his time trying to invent such mechanisms. His taste for doing this evaporated with the realization that there are an infinite number of such possible mechanisms, so that there would be no possibility of proving that any particular mechanism was really the correct one. At the same time it must be recognized that there is an element of "reality" here because most physicists would recognize that there is a certain sense in the question "Are there really particles in nature?" Now I do not believe that the physicist, although he might be willing to ask this question, would admit that he was thereby implying that he could answer it. The meaning of his question must be sought on a different level. What he is in effect asking is: "Do you think that there will ever come a day when experiments cannot be devised which might conceivably yield such a result that their explanation would require some sort of structure in particles for which there was previously no evidence of structure?" If always when such experiments had been devised and executed, the result had turned out to be inconsistent with internal structure, then we might be really saying something about nature and not about the way we handle nature when we say "there are particles in nature".

I may perhaps be permitted to record my suspicion that the simplest way of stating the significance of the recently discovered violation of the principle of parity may turn out to be to say that there is structure within the electron, but so deep-seated that its effects do not usually manifest themselves.

It is perhaps not too surprising that particles are so easily treated by probability methods, for having come to the end of the effects of structure we have also come to the end of the possibility of explanation in causal terms.

CREATION AND EMPTY SPACE

The notions of "creation" and conversely of "annihilation" should obviously be examined. We have already examined certain aspects of this situation in connection with "verbal compulsion". We may define creation in some such way as this: "If we now observe some object inside a closed surface which was previously empty, and if the object did not enter through the surface, as proved by the failure of sentries posted all over the surface to observe the passage of anything through the surface, then we shall say that the object was created inside the surface at some time between the present and the past instant when it was not there". Conversely for "annihilation".

This begins by being a pure definition of how we would name a phenomenon if we should ever observe it. The connection of such a situation with situations which in former discussion I have described as pure conventions suggests itself. It would seem, however, that all the connotations of "convention" do not apply here, because we are here confronted, by hypothesis, with a well defined experimental situation, in spite of the fact that for the present, at least, there is no second way of getting to the experimental terminus. But now the verbalisms get to work. We ask ourselves, "How can you be sure that the object got there by creation and not by some other method?" This sort of question is at first meaningless, that is, so long as the only experimental knowledge we have is that at one instant the object was not there and at a later instant was there. From this point of view there is nothing more to be said, and the word we have agreed to use is "creation". We recognize, however, a certain verbal compulsion in the situation. But the question itself suggests the possibility that search might disclose more to the experimental situation than is mentioned in the definition. Perhaps we can split the act of creation into finer details and, for example, observe the object when it is only half created. If so, then we may also envisage the possibility of different sequences of partial creation, reaching from the initial nothing to the final consummation. And if we choose, after discovering the new experimental facts, we can go back and modify our original definition, and reserve "creation" for only one of the sequences. However, we would be more inclined, I believe, to deal with such a situation by saying that there was more than one method by which the object could be created. In any event, the situation alters when we acquire more than one method of getting to the terminus.

Until creation has been observed, our definition is only a program to direct experimental exploration. But it contains a hypothesis which would hardly have been recognized as a hypothesis twenty-five years ago, and which may vitiate the entire program and point of view. We specified that we should start with an "empty" closed surface. But are there empty closed surfaces, and is this a permissible concept? The question would have seemed trivial twenty-five years ago, but the matter is now by no means self-evident, since we have come to recognize the fluctuating zero-point fields in "empty" space. It would seem that the whole concept must be reexamined from the beginning. We have already seen that "empty space" can mean nothing in terms of direct instrumental operations, because the instrument which might show that the space is empty destroys the emptiness by being there to show it. There is evidently a close connection with the thesis that all we need is a complete description of the readings of instruments on the surfaces that enclose any arbitrary three dimensional region. On the ordinary scale, exploration with light beams affords the simplest criterion whether a given three dimensional region is empty or not. Given means for stationing light sources at any points on the closed boundary and also means for detecting the light received from these sources at all other points of the boundary, then if the received light for all possible arrangements of the sources can be calculated from the emitted light by assuming straight-line propagation through the three-dimensional space with no scattering, the space would be declared "empty". Ideally it is now believed that this situation would never occur, for the reason that there are zero-point fluctuations of the electromagnetic field at any point within the enclosed surface, and these zero-point fields interact with the photons of the beams of light used as probes. Any such interactions are so small that it will doubtless be a long time before they are established by direct experiment. It is in any event a bit shocking, I think, to realize that the concept of empty space, which appears unavoidable and a necessity of thought, can have no guarantee that it is anything more than an artefact of our thinking. In view of all this are we going to be forced to speak of "transformations" instead of "creations" or "annihilations"? Again there is an element of pure verbalism. We might perhaps want to speak of creation by transformation even if we accept that we cannot speak of creation out of nothing.

The foregoing would make it seem that it is going to be difficult to set up a definition of creation which does not involve the notions of space — an object is created when it suddenly appears within a closed surface without having come in across the surface. But the notion of closed surface is a spatial idea and becomes meaningless, except in paper and pencil terms, when we are driven to talk about distances of the order of 10^{-13} centimeter. Our definition of creation would also seem to imply ordinary time, at least to the extent that we talk about an earlier and a later state of the system. It would appear, therefore, that in domains in which our ordinary space and time concepts fail, the ordinary notions of creation must also fail, and must be replaced by others.

EVENTS

Somewhat similar to the points which we considered in an earlier chapter and to the particles which we considered above are "events". Events are usually thought of as the building stones of the actual world of happenings. If we could reproduce all the events we could reproduce the world. The event plays a fundamental role in general relativity theory. Here the event is a complex of four numbers, three space coordinates and one time. These events are usually thought to have the additional attribute of publicity, so that an event accessible to only one person, like the events of introspection of the psychologists, would be a self-contradiction. The events, in terms of which the world is to be described in general relativity theory, are thought of as intersection nodes of the coordinate "mollusc". No matter what the transformation of coordinates, the intersection nodes cannot be transformed away, but persist in all systems, and it is this invariant background of nodes of intersection that corresponds to the physical "reality". But there is no general relativity theory of what the nodes represent. The implication seems to be that they represent some sort of discreteness or singularity in the solution of the underlying equations, and that there is nothing more to be said about the situation than the mere fact of the existence of the discontinuities. This implies that there can be no further parameters characterizing the discontinuities than their mere existence, and would mean that, given the mesh system, the physical nature of the corresponding system is fixed. This to me does not seem right. There must be something more to it than just to say that there is a discontinuity. It would seem that one should also say what sort of a discontinuity it is. The specification of the mesh system by itself will not determine whether it is electrons or protons or photons that are situated at the points of the mesh, and surely our experience and the world will be very different depending on what it is. Given only the mesh system, that is, the "events" in the relativity sense, the physical system that gave rise to the mesh system can by no means be reproduced. There is more to it than the mesh system. This it seems to me is a fundamental defect in Einstein's whole generalized relativity outlook.

"Events" seem to play a somewhat similar fundamental role in Whitehead's philosophy.

A good many years ago I had something of this sort in mind and was making my objections to Hermann Weyl. He agreed with me — at least I thought he did, and I remember that he said "Alles ist nicht Coincidenz".

V I

ON THE FRINGES OF PSYCHOLOGY

So far we have mostly been concerned with special disciplines such as physics or mathematics or logic in which a high degree of objectivity or impersonality prevails. The material and the procedures of these disciplines are to a large extent public in the sense that every qualified person can perform the operations and obtain the same results. This applies to a large extent also to the conventional biological sciences. Consequently we do not have to pay much attention to the individual in these fields. But even here there are situations in which the individual cannot be lost sight of, as we have seen in the matter of proof. When, however, we come to situations in which other people play an essential role, questions of meaning and operation become insistent which we could ignore in a more impersonal setting.

We can roughly recognize two kinds of situation in which we are concerned with other people — situations in which we are concerned with them as individuals, and situations in which we are concerned with them in groups, that is, in society. The word "psychology" in the title of this chapter is intended to suggest that in it we shall be concerned with people as individuals. The title is not at all intended to indicate an exhaustive or even systematic treatment of the topics conventionally covered by the professional psychologist. We shall be concerned with only restricted aspects of a few of these topics which are of special interest to us, and I shall not hesitate to introduce other topics not traditionally associated with psychology if they are pertinent.

THE THESIS OF SUFFICIENCY OF ATOMIC ANALYSIS

One very broad characteristic of the topics which we are now to consider, broader even than that we are concerned with people, is that we are in one way or another concerned with living things. I do not intend to attempt any discussion of conventional biological problems, but there is one feature of the thinking of biologists which has, I believe, a reaction on everyone else at the present time concerned with living things and which therefore requires express comment. Most present-day biologists are, I believe, nonvitalists and "materialists" in the sense already expounded in Chapter III. So far as I can make out this is also the attitude of most psychologists — at least if they have a different one they appear a little unwilling to say exactly what it is. This attitude may be formulated in a very general way in the statement that it is not necessary to assume any new principles not already operative in the physics and the chemistry of nonliving matter in order to explain the functioning of living matter. It may alternatively be given a more specific and sharpened formulation. This sharpened formulation is: "Given a complete description in physical terms of any organism, then there is nothing more to give, in the sense that all the present behavior of the organism and its future behavior in a completely specified environment is fixed". Here what is meant by a "complete" description may be made specific by saying that it demands that the state of every atom in the organism be completely specified. It may well be that specification in such minute detail is not necessary, but by going to the limit we have at least done no harm and it may be that future experiment will show that it was necessary. I shall call this "the thesis of the sufficiency of atomic analysis". As stated, this is the thesis in the classical prequantum form. Quantum theory demands some modification, but not such as to change the essential situation. We will consider later what any such quantum modifications may involve.

So far as I can judge most present-day psychologists as well as biologists would accept the thesis of the sufficiency of atomic analysis. "Explanation" in such a context would merely mean deducing the functioning of the organism from the already known laws controlling the interactions of the atoms. Most psychologists who accept the thesis would, I believe, state further that so far as their own particular purposes go the most important part of the atomic specification is concerned with the atoms of the nervous system and in particular with the brain.

Everyone will admit that in the present state of technology we are fantastically far from being able to implement such a thesis to the extent even of being able to specify the state of all the atoms in the brain, to say nothing of deducing the future unrolling of such a system. The operational meaning of such a thesis is almost exclusively as a program, a program justified by the conviction that there is no presently known fact which would suggest that it is impossible to carry out such a program "in principle". In spite of the fact that we cannot implement the program, and that it is even very doubtful whether it can usefully suggest specific lines of attack to the psychologist in his laboratory, the thesis nevertheless serves a very real function. It provides a basis for communication. The ideological background of psychologists and other interested persons is sufficiently homogeneous so that the imagery brought up by the thesis is enough alike in different persons to permit communication. It permits meaning to be assigned to concepts whose meaning would otherwise be so difficult to make precise as to endanger communication. In thus conceptualizing the situation a certain vagueness is permissible. One does not need a resolution of the difficulties in the concept "state of the atoms", difficulties which the discussion in Chapter IV has shown are considerable. Neither does one need to keep explicitly in mind the hypothetical details of the manipulations by which the atomic analysis might have to be made in practice. Thus, I can think about the simultaneous state of all the atoms in my brain with all the implications with which I think of the simultaneous state of all the atoms in your brain, unmindful of the fact that I would have to commission someone else to determine the atomic state of my own brain, whereas I myself could ideally make the determination for the brain of anyone else.

Another advantage of the thesis is that it has sufficient flexibility to adopt itself to psychologists of different outlooks, except, of course, that it will not accommodate itself to the vitalist point of view. It is, however, flexible enough to adapt itself to the most uncompromising behaviorist and to the dyed-in-the-wool introspectionalist. The behaviorist would certainly expect that two organisms with identical atomic analyses would exhibit identical behavior. In fact, the behaviorist might, if he is of an extreme enough type, maintain that we have here only a tautology, because any reactions of the organism with the instruments which are used in making the atomic analysis are by definition part of the behavior of the organism. If the behaviorist is not of this extreme type he would certainly expect that two organisms with identical atomic analyses would exhibit identical behavior in all observable respects. Of course he would not invert this, but would expect that two organisms with identical observable behavior might, and probably would, have different atomic analyses.

Opposed to the uncompromising behaviorists are psychologists who want to talk about consciousness and feelings. An example of the position of such a psychologist is given by the following quotation from W. S. Hunter's biographical memoir of James Rowland Angell.[1] "In brief, Angell's position was as follows. Consciousness appears (and appeared phylogenetically) when reflexes, instincts and habits fail to solve the problems which confront the organism. Consciousness aids in the solution of the problem and then, no problem existing longer at this point, passes on to other points of conflict in the organism's behavior. Were consciousness not in general a problem solver it would have no adaptive value and hence would not have survived as a function of the organism". Such psychologists can also express their point of view in terms of the thesis of the sufficiency of atomic analysis.

We pose the question: How might such a psychologist, who believes that "consciousness" has "objective" meaning, go to work to reduce consciousness to atomic terms? In answering this, in order to avoid issues which will appear later, I will suppose that it is I who am trying to find the atomic background for my talking of myself as conscious. Imagine now a record kept in two parallel columns. In the one column is the complete atomic analysis of my brain as a function of time. (It will not change the argument if it should turn out that an atomic analysis of my whole body is necessary instead of my brain only.) This atomic analysis column will obviously have to be made by someone else. Paralleling the atomic analysis column is a column which I myself make, in which I record all my conscious activity, including in particular a record of the occasions when I recognize that I am conscious. Now it seems not unreasonable to anticipate that whenever in the conscious states column I am describing myself as conscious, some regularity of pattern will recur in the atomic analysis column, and, conversely, whenever this pattern recurs I am being aware that I am conscious. If this program is carried through, and conceptually it is of little import that there is no present prospect of carrying through the program, then I have a method for getting my private consciousness, with which I started, onto a completely public level. For the two columns, atomic analysis and introspectional, are by hypothesis completely public, for all to see. Furthermore, I can by the same procedure get *your* consciousness onto a public basis, if it should turn out that when you conduct the same sort of parallel column analysis the same atomic pattern recurs which I found for myself. I think that in most persons the expectation would be very strong that some similarity will be found in the atomic patterns corresponding to your consciousness and my consciousness. The strength of this expectation is doubtless partly a result of our social conditioning which has taught us to say that I and my neighbor are alike. But we should be prepared to find that there is no significant correlation between your report that you are conscious and my report that I am conscious. If such should prove to be the case, I think we would be much less inclined than at present to say that you are conscious in the same way that I am conscious, even if we were unable to specify further what constitutes the difference.

It would seem, therefore, that we have here a conceptual tool which is capable in general of reducing the private to the public. Now this is apparently what most psychologists want — the world for them is one and real and public. Such a psychologist will sometimes talk of what I call private experiences as events accessible to me but inaccessible to him. Conceptually, the inaccessibility is thought of as only due to some irrelevant accident. The thesis of atomic analysis now enables a meaning to be given to "inaccessible event", a combination of words which from one point of view is self-contradictory.

The procedure above can be carried further in giving meanings. For instance, a meaning of sorts can be given to the consciousness of animals. It is only necessary to suppose that in the atomic analysis column of an animal (the animal, not being able to talk, the parallel column method is not applicable) atomic patterns will be found which are similar to the patterns already associated with consciousness in people. It is this possibility which gives a certain degree of intelligibility to the position of psychologists like Angell. Whether the discovery of a similarity of pattern should appreciably alter my treatment of my dog or my cat probably admits of no answer without strong emotional overtones. It is to be anticipated, however, that as one goes down the scale to animals of less complicated organization, the similarity in the atomic pattern that is taken to indicate consciousness gets more and more fuzzy, so that in the end one gives up the attempt to associate consciousness with a sufficiently lowly animal.

The thesis of atomic analysis is capable of giving meaning to such an at first sight meaningless concept as a forgotten dream. When a remembered dream occurs in the conscious experience column there is a parallel entry in the atomic analysis column. It is to be expected that there was an anticipation of the entry in the atomic column at an earlier time with sufficient resemblance in pattern to the present entry to justify calling it the atomic account of the dream as it was occurring. It is to be expected that a subpattern in this earlier pattern will be found which by definition is associated with consciousness, for in my dreams I am always recognizably conscious. Furthermore, as part of the larger pattern it is to be expected that some characteristic will be found that declares that a dream is now occurring. Now, since the dream is by hypothesis remembered, it is to be expected that a continuous thread of some sort will persist throughout the entire atomic column, linking the actual occurrence of the dream with its present recollection in consciousness. There will, of course, be no entry at all in the conscious experience column at the time the dream is occurring in the atomic column. This will be one of the marks which distinguishes a remembered previous waking experience from a remembered dream — whether it is the only distinguishing mark we do not need to speculate. So much for a remembered dream. A forgotten dream will be said, by definition, to have occurred whenever a pattern is found in the atomic column, at a time when there is no entry in the conscious experience column, which has characteristics which have been found to accompany all remembered dreams, including the characteristic pattern of consciousness, but which has no issuing stream of connectivity running down to a similar pattern in the present experience column.

Perhaps one's first impulse is to say that "forgotten dream" is meaningless because it conceals a self-contradiction, but this analysis shows that this is not necessary. It suggests that there may be other sorts of physical manipulation besides the highly idealized and impractical ones used above, in terms of which it might be possible to give meaning to "forgotten dream". The psychologists tell me that they are indeed on the track of phenomena which will enable them to speak meaningfully of forgotten dreams.

It seems to me that the psychoanalyst, as distinguished from the psychologist, and whatever the school to which the psychoanalyst belongs, need find nothing inacceptable in the thesis of atomic analysis. There is nothing inconsistent in supposing that the various modes of subconscious activity to which the psychoanalyst gives special names such as "id" or "superego" correspond to recognizable patterns in the atomic activity of the brain. Whether it is sufficiently profitable to attempt to analyze out of ordinary behavior characteristics which might correspond to such patterns is another matter.

The thesis of the sufficiency of atomic analysis thus serves a real function in enabling us to form conceptions in operational terms which otherwise might give some difficulty. Some other examples will be given later. Many of these concepts can be made definite enough to permit us to communicate with each other in terms of them. The thesis also serves a function in suggesting possible characteristics of the pattern which will be found to correspond to consciousnes. One of the most striking characteristics of the conscious experience column of our analysis and of the consciousness which presents itself to introspection is the coarseness of its temporal structure as compared with the atomic possibilities. The "psychological present" has a duration of 0.01 second and our introspectional analysis cannot recognize intervals of time shorter than this. This suggests that we may find that consciousness is correlated with some comparatively stationary episode in brain functioning. Even simple dynamic systems have such stationary episodes. A ball thrown into the air is temporarily motionless at the top of its trajectory — a clever photographer knows that he can get a sharp picture if he exposes at the moment when some displacement has reached a turning point. A still more vivid picture is offered by the waves on a gently shelving beach. At any moment there is a well defined locus where the water has reached its maximum distance and is in process of reversing its direction of motion. This locus of temporary rest and maximum displacement moves back and forth irregularly along the beach in a way suggestive, perhaps, of the flickering of consciousness around the brain. The grains of sand may be thought of as playing the role of the atomic background. It is almost certain that the brain is the seat of continuous excitation of some sort, which at any location must reach a maximum and die away again. Why may not at least part of the pattern in the brain of temporarily stationary excitation correspond to consciousness? The temporary stationary character may be purely geometrical, determined by maximum displacement from the initiating center, or it may be chemical and measured by a maximum rate of return of ionized atoms to their initial configurations, or it may be even more complex and correspond to a stationary state in the n-dimensional space required to represent brain activity fully. The stationary state might be some general attribute of the activity of the brain as a whole, something consistent with the fact that certain brain functions appear not to be sharply localized.

There would seem to be plenty of possibilities here, and also plenty of possibilities in the complexity of the stationary pattern to account for all the recognizably different conscious states. The number of conscious states allowed by possible brain configurations is enormously increased when it is considered that a conscious state may correspond to a sequence in time of stationary atomic configurations, instead of to a single stationary configuration, the length of the sequence being limited only by the duration of the psychological present. It may well be that the pattern of stationary states or whatever other characteristic of the atomic configuration corresponds to consciousness will be found to be located in a limited part of the brain structure. If such should prove to be the case I suppose those physiologists and psychologists who want an "organ of consciousness" will have their answer. Or it may be that the stationary states in only a particular type of substructure, wherever it occurs in the brain, will be found to correspond to consciousness.

If ever we find this sort of thing it seems to me that it will be all that we shall need and that nothing further in the way of explanation is required. We are definitely not to ask *why* it is that a stationary state, or whatever other characteristic configuration we find, corresponds to consciousness, nor must we seek in the stationary state the "quality" of consciousness as it occurs in introspection. So far as this method of attack can go, the stationary state (or other configuration) *is* consciousness. Occam's razor, the principle of intellectual parsimony, demands that we be satisfied with this. There is no second method, in this context, of getting to any meaning that we might ascribe to consciousness. If, for example, we require an explanation of what is perhaps the most striking feature of the consciousness of introspection, namely, that I am always one, never double or multiple, we have to discipline ourselves to be satisfied with the observation that consciousness, yours or mine, is always associated with one body and in particular with one skull. We have an invariable correlation, and that is all we need. This does not rule out the possibility that an organ of consciousness will some day be found, but there is no necessity for such a discovery.

If one still feels an uneasiness in contemplating the uniqueness of consciousness it may perhaps offer some consolation to reflect that every system whatever, simple or complex, is the center of a uniqueness, namely its relation to itself. The more complex the system, the more complex the relationship. The nervous system has a high complexity. May consciousness be merely certain aspects of this complex self-relationship, *seen from the inside?*

There are other situations in which the thesis of atomic sufficiency enables one to find a meaning in expressions which an unsympathetic interpretation might dismiss as meaningless. Thus I have found that most people will assent to the proposition, "There is no method by which it can be established that the quality of your sensation of red is really the same as mine." One says this when one sees that the only method by which your sensation and mine can be compared is in behavioristic terms. But behaviorism is not what is wanted in this situation — what one encounters here is a groping realization of the incommensurability of the public and the introspectional worlds. This "quality" which cannot be communicated is nevertheless something with public attributes, as shown by the mere fact that we are talking about it. Strictly, the situation which everyone appreciates when they make the statement above is one that cannot be got into words at all. But we do verbalize it — what can we mean by such a verbalization without stultifying ourselves? We can find a meaning of sorts in terms of our thesis. We again imagine the device of parallel columns, the record being kept both for you and for me. Our two atomic analysis columns are compared corresponding to the report by each of us that we are seeing red. If the two atomic analysis columns should show a high degree of similarity under these conditions then we would feel justified in saying that we were having similar experiences and in particular were experiencing the same quality of red. Hence a meaning of sorts can be given to "quality of a sensation". It is true that with such a meaning we have to modify our original statement and say that in the present state of technique there is no method by which it can be decided whether your sensation of red is the same as mine, but, nevertheless, the original statement was not as devoid of sense as it could be made to appear if we were malicious.

Carrying the same idea further, the thesis enables a public meaning to be given to pain. The expression "as private as pain" is a common one. If whenever I report that I am feeling pain my atomic analysis column discloses a pattern similar to your pattern when you report that you are feeling pain, then we have a basis to giving a public character to pain. Specific similarities in the patterns would give the basis for saying that the quality of your pain was the same as mine. A possibility such as this does not prejudge the answer to the question whether all types of pain will be found to have a very closely similar atomic pattern and whether social conditioning has not brought it about that we have learned to use a common word for a group of unpleasant experiences which may not have very much in common to unsophisticated apprehension. Neither does the possibility of a description of pain in atomic terms preclude the possibility that a satisfactory correlation may be found on the conventional behavioristic level. It may not be necessary to push the analysis to atomic depths.

The thesis of the sufficiency of atomic analysis in "classical" terms presents the atomic analysis column as completely deterministic if the future course of the column is determined by its present. If one wants to adopt the general thesis of essential correlation instead of the more conventional causality, one need not rule out the possibility that the future is determined by the present and the past together. On the other hand, the conscious experience column is not at all deterministic, in that any given conscious state may correspond to many different atomic states, and may be followed by a multiplicity of future conscious states. The concept of "free will" occurs only in the conscious states column and is somehow associated with the fact that this is not a deterministic column. This clean-cut classical picture now has to be somewhat modified in the light of quantum theory. The atomic description column still remains a "complete" description of the system in atomic terms in the sense that it contains the results of all the physical measurements that it is possible in the nature of things to make, but it is not "complete" with the old connotations, because it is not possible to give both position and momentum of every atom, something which according to the classical picture was not only possible but necessary. Furthermore the atomic analysis column ceases to be completely deterministic. Predictions of a sort can still be made. These are not indefinitely precise, but have a fringe of fuzziness, with the result that the longer the range of the prediction the more blurred does it become until, in the limit, one has lost the possibility of foreseeing even the most general characteristics of observable behavior. I do not believe that all this seriously modifies the picture for the biologist or the psychologist, or prevents him from thinking profitably in terms of the classical thesis. For most biologists would not claim that an analysis so profound as down to atomic terms is necessary for their purposes, but that an analysis down to larger units, such perhaps as the protein molecules with their many thousands of atoms, is adequate, and that such an analysis can give results approximately deterministic over long enough intervals of time to serve all present purposes. Quantum effects would thus appear to be of the nature of a perturbation of a system classical in the main, and even when specific effects appear which probably are of quantum origin, such as mutations in the germ cells, these effects are slow acting and have no measurable effect on the immediate future of the organism.

The thesis of the sufficiency of atomic analysis is thus one which does not commit one to any one single point of view with regard to consciousness or sensation or behavior. It is in harmony with the general temper of the times, so that many people of various outlooks can use it in their thinking and as a basis for communication. In particular, it enables those psychologists who want to, and others who may look on things in the same way, to get everything onto a completely public basis. It is not necessary that the thesis be explicitly formulated, and as a matter of fact it is seldom formulated in the way that we have adopted in the discussion above. But I believe that even if the thesis is not consciously present, most present-day biologists and psychologists do postulate something roughly equivalent in its practical effects. Otherwise, too many of the conventional ways of talking are devoid of meaning. This "something roughly equivalent" may be only the inarticulate belief that the "true" meaning of every word whatever has to be on the public level.

In spite of these many desirable results of accepting the thesis, acceptance carries implications that should be subjected to analysis. In the first place there is the legitimacy of assuming that an atomic analysis of a living system is possible in principle. Bohr has strongly suggested in his discussions of his general principle of complementarity that he believes it is not possible in principle, the reason being that the reactions of any physical instruments which we might use in making the atomic analysis will be so disturbing as to destroy the very life whose nature we are trying to discover. So far as I can discover, this view of Bohr's has not received wide acceptance among biologists, any necessary connection between the disturbance by the measuring instrument and the organism being at the present time thought to be too vague and incompletely understood to justify such a sweeping conclusion as that of Bohr. But the difficulty of Bohr suggests another kind of difficulty, which I believe much more formidable. This is the difficulty of determining simultaneously the configuration of all the atoms in *any* material system, whether living or dead, and therefore the difficulty of giving meaning to "state of all the atoms". The difficulty arises because there is not room enough in space for all the instruments that would be required to measure the position of all the atoms. "Simultaneous position of all the atoms" is, I believe, an illegitimate concept as applied to any physical system not of the most primitive simplicity. Here again is a situation where we say "all" but do "any". In the inorganic world the resultant difficulty need not, perhaps, be too serious, because of the approximate homogeneity of large tracts of inorganic systems, which reduces the number of instruments required to give adequate characterization. Or another method of turning the difficulty for inorganic systems is the method of identical replicas. By making successive measurements on identical replicas the entire system may eventually be covered by measurements, which are then lumped together as fictitious simultaneous measurements on a single system. But in an organic system, in which small-scale structure may play a vital role, the difficulties and doubts would appear more formidable. Organic systems are not homogeneous over as wide ranges as inorganic systems, and the method of identical replicas becomes questionable for organic systems because of the difficulty, or impossibility, of acquiring the fineness of control necessary to ensure that the replicas be identical. These considerations cast doubt on the legitimacy of assuming that the first column, the column of the detailed atomic specification of the system, can be constructed. The difficulty arises from the purely physical character of the instruments involved without regard for any difficulties arising from the fact that the instruments must be used by human beings.

Another even more serious form of the same type of objection appears if we take to heart our fundamental requirement that any eventually acceptable account of the world has to include an account of the mechanism which is thinking about the world and giving the account. From this point of view it is utterly impossible to require that I, or anyone else or all men together, give an atomic account of my own mental processes. My conscious states, in terms of which my account is given, succeed each other at a rate certainly less than 100 per second. In my whole lifetime the number of my conscious states is less than something of the order of 3×10^{11}, which is so much smaller than the number of atoms in my brain that it would take something of the order of 10^{14} lifetimes to even mention all the atoms, one by one, to say nothing of mentioning all their combinations, which according to supposition correspond to my different mental states. It is not often that we have to take account of the finiteness of the possible experience of any individual or of the entire human race, but here it seems to me is a place where this sort of consideration definitely blocks a tactic which we would like to follow.

In addition to the numerical difficulty just discussed, I believe that there is the further difficulty that the construction of the conscious states column involves a divergent process. The verbalizing of one's conscious experiences is itself a conscious experience which requires to be verbalized. It would appear that the material to be verbalized must grow in virtue of the act of verbalization faster than can be kept up with. One is reminded of the Irishman who suddenly started painting his fence as fast as he could in order to finish before his paint gave out. One can deal with the situation in practice only by leaving out whole blocks of experience which one can only hope will not turn out to have been important. We are not yet in a position to decide by experiment whether such omissions are important in fact.

MEANING AND COMMUNICATION

It thus appears more clearly than before that the present function of the thesis of the sufficiency of atomic analysis is to give a justification of sorts to our use of public language in talking about ourselves, and also to provide a basis for communication. How does the fact that the thesis is impossible in principle affect its practical use? Does it mean that our assumption that we have here a basis for meaning and communication is illusory? There are interesting implications here for the whole subject of meaning which we now examine. We must always keep in mind our cardinal principle that our meanings are to be meanings *now*, and that meanings cannot be altered by anything that may happen in the future, although they may be altered by what we now expect may happen in the future. This implies that for some purposes we can get along with less than a full uncompromisingly operational specification of meaning so far as we require that the operations have to be of known feasibility. The operations play a conceptual role. If I can imagine myself performing the operation, that is sufficient to give meaning to me, and if my neighbor can imagine himself performing the same operation, that is sufficient to enable me to communicate with him. If I and my neighbor can both imagine ourselves on the far side of the moon, looking at it, that is enough for communication, even if neither of us can imagine how we might get there. Accepted communication is one of the aspects of meaning, and in fact from the popular point of view is probably the most important aspect. For if my neighbor responds to my communication in the way that I wanted him to respond, it would seem pretty natural for me to say that what I had said had some sort of meaning and my neighbor knew what it was, even though both of us might have been talking about some such thing as absolute length or absolute simultaneity, which from the operational point of view of the physicist is meaningless. In this sense my neighbor and I can mean something by a statement, even if it can be shown that we are both deceiving ourselves.

Communication involves at least two things: securing the wanted response from the person addressed, and the feeling of meaning on the part of the utterer. What we have called "verbal perception" is involved here. I have certain expectations with regard to how my neighbor will respond when I use a word and with regard to the associations that the word will call up, and these expectations may be made the basis of communication. Successful communication doubtless tends to survive as such entirely apart from the nature of the program of actual action involved. Even actual inconsistencies in the imagery associated with a given word is no deterrent to communication, provided the word is used consistently in any one context. Compartments in one's mind are common enough.

The thesis of the sufficiency of atomic analysis is thus a thoroughly workable thesis within the appropriate contexts. It is a thesis which I myself can and do use, and it often, I believe, clarifies my thinking. The aspect of its use which is of principal concern to us here is as a device which enables us to get various primarily introspectional words such as "feeling" and "consciousness" onto a completely public plane. To many people this is an objective greatly to be desired. It portrays the world with a unity and simplicity which is found highly acceptable. A thought is a thought, knowledge is knowledge, and pain is pain whether it is mine or yours, and whether or not the physical substratum is accessible to you or to me.

Most people apparently take the objective, impersonal, unitary nature of the world so much as a matter of course that they cannot see that there is even a problem in getting the private and the public onto a common basis. Those few who do see that there is something here for consideration seldom if ever offer anything so articulate as the thesis of the sufficiency of atomic analysis in defense of their reduction of the private to the public. It would appear, however, that thoughtful people have always felt intellectual uneasiness in the face of this situation and have demanded some sort of conceptual invention to allay it. In the earlier days the conceptual invention might take the form of "existence in the mind of God". Such a conception can give a basis for communication very similar to that offered by the thesis of atomic analysis. However, few in our present culture could accept such a tool in thinking, but have to find some substitute. The substitute which they use is doubtless vague and ill-formulated, but insofar as it could be formulated in operational terms at all I believe it is probably essentially equivalent to the thesis. And once the formulation has been given as explicitly as in the thesis, I believe that the background of present-day thought is homogeneous enough that the thesis can be made the basis of communication.

Although it is thus possible to get the introspectional words onto a public basis, we have to pay a price if we choose so to do. It is possible that we may regard the price as too high and refuse to purchase the possibility allowed us by the thesis. I for one regard the price as too high, for reasons connected with the resultant verbal usage which I will give presently in detail, and I propose to substitute for the verbal usage which appears to me objectionable another specialized verbalization which appears to me less objectionable. It would appear that the behaviorists also, or at least some of them, regard the price as too high. Their refusal to pay the price takes the form of a specialized verbal usage different from the one which I advocate.

THE REACTION OF THE BEHAVIORIST TO THE THESIS

Let us consider the attitude of the behaviorist first. The present behaviorist position has its roots in the early history of psychology. Early psychology was primarily introspectional. In trying to coordinate the findings of introspection, an attitude was adopted which was an uncritical survival from earlier habits of thought. Early thinking was often frankly animistic and indulged in meaningless reification. Consistent with this style of thought the early psychologists invented or accepted various "faculties" such as the will, or the soul, or the mind, or consciousness, to which they ascribed an explanatory and causal function. As psychologists grew more experienced they realized that they were not "saying anything" in talking about their various invented faculties in the role of causal agents. They came to see that they were dealing only with a sterile verbalism — there was no second method of getting to the terminus. The fact that the verbalism was sterile was proved by the fact that they could get along without it. Growing appreciation of this situation is often linked with the name of Pavlov. Instead of saying, "The dog eats voraciously because it is hungry", psychologists saw that it was sufficient for their purposes to say, "The dog eats voraciously because it has been deprived of food". Since then psychologists have been whittling away with Occam's razor and have discovered that they can get along without a great part of the traditional verbal apparatus. Many behaviorists carry their reaction to a logical conclusion by refusing to use at all such words as hungry, or feeling, or sensation, or conscious. Skinner[2] is a well-known advocate and practitioner of this practice, and I have had long conversations with him on the subject. Now I have the greatest sympathy with Skinner's position in many respects — I can find no more meaning than he in a "mind" or a "feeling" or an "ego" as a causative agency, and I have the highest esteem for Occam's razor as an instrument of intellectual emancipation. But I do not think that Skinner's solution is the only possible one or that it is a solution that takes into account all that we can see or is significant. Furthermore, I believe that at least some psychologists find this solution congenial because they take it for granted that the world has to be public and one. It follows that any solution consistent with this conviction stands a better chance of being adopted without searching analysis of all the implications.

INTROSPECTIONAL WORDS IN THE PRIVATE MODE

My solution is somewhat similar to that of Skinner in that I also recognize that the introspectional words are in a special class, but my solution differs from his in that instead of discarding these words altogether I retain many of them, but with a restricted meaning. The special nature of the introspectional words becomes obvious when one tries to give an account of what is involved operationally in using these words on both the public and the private level. These words are a subclass of the more general class of words the operational meaning of which depends on who it is that is performing the operations. We have already recognized the occurrence of such words in Chapter III. In the case of the introspectional words the operational heterogeneity is especially obvious: one is tempted to say — especially aggravated. Consider, for example, what is involved in carrying out the injunction "Verify that individual X has a toothache". The operational verification is entirely different dependinng on whether the individual X is myself or another. When it is I that have a toothache my operation of verification is direct, immediate, and so elemental that it is well-nigh impossible to describe to another how I do it. Whereas if I have to verify that some other individual has a toothache, my operations are complex, roundabout, and I can never be sure that I may not be mistaken — the unreliability of the lie detector is notorious. If it is not I that am enjoined to verify that X has a toothache but someone else, let us call him A, then as I observe A making his verification I see that he goes about it with much less fuss and feathers when the individual

X happens to be A himself than when X is another. The operational dichotomy in these situations is so intimately involved with everyday experience that it seems to me I can ignore it only at my peril. It is not enough that the operational dichotomy can be played down, as does the behaviorist, by saying that X's toothache is accessible only to X; I want to emphasize the dichotomy. In fact, I believe, as will appear in detail later, that serious social consequences follow the ignoring of the dichotomy.

It seems to me that there is something here which not even the intransigent behaviorist can ignore. The moment that he can recognize that there are events accessible to only one person, he also has to admit that there are operations which are performable by only one person, namely, the operations by which the person to whom the events are uniquely accessible handles the events. The class of operations performable by only one person may very well have a calculus of its own, and part of the task of the behaviorist is to investigate what this calculus may be. In investigating these operations the psychologist may, if he chooses, remain on the public behavioristic level, the uniquely performable operation being described in public behavioristic terms, the same for all of us. To this extent I can act as does the behaviorist. But I want to push the matter further. In the class of operations performable by only one person there is a subclass which is so sharply set off from all the others that I think it demands special treatment — this is the subclass of operations which only I can perform. The dichotomy between the operations by which I decide that I am having a toothache and any of my neighbors is having a toothache is so sharp and spectacular that it is to be emphasized by every means in my power. This dichotomy is the most insistent and uncompromising of the characteristics of my world — I do not see how I can neglect it and possibly hope to give an adequate description of what happens to me, or to adapt myself to living in the world.

In order to minimize the peril of neglecting this operational dichotomy, I propose to restrict my use of the more important and more dangerous of the introspectional words arbitrarily to an operationally unique sense. In particular, I propose to use such words only in my private aspect. Such usage is consistent with the vision that I cannot get away from myself. Because of this, any "ultimately true" account that I can give of the world has to be from myself as center — any valid report has to be reducible to the first person singular if it is not actually already in the first person. In order to give this first person account with the greatest vividness and immediacy I find it almost unavoidable to use such words as "think" and "feel" and "remember" and "conscious" in describing my direct experience, that is, to use these words in their private aspect. Of course I could, if I wanted to, avail myself of the permission granted by the thesis of the sufficiency of atomic analysis and express my introspectional experience in words of solely public import. This is essentially what the behaviorist does. But if I did make such a choice I would have to keep in mind a structure of such operational complexity as to be completely unmanageable, and I am not willing to pay the price.

It is most fortunate that restricting in this way the usage of some of the introspectional words offers no impediment to communication. As a matter of fact most people do now ordinarily use these words predominantly in their private mode. Each of us talks out loud in his own private mode, and we find that we perfectly understand each other. If ever some special situation should make desirable usage in the traditional public mode, it is always easy to give express notice to that effect. We will return to this question of communication.

Another reason that I am not willing to pay the price is that it obscures, or even makes impossible, what is for me one of the essential visions, namely, that the world of introspection is a different sort of world than the noonday public world of common experience. It is difficult to express this in ordinary language; doubtless one of the reasons is that language is an evolutionary social product, with all the emphasis on the public aspects. We will return later to an examination of some of the respects in which the world of introspection differs from the public world.

If it is agreed to use the introspectional words only in their private mode, then these words thereby become "relational" words, a class of words which we have encountered earlier. In general, we can discover the occurrence of relational words by an analysis of the operations which give them meaning. If we formulate the operations in public terms, and if it turns out that the nature of the operation is different according as it is I or someone else who performs the operation, then the corresponding word is relational. By far the commonest relational words are "I" and "you". The referent of these words is neither a specific individual nor a class, but is an individual who varies with every user of the word, and who is characterized by standing in a certain relation to the user of the word. In the case of "I" the relation is of identity, and in the case of "you" the relation is that of hearer. In the same way, the experience which is the referent when I use an introspectional word in its private mode is the experience of just one person, myself. When *I* say "conscious" in its private mode I can be referring only to my own experience. In this sense only I am conscious and conscious in this usage is a highly relational word. But I also hear you say that you are conscious. What meaning can I ascribe to a statement like this by you? The specific answer to this important question will be given presently. In the meantime one must not assume that in order to answer it we must readmit the usage of "conscious" in its public mode. The convention which I accepted prescribed only how *I* should use certain words. I can continue to keep the convention no matter how you use them.

There are a great many words with relational aspects, but most of them have other aspects also. The words "I" and "you" are almost unique in that they are used only in a relational mode, whereas the others have both public and private components and if usage is to be in one or the other mode exclusively it has to be by agreement and convention. Furthermore the line of division between the two modes is not always sharp, so that sometimes it is not profitable to set up a convention restricting usage to one or the other mode, but usage in both modes has to be retained and we have to content ourselves with calling attention to the ambiguous usage and trust to the context of the usage to provide any necessary clarification.

If Skinner would formulate a definition of the class of words which he would not use at all, I probably could use the same definition to specify the words which I want to use only in the introspectional mode.

THE OPERATION OF PROJECTION

A fundamental question already hinted at is communication. If I agree to use words like "conscious" only in their private mode, so that the operations which give meaning to my use of "conscious" are operations which only I can perform, how is communication at all possible? If my neighbor adopts the same convention as I, and I hope that he does, what are the operations which I perform by which I give meaning to the "conscious" which I hear uttered by my neighbor? There must be some meaning, for I cannot admit that my neighbor might be stultifying himself by adopting a convention which I urge, but whatever the meaning, it cannot be specified in terms of the same operations which give meaning to my use of the same word. At first thought, this may seem disturbing, but on further reflection it need not be, for we have seen that always, "in principle", part of the operational picture involved who it is that performs the operation. For us the problem is to put our finger on the specific difference of the operations in the two cases before us. It seems to me that the operation by which I give meaning to your use of "conscious" is a simple one in the sense that everyone uses the operation. I shall call it the operation of "projection", I "project" myself into your position, that is, I imagine myself in your position, and I ask myself what I would be saying or doing in such a position. If I can imagine that I myself would be using the same word in that position, then I understand the meaning of your word and you have been successful in your communication. For present purposes it is not necessary to attempt to analyze the operation of projection further. Simple observation shows that it is an operation which I continually perform without hesitation, and I believe that you also perform the same operation. Because of your ability to perform this operation easily, I believe that it will be easy for you to adopt my convention to use the introspectional words only in their private mode. Without the ability to perform the operation of projection, social cooperation would doubtless be much more difficult than it is, so that it is natural to think that ability to perform the operation is the product of evolutionary pressure.

The operation of projection thus serves a much broader function than merely to give meaning to the private words which we use in talking to each other. In its general social context, as an operation by which we anticipate the actions of our fellows and adapt ourselves to them generally, it is what a physicist would call a first approximation. We know that our fellows do not act exactly as we would under all circumstances. In coarse outline all human beings are alike, but in finer detail they differ. We correct the operation of projection by using the specific knowledge that we have acquired of the particular individual with whom we are dealing. If our acquaintance with the individual has been intimate and prolonged we know intuitively what to expect of him, and the operation of projection may not consciously enter. But I think the operation of projection or something essentially equivalent has to be involved if I am to mean anything when I speak of my neighbor as being conscious. Furthermore, it appears that this is all that I need, so that it would violate the principle of intellectual parsimony to search for anything more.

The fact that the present-day adult member of society can use the operation of projection intuitively as an unanalyzed is not inconsistent with recognition by the psychologist that this operation has a very complex background. There are psychologists who claim that the awakening awareness of the child to himself as a person can occur only in a social setting. The contention is that the child first becomes aware of other people and that only after this does he say to himself, "I am a person just like those others". This may well be the case, although it is a little difficult for me to imagine that the child was incapable of saying "This is my leg" until after he had learned to say "That is your leg". But if this is actually the historical development for any individual, it would seem that somewhere along the line there must be an inversion, for contemporaneous socially mature man apparently thinks of others in terms of himself, not of himself in terms of others. At least that is what simple observation shows is happening in my own case and I think I hear most of you say the same thing.

If one pushes to their conclusion some of the lines of thought suggested in the last few paragraphs it becomes obvious that the distinction between public and private cannot be made sharp in all respects and that one cannot permanently confine oneself to a single level of operation. So long as I am concerned only with my own introspectional experiences I can be fairly well satisfied with my understanding of "private" — it is somehow concerned with something that can happen only to me. But what happens when I hear my neighbor use the word "private"? We have seen that communication is possible here with the aid of the operation of projection. But there is more to it than this. How shall I think about situations in which I have to use the operation of projection? Any uttered word is public — my neighbor by the mere act of making a communication about his private experiences and I by talking about them have introduced a component of publicity which cannot be exorcised. Insofar as I talk about them, all my dealings with my neighbor have to be on a public basis. (This is essentially the thesis of behaviorism.) But shall I recognize subdivisions in this publicity corresponding to different ways in which my neighbor talks? Shall I recognize in the totality of publicity that is my neighbor a subdivision which I may call "private for him" and another part which I call "public for him"? It is possible to make such a division in purely observational behavioristic terms. What happens when I attempt to express in the same language what I hear him saying about what he observes in me? I would seem driven to recognizing a "private for me which is public for him". The regress can be carried to infinite lengths and offers possibilities of infinite confusion. It seems to me that in its entirety this is a situation with which language is essentially incapable of dealing. Even the nimblest hopping back and forth from one level of operation to another is of no avail. Communication is at all possible only by the exercise of good will and by ignoring certain aspects of the total situation. It is an art to know what aspects to ignore, an art which can be acquired only by prolonged social and cultural experience.

If for some compelling reason we need an explicit verbalization for dealing with the next stage of approximation in dealing with the public-private dichotomy, we might find it adequate to recognize a "private-for-me", a "private-for-you", and a "public-for-all-of-us", or simply "public". This "public" is public in no absolute sense, but is rather "public-for-the-human-race".

DETAILED ANALYSIS OF SOME INTROSPECTIONAL WORDS

We are now nearly ready to examine in detail how some specific introspectional words appear when used only in their private mode. But we have to deal first with a certain vagueness in the word introspectional itself. There are some verbalisms such as "the self" or "the will" or "the mind" or "the soul", used with the connotation of a causative agency, which many people will doubtless want to call introspectional. To me these particular words are as meaningless and unintelligible as to the most ardent behaviorist. They are unintelligible because I cannot do the sort of thing that I am obviously expected to do if I am to use them. It seems to me that the impulse to use these words arises from bad introspectional observation. In the presence of these words I experience an inhibition. It appears to me that this inhibition has been growing upon me — when I was younger I could use these words. I like to think that this experience of mine is significant. At any rate, with my present inhibitions I shall naturally not try to find the meaning of these particular verbalisms or others similar to them.

Perhaps the most important single word to be affected by our convention to use it only in the private mode is "conscious". There is obviously a possible public mode here as shown by the quotation on page 203 from the biographical notice of Angell. I think most psychologists would now be willing to say that the operational background of any such public usage is at least obscure. Usage exclusively in the private mode has now become such a matter of course with me that my first impulse is to see no meaning in the question whether you are conscious in the same way that I am. Any operational meaning that can be attached to this question is at least exceedingly complex, and probably involves something equivalent to the thesis of the sufficiency of atomic analysis, as we have already seen. I do not regard it as an answer to say, as some people do, "I cannot *certainly* say that you are conscious in the same way as I; I can only say that the *probability* is that you are similarly conscious". To me such an answer betrays lack of appreciation of the point at issue.

Used only in the private mode, "conscious" is as uncompromisingly a relational word as is "I". In fact, one who sees nothing of a causative agency in consciousness could argue that except for differences in grammatical usage "I" and "conscious" are practically synonymous. The relational aspect of "conscious" may perhaps be made more vivid by coining a new word. Instead of saying "I am conscious" say "I am *mes*cious". Perhaps it does not require so much argument to convince one of the propriety of saying "Only I am mescious" as of saying "Only I am conscious". (Euphemism suggests that "*mes*cious" is preferable in some respects to the perhaps more natural "*I*scious".) The same scheme could be adopted in speaking of others. I can say that you are "*you*scious". I can also say that *only* you are youscious. This is the level on which I might be talking about the "private-for-you" as already suggested. Similarly I can invent the word "*he*scious", but *we*scious or *they*scious would make no sense.

Before passing to an examination of some of the other words in their introspectional mode, it may pay to try to characterize a little further this introspectional consciousness. One is faced with a very real embarrassment in this attempt; one is almost forced to proceed in negative terms, telling various things that consciousness is not. In the first place the statement "I am conscious" is not to be analyzed, as are most statements, into a sequence of words each with its own meaning, such that the meaning of the whole can be built up from the meaning of the words separately. I am not saying that there is something, "I", which has the property of being "conscious". As already suggested, "I am conscious" is essentially a tautology. The statement "I am conscious" is not subject to verification — to say it constitutes the only sort of verification of which it is capable. Hence the apparent statement "I am conscious" is properly not a statement at all, but only a pseudo-statement.

The word "aware" used in the introspectional mode is closely synonymous with conscious. It is almost the same thing for me to say "There is awareness" as to say "I am conscious".

"Consciousness" has no describable quality and so far as I can see no recognizable quality, using "quality" in the sense in which I speak of the quality of my sensation of red. So far as I can see there is no component of memory in the experience that I call consciousness. I can find no awareness in my present conscious experience that what is now consciousness is similar to what I called consciousness in my previous experience. There is, on the other hand, a definite component of memory in my recognition of the quality of red, for example, in a present sensation, because I am aware that the red which I now experience is similar to the red which I formerly experienced. Although I cannot communicate the quality of this sensation, I recognize it when it recurs, and this recognition is an essential part of the situation. But there is no such recognition of a past experience when I recognize myself as conscious. The word "quality" is not applicable to consciousness. We would seem to be concerned here with something that has to do only with the immediate present and that is of an unanalyzably primitive simplicity. The only thing that I can find in introspection of a comparable unanalyzable primitiveness is my perception of the flight of time.

The fact that the present experience which we call consciousness contains no recognizable element of memory does not mean, however, that we cannot remember that we have been conscious in the past.

Precisely what this thing we call memory of consciousness consists of I find difficult to analyze.

Let us next consider what we mean when we talk about the quality of a sensation, such as the sensation of red. This "quality" has public and private aspects which require untangling. I have found that most people are willing to say "There is no method by which I can verify that the quality of your sensation of red is really the same as mine". This on the face of it is a fairly straightforward sort of statement, and involves perhaps nothing more than a realization that any obvious check would be simply a check on similarity of overt response in similar situations, not a check on the similarity of the "quality", whatever this may mean. If one reacts to reflection on this situation by saying "I recognize that I cannot *certainly* check that the quality of your sensation is really the same as mine, but the best I can do is to establish a high probability", it seems to me that he has not seen the issue. The same situation arose with regard to "consciousness". The point would seem to be that "quality" of a sensation, with the connotation of communicability, is a word which is simply not applicable in this situation. I doubt whether even the device of parallel column report which we used in making plausible the thesis of the sufficiency of atomic analysis would avail in this situation. What I am essentially saying when I say that I cannot communicate the quality of my sensation of red is that "quality" is a word which has meaning only in the introspectional mode, or, in other words, that it is a relational word, and that the subject of the relation is myself. There are not many words in which the public component, even in popular usage, is so small as in "quality".

Although a quality may not be communicated, nevertheless there are some things that may be said about it. Perhaps the most important of these is that I can remember the quality of my sensation of red. Perhaps this is nothing more than saying that I can remember my sensation of red and recognize it when it recurs. This is an introspectional statement. It can, nevertheless, be subjected to a check of sorts. I can fasten a label to a red object, recording that this object appeared red to me at some date, and then I can verify at a later date that the object still appears red. In practice this procedure is subject to the hazard that some painter may have wielded his brush between the two dates. We have learned how to deal with such hazards by methods which need not concern us further. There is frequently an involvement of the word "red" with the sensation, but the verbal involvement appears in no way necessary. However, some sort of involvement, whether verbal or not is unessential, of the present experience of the organism with its last experience would seem to be an almost necessary condition for survival, especially if the environment is at all complex. "Quality" of a sensation, so far as it can be given meaning at all on the public level, may be merely one of the artefacts of the mechanism by which the organism makes connection with its own past.

"Sensation" is a word which in popular usage is closely similar to "quality of a sensation", and it also has predominantly a private introspectional meaning. Doubtless this is the reason that Skinner and others of his school will not admit it at all. Nevertheless, I think that "sensation" has a distinctly greater component of the public than does "quality of a sensation". I would be more sanguine of being able to find some correlation between the two columns of an atomic analysis which I could associate with "sensation" than I could with "quality of a sensation". And it may perhaps be significant that I do not feel a very strong inhibition against saying "You have sensations as well as I", although I am strongly inhibited against saying "You have sensations *like* mine". In spite of all this, the fact remains that the operations which justify me in saying "I am having a sensation" are sharply different from the operations which justify my saying "You are having a sensation".

In the word "pain" the swing toward the public side goes perhaps a little further than in "quality" and "sensation", in spite of the fact that "private as pain" is a common expression and that most people seem able to handle pain in the private mode. The private aspect of pain is easy to see. I know when something hurts, and it makes absolutely no difference what my neighbor says about it — unless he hypnotizes me — whether he says that *really* I am not feeling pain, or that I *should* not be feeling pain, or even if he concedes that I have a right to think that it hurts. Furthermore, I need no method of confirming that I am feeling pain in spite of the fact that I know that there are public proceedings which offer a second method of getting to the same terminus and which may be made the basis of confirmation. Several such public proceedings suggest themselves. Thus in many cases when I feel pain I make characteristic avoidance reactions which both I and my neighbor can see and which he can correlate with my statement that I am feeling pain. Another possible procedure is as follows. Suppose that I am subjected to a stimulus of gradually increasing intensity, as independently measured in physical terms perhaps by an energy input, and that I simultaneously report my estimate of the intensity of the stimulus as I feel it. It seems to be a fact of observation that most people are able to make an estimate in numerical terms of the intensity of the stimulus which they feel. If now it should turn out that the curve plotting my estimate against the physically measured intensity should pass through some distinctive episode, such perhaps as an abrupt change of slope, immediately before I reported that the stimulus was intense enough to give pain, I think that the psychologist or physiologist would feel that he was getting something significant. Still more, if it should appear that the intensity of the stimulus which produced pain was accompanied by some recognizable change in the chemical response of my nerves, such perhaps as actual destruction of some of the nerve cells, I think the psychologist would be still more pleased. He would feel that he had found out something about the "nature" of pain and would think that he had got it onto a completely public basis. He would probably even change the definition of pain, and say that pain occurs whenever there is the characteristic degeneration of the nerve cells. Such a definition, although in public terms, will nevertheless remain a convention and a sterile verbalism unless there is some second method of getting to the terminus. There has been such a second method in the instances examined above, in the report made by the subject who experiences the pain. Another method not requiring the active cooperation of a subject would be presented if, for instance, the characteristic degeneration in the nerve cells was always correlated with characteristic avoidance reactions.

There is thus a very large component of the public in the concept of pain. This is sometimes carried to the extreme of complete publicity, as when the attempt is made to give a legal definition of what constitutes cruelty to animals. In the case of the pain of animals usually one has only the avoidance reactions, and so long as one has only this, one is strictly dealing with a convention when speaking of the pain of animals. It is hard to deal with this situation in a thoroughly rational manner. What shall I say to my neighbor who claims that my dog is not like me at all, because my dog *enjoys* making avoidance reactions whereas I dislike it. It would seem that the tenderhearted people who are concerned with giving pain to animals actually deal with the situation by projecting themselves, thus introducing a second method of getting to the terminus and thus removing the purely conventional character. Such a procedure is methodologically heterogeneous, for one is simultaneously operating on the private and the public levels. It does not seem as though such methodological heterogeneity does much harm in this case.

"Think" is a word with mostly private overtones as it is commonly used. The operational difference in the use of the word "think" as applied to myself and to you is as well marked as it is in the case of the word "conscious". In fact, in some usages "I am thinking" is almost synonymous with "I am conscious". However, there are differences. I am never aware that I am merely thinking, but always at the same time I am aware of what it is that I am thinking about. On the other hand, I may believe that you are thinking because of something in your facial expression or other behavior, but that does not enable me to guess what you are thinking about, and I may say "a penny for your thoughts". "Thought", by the way, would seem to be a reification created by the exigencies of grammar — a thought is "what" I think. Although I can often make the unequivocal statement that I am thinking, the word nevertheless has an unusual amount of ambiguity even when used exclusively in the introspectional mode. Thinking is not usually considered to be synonymous with all conscious mental activity, but only restricted aspects of it. It is not easy to formulate acceptably what should be included in the restrictions. This is shown by the difficulty in agreeing whether "think" can properly be applied to calculating machines as they have been constructed up to the present, or indeed whether any conceivable artificially constructed system should be said to think. I doubt if the usage can be made very sharp. In my own case I believe I use the word mostly in connection with conscious mental activity that has a recognizable component of problem solving, and would not be inclined to use it for sensation or for the perception that usually accompanies a sensation. But if one tries to formulate this distinction one would have to define more specifically what problem solving consists of and to decide whether it is proper to speak of one's mind unconsciously solving problems. Many people do speak in this way, and when I hear them talking in this way it seems to me that they are communicating something which I can find also in my own experience. The upshot of these considerations would seem to be that "think" is mostly introspectional in its connotations, but that it is vague, and preferably to be used as little as possible when precision is demanded. For example, we prefer, if possible, not to use the operation specified by "Report what you think under such and such circumstances" although doubtless such a specification is admissible in principle. The same may be said of the use of others of those words which we agree to use only in an introspectional mode in formulating the specification of acceptable operations.

In the last paragraph the word "mind" naturally slipped in. This word has a history of much abuse and misconception. People would like to use it in a completely public sense and furthermore to think of mind as a causally efficacious agent. At the same time it has a large introspectional component. I am sure that I myself have a mind, but whether you, or my dog, or my elm tree, or my calculating machine has a mind or not can only be inferred by indirect means unlike the means which I use to decide about my own mind. There is no agreement here — some people find it meaningful to talk about the mind of plants. Other people want to talk about mind only when there is a nervous system with which it may be associated. In any event we do not have to decide what mind *is*, but need only to decide under what conditions we want to use the word mind. It may be that enumeration of all the specific instances in which one wants to use the word "mind" will disclose some easily recognizable common characteristic sufficient to justify its retention. It would appear to me, however, that even more than in the case of the word "think" usage of the word "mind" should only be pictorial and rhetorical, as in the last paragraph, and the attempt should be abandoned to use it in a precise sense.

One of the perennial topics of discussion is free will. We have already seen in the first chapter that it has purely verbal aspects. "Free will" is something that we say that we have. It also obviously has both public and private aspects. We here encounter the logical difficulty of reconciling freedom of the will with determinism and the ethical dilemma of reconciling determinism with responsibility. This responsibility is often considered a direct consequence of freedom, and it is furthermore often supposed that acceptance of the concept of responsibility is necessary to the successful functioning of society.

It seems to me that the most important aspects of the concept of the freedom of the will are relational and private. I am free because I feel that I am free, and this is what I mean when I talk about freedom of the will — I really mean "my-freedom" of the will. We can analyze, if we please, how it comes about that I have this feeling of freedom. We can perhaps account for it sufficiently well by observing that in the past I have never been able to predict how I would act (that is, I have not been able to find in introspection the factors which would determine my future action), and by observing that my neighbor has never been able to exert a compulsion upon me capable of controlling the detailed sequence of my thoughts. But *your* freedom is a different matter. I will accept it and tell you that I accept it when I want to get a handle by which I can control your social actions through the concept of responsibility. But I will reject it when I scheme how I can make you do as I desire. Now it is from my point of view regrettably true that in the past my attempts to make you do as I desire have not been very successful. I am, however, continually improving my technique, and with the brain-washing techniques of the Communists, and the reinforcement of animals by the comparative psychologists, and the specific effects of some of the new drugs, and perhaps the ultimate possibility that I may be able to graft my nervous system onto yours or attain electrical control of microscopic areas in your brain, I am optimistic that my ideal of eventual complete control by me of your actions is not an impossible one, in that it at least does not imply a logical inconsistency. By the same token, it is to be remarked that my feeling of my own freedom occurs against a background in which I have never found myself exposed to any of the forms of compulsion suggested above. It is quite conceivable that if I had grown up with such a background, my present conviction of freedom would not have arisen. In this connection I notice that as I grow older my youthful militant conviction that I am the originator of my own actions loses its militancy, and

I feel myself more in the passive role of an observer of my own mental activity. Freedom becomes more an attitude toward a program.

One of the difficult points connected with the concept of freedom of the will is how to give it operational meaning. If you say to me that you are free to take either the right- or the left-hand turning of the road, and, as a matter of fact, choose the right, by what operation can you prove to me that you were free to take either? No operation readily suggests itself. Recently, however, a possibility has come to light, suggested by an article by D. B. Silversmit,[3] by which a novel twist is given to the situation, permitting a slender modicum of "objective" meaning to a statement about your own freedom by you. If you say "I will take the right-hand turn whenever the coin which you toss comes heads and the left whenever it comes tails" and if your prediction turns out to be correct for a great many trials, then I think I would perhaps be more inclined than before to admit that you have some justification for saying that you are free to take which turn you please. But notice that we have been able to give your statement meaning only in a context of indefinite repetition and in conjunction with the probability concept that the tossing of the coin is something which is unpredictable "in principle". I still can see no way of giving operational meaning to the concept of freedom for your individual act after it has been performed. There is, furthermore, an element of paradox in the repetitive situation. For my neighbor, apparently by giving up his freedom and coupling himself invariably to a chance event over which he has no control, is said to demonstrate his freedom. But what is it that he actually has thus demonstrated, his freedom to couple himself invariably to a chance event, or his freedom to choose the right or the left? Viewed as a whole from the outside and without the element of prediction, which perhaps is the kernel of the situation, one would rather say that it is the tossing of the coin which is free rather than the choice of my neighbor. Here probability and freedom appear closely related — ordinarily, chance and freedom are regarded as antithetical.

One hears much discussion of the control of human behavior, both whether it is possible in principle and whether it is desirable. The psychologists have made impressive advances in their mastery of this situation, but I think that even the most ardent psychologist would claim only that it is probability of behavior that, in the present state of technique, is subject to manipulation, not behavior in the individual case. Statistical analysis is an essential tool in all present reinforcement experiments with animals and humans. I think that no psychologist would claim more at present than that if he were given control of education he might perhaps bring it about that 7,000 out of every 10,000 voters would vote Republican, but I think he would not guarantee that any specific voter would vote Republican. I suspect that behavior control will always have to be on a probability basis — even if one accepts the thesis of the sufficiency of atomic analysis, the instrumentation necessary to completely control any single individual would be so complex as to entirely swamp the individual.

"Perception", a word which we have frequently used, has a strong private component, somewhat like the quality of a sensation. Perception implies that I perceive something — it is the nature of this something that determines for me whether the word perception should be used. There are in the literature various usages of perception. For me, perception implies that the object of perception has a certain degree of recognizability and familiarity — it is placed and fits into a scheme. When I have a perception I see that something or other is thus or so — I see that the object is out there is space, or that it is red, or round, or that the sound I am hearing is the note of a piano. What this extra something is beyond the pure sensation or the naked sense stimulus it would be very difficult to say, but there is no doubt when it is present, or absent, and the recognition of its presence or absence is something that occurs only to me — I cannot say whether my neighbors have my perception in my private sense any more than I can say whether their red is the same as my red. The transformation of a sense impression into a perception is a common experience. How often do I say "I can't see *what* it is" only to be followed presently by "*Now* I see what it is". Perceptions are often the accompaniment of direct sense stimulation — whether one would want to say that he has perceptions in his dreams is mostly a matter of choice. One might perhaps speak of indirect perceptions or remembered perceptions under such circumstances.

It is a matter of experience that a perception carries with it no guarantee of truth, but that the truth has to be checked. When one has a perception, the truth of which is proved to be illusory by an appropriate check, one has had an "illusion". By a study of illusions, as was done systematically by Adelbert Ames, Jr.,[4] among others, the very complicated nature of the machinery back of the perceptual act is brought to light. Introspection here makes it seem very reasonable for me to say "If there were no memory there would be no perception", for I think I can always detect a component of memory in what I want to call a perception. Whether the urge to say this has any present value I do not know. It at least leads to the expectation that a perception involves a wider area of brain activity than a sense stimulation, and therefore to the expectation that perhaps our eventual brain analysis will be able to distinguish between the two.

We cast the world into the mold of our perceptions. Because we always see things out there in space at some time or other we ascribe a universal significance to space and time, in the sense that every observer, no matter what his frame of reference, has to describe the world in terms of his own space and time. Quantum theory and cosmology may make us question whether after all the mold of space and time is a good mold. However, the substance of our skepticism is mostly verbal, for we do not see in what other terms we could describe our experience.

The following five words I take from an article analyzing some of the problems of psychoanalysis by Anthony Flew.[5] "Motive", "intention", "purpose", "wish", and "desire" recognizably have something in common and all have a private component. I often find myself in a position where I use one or another of these five words, and when I do find myself in such a situation I can say what my wish or purpose, and so forth, is by direct introspection. But the dividing line between the public and the introspectional use of these words is less sharp than for some other words. It is easier to set up behavior for the possession by you of the corresponding attributes than it is in some other cases, and it is less easy for me to deceive you by lying. This is true in different degrees for the five words. Notice, however, that the behavior in terms of which you give meaning to my motive, intention, or purpose demands observation by you over an interval of time. You have to watch how my actions unfold in a sequence to guess at my purpose, and you are not able to judge my purpose from a single instance of my behavior.

There has been much discussion of "purpose" recently in the

context provided by cybernetics and information theory. Under what circumstances may the motions of a machine be said to be purposeful? I think much of this discussion is confused because of failure to recognize that in actual usage "purpose" has two modes, so that in consequence "purpose" is often confusedly used in both modes in the same context.

The situation with regard to these five words is still further blurred by the decision of the psychoanalyst to "extend" the meanings of these words. He speaks, for example, about my unconscious motives, motives which he says are at present inaccessible to me and which remain inaccessible until made accessible by some psychoanalytical technique. The psychoanalyst says that he finds it profitable to thus extend the meaning, and if he does there is no reason why he should not, so long as he knows what he is doing and takes us into his confidence. Such an extension does, however, displace the word motive into the category of the almost completely public, and runs counter to the emphasis on the private component in these words as commonly used. I believe that important social consequences are tied up with such private usage. Many people will militantly maintain that there is no method by which you can discover their real intentions, and regard it as an invasion of privacy for you to attempt to say what they are.

We thus see that the private component in a word may be greater or less. There is at least one extreme case in which there is no private component at all — this is the word "death". Every individual hears his fellows talk about death, his own included. He comes to think of death in impersonal terms, a sort of average of the thinking of everybody, but his own death, because it is his own death, he thinks of in special terms, that is, in terms of his own experience. The resulting concept is an incongruous hodge-podge, because if there is one thing which my own death is not it is a form of my own experience — when I am dead I no longer have experiences. The man who says "I shall never die" cannot be confuted. The meaning of "my death" is not to be sought in my expectations of future experience, as the meaning is to be sought in other expressions having future reference, but is to be sought in other aspects of the programs of action which I now adopt. But just as popular usage minimizes the private aspects and mistakenly emphasizes the public aspects in the case of a word like "conscious", so in the case of the word "death" popular usage minimizes the public aspects and mistakenly ascribes private aspects to it. The result is that the programs for action which most people draw up in anticipation of death simply do not make sense. And yet it is obvious that these illogical programs constitute a most powerful social cement and that if society were suddenly deprived of them it would probably pass through an initial period of high instability. For instance, a man's conscious motives in providing for the future well-being of his children would be drastically altered. I have examined in detail in my *Intelligent Individual and Society* some of the social consequences of irrational thinking about death. I have not always found it easy to divest my own thinking about my own death of the implication that it is a form of my own experience, but intellectual integrity demands it.

We now finally consider a few words in which the balance is approximately evenly divided between the private and the public aspects. One such word is "value". We have economic values, almost entirely public, set by the mechanics of the market place. The value which the market sets on an article need not be the value which I set on it. The value which I set on it is in a sense private, because it is I who set it, but it is also public to the extent that my neighbor can find out what my valuation is, without having to rely on my say-so. He can do this, for example, by observing my top bid when the article is subject to competitive bidding. This, however, presents only a small part of the picture, because I value a much greater range of things than the articles of the market place. In particular, I value abstract things such as friendship, for which it would be difficult to find a numerical measure. It is true that one can set up procedures to determine whether I attach a greater value to this than I do to that, even if one or both are abstract. This can be done in principle by cunningly devising situations in which if I am to have one of two alternatives I have to give up the other. But the system of values established in this way will almost certainly not have the desired properties of the series of numbers, and we must be prepared to find instances where I prefer A to B, and B to C, and C to A on Monday and the inverse on Tuesday. The value for me of a thing, material or abstract, is complex. Its importance will depend on my purposes. But, in addition to the ingredient of "importance", a more nebulous ingredient involves my personal feelings, such as esteem or dislike. These feelings are close to the exclusively private. I usually have a pretty distinct idea of whether I like or esteem something or not, and it is not unusual for me to keep these feelings to myself, for reasons of social policy, and even to practice deliberate deception, sometimes innocent and sometimes guilty, with respect to them. So far as the value which I set on something depends on feelings of this sort, my values are private.

A value is not a value for me unless I accept it. The operation of acceptance is one which society tries to make public by every device in its power, and we have such public rituals as reciting the Apostles' Creed, or pledging allegiance to the flag, or taking the temperance pledge. In spite of all this I know that for me acceptance is a purely private operation. It is I who know whether I accept or not; I may or may not choose to deceive you about my inner feelings, and I know that you cannot certainly know whether I am really accepting or not. That I and my fellow say things like this seems to me a rock-bottom fact about the way things are with people, and a disregard of it in the construction of society is, I believe, responsible for many of our social difficulties.

Another closely related word is "belief". This, I think, is more nearly entirely private in nature than "accept". I think, however, that the individual usually has a mistaken idea of the role which his beliefs play in his conduct. A belief frequently has the connotation of something sacrosanct, something to which a man owes loyalty, to which he will adhere through thick and thin, often even in the face of the evidence. There is no doubt that the actions of many people are determined by their beliefs. We have already in Chapter II discussed how belief or faith enters the activity of the scientist. I think that similar remarks are applicable to all of us as well as the scientist, and that the actions of all of us could be determined by something less uncompromising than belief, something more nearly of the nature of a tentative program, followed because in the light of all presently available evidence it is the program which seems to have the greatest prospect of success. In other words, beliefs are a luxury which we can get along without, and intellectual good form, as symbolized by Occam's razor, demands that we should. For me, "belief" implies a metaphysical background, and metaphysical in the bad sense at that. It has always been a puzzle to me to understand why society treats a man's beliefs with so much respect. Such respect is understandable only with a metaphysical background, a background which associates belief with the voice of conscience and the voice of God. The respect of society is understandable only because so many people adopt this attitude.

Another similar word is "guilt". It has a recognizable private component. I know when I have the feeling of guilt. It is closely connected with "acceptance", in that I am likely to have the feeling of guilt when I violate a canon of conduct which I have accepted. This is not the only occasion, however, on which I feel guilt, but I may respond to the public component and feel guilt if my neighbor is sufficiently insistent in telling me that I ought to feel guilty. This sort of guilty feeling was fairly common in my youth, but lately I have this sort of guilt complex more and more rarely. This is doubtless a consequence of the fact that I become increasingly willing to pit my own judgment against that of my neighbors. My feeling of guilt may be of widely varying degrees of complexity, from that when I am discovered raiding the icebox to that when I abscond with the savings of widows and children. In spite of all these private aspects of guilt, the word has a larger public component than many other associated words, because my feeling of guilt is so often associated with secondary reactions which my neighbor can exploit to assure himself that I am not deceiving him when I tell him that I do or do not feel guilt. This may not be unconnected with the fact that the guilt complex is almost entirely of social origin — if it were not for the pressures of my neighbors I doubt whether I would ever have the sentiment of guilt. If I had grown up alone on a desert island I might feel frustration or exasperation with myself, but not guilt.

Another word for which I believe the private aspect is much more important than ordinarily realized is "proof". This has already been discussed in Chapter II. Here I shall only reiterate my opinion that a proper appreciation of this will alter the common picture of science as something essentially public into something essentially private. But here my ideas are unorthodox, and I have sufficiently expanded them in another place.

The above is only a small sampling of the words which have recognizable public and private components. Others will be commented on specifically later as we run across them. I suggest that one can make an estimate of the relative magnitude of the two components in terms of the relative difficulty of deceiving his neighbor about his true state of mind, no holds being barred in the sort of deception that one allows himself to practice. Of course it is I myself (or you) that must be the judge as to how successful we have been in deceiving our neighbor about our true state of mind, for this is the only context in which "true state of mind" has a meaning. "True state of mind" is thus incidentally demonstrated to be of a private relational character.

THE NATURE OF THE WORLD OF INTROSPECTION

Let us now turn to an examination of the world of introspection which we have been encountering in all this analysis. We are now almost of necessity limiting ourselves to questions arising in human psychology. The animal psychologist is practically limited to the conventional behavioristic approach. In the first place, the world of introspection is not a sharply limited world. In introspection we find the transient and the fleeting; we watch things coming into existence or meanings still only half formed. We cannot expect to describe such things in the ordinary language of the *fait accompli*. I publicize the results of introspection by expressing them in language, but I can see that something was happening before the language emerged. It would seem obvious that not all the details of the verbalization mechanism can be correlated with the data of introspection. The words simply come, one knows not how. These words correspond to memories and vague familiarities, which one associates with the immediate experience with sufficient confidence and definiteness to be able to assure oneself that one is using the word correctly, but what it is for which he is using the word correctly he finds it not so easy to say. By effort we can doubtless educate ourselves to the recognition of ever finer introspectional details. I have sometimes spoken of the desirability of the invention of an introspectional microscope. After we have become sufficiently familiar with new introspectional detail we shall doubtless find some sort of verbalization for it. But always at the edge of my introspectional exploration there will be an inchoate limbo of half-created things in the process of coming into being which may not be spoken of in the noonday language of ordinary social discourse.

Not only may ordinary language not be used in talking about the nebulous edge of the introspectional world, but operationally the introspectional world is different from the public world. The operation of verification is not applicable. There is no method of verifying that I am not making a mistake or am not the victim of self-deception. In the public world the operation of verification is of cardinal importance — without it we could, for example, hardly have formed the concept of "object". One of the most potent means of verification ordinarily is repetition. But situations cannot be made to repeat at the limit of introspection. It is true that we can remember previous events and remember that they were similar to present events, but it would not be memory if there were also not a recognition that the past event is not the present event. What other method can we adopt to verify our recollection of a past event if repetition is not available? In practise we scrutinize every aspect of our recollection that we can — we try to remember the associations that were called up and we make an indirect check in terms of the consistency of these associations. But all this is possible only as the remembered event recedes in time, because all these operations of indirect verification take time to perform. In general, we check against error in our recollection by exploiting the involvement of the recollection with other recollections. But these involvements grew in time. The naked event, as it first occurred, had no involvements because it had no time to grow any, and no check can be made on it. In other words, there is no second method of getting to the terminus. The notion of error, which is universally applicable to the events of ordinary experience, is not applicable to the starkly simple things on the limit of introspection, such as the perception of the flash of a firefly on a summer evening. This can only be accepted. Where there is no possibility of verification there can be no error, and "truth" becomes meaningless. As it first occurs, introspectional experience is unlike ordinary experience — it transforms itself into ordinary experience as it recedes in time and grows an involvement of memory. The "reality" of the public world is something that emerges with the passage of time as the elemental things of the introspectional world intertwine.

In the light of all this it is particularly obvious that the ordinary concept of the past does not apply at the limits of introspection. Ordinarily events of the past are conceived as having an autonomous existence, which persist through all future time. What meaning can we ascribe to the existence of a past event at the limit of introspection if its occurrence cannot even be verified? Here it seems to me are some of the things which, accepting the suggestion of quantum theory, we may have missed on the scale of everyday experience. I have expanded this idea in an article, entitled "Error, Quantum Theory and the Observer," in the volume in honor of Arthur F. Bentley, entitled *Life, Language, Law,* published by the Antioch Press, 1957.

On reflection it is not surprising that there should be a difference between the two worlds. Every electrical engineer knows that there is a qualitative difference between transient and steady-state phenomena.

What significance should be attached to the observation that the world of introspection is qualitatively different from the public world? The uncompromising behaviorist or any others convinced of the possibility and desirability of getting everything onto a completely public basis will doubtless see only minor significance. They will think of introspectional experience as only one aspect of events which in the present state of technique are accessible to only one person, but which someday may become completely public by developments like those suggested by the thesis of the sufficiency of atomic analysis. This attitude is doubtless fortified by the conviction that introspection is incapable of giving a complete account of all that is of present interest to the psychologist. This conviction is strengthened further by the lesson of psychoanalysis that there are processes occurring in the brain or nervous system which do not ordinarily get into consciousness at all, but which can be brought up to the level of consciousness by appropriate techniques. The same conclusion is forced by a calculation of the fantastic richness of the possible number of states of the brain allowed by the combinations of its 10^{10} neurones compared with the relative poverty of conscious experience, limited by the psychological present with its duration of 0.01 second.

It seems to me that it must be granted that there is much truth in these contentions of the behaviorist and others like him. But I think that any thoughtful behaviorist would admit that in the present state of technique he is hopelessly far from being able to make all the events of any introspectional report publicly accessible. Until that day comes, the question is what present tactics should be followed. One possible tactics is to ignore introspectional report as a subject for investigation by psychologists. This is a perfectly possible course of action. It may well be that the working psychologist is convinced on the basis of his experience that introspection is not a very promising tool and that there are other problems which can be attacked instrumentally in various ways which offer much greater prospects of immediate return. In this case such a psychologist would be foolish to waste his time with introspection. But it seems to me that if introspection is to be excluded it should be on some such basis, not as a matter of general principle. For introspectional report is, by the very fact of being a report, public, and, as such, proper subject for psychological inquiry. In fact, it is to some extent a necessary subject for inquiry, for the task of the psychologist is not completed until he has accounted for that aspect of behavior which is introspectional report. It is not meet that an outsider like me should question the judgment of the psychologist that he can at present spend his time more profitably on more public matters than introspectional report, but as a physicist I may be permitted to express a mild surprise that this should apparently be made so much a matter of principle by the behaviorist, or that any method should be discarded which might conceivably help in unraveling the incredibly complicated maze of present psychological phenomena. I cannot believe that the behaviorist can at present set up a correlation between all the items of introspectional report and the observable features in other behavior. It would in fact seem that there are many at present inaccessible goings on in the nervous system the existence of which the psychologist would not even suspect if it were not for verbal introspectional report. May not some of these be of significance? There is, for example, the state of tension into which I place myself when I try to remember a name, or the process by which I assure myself that the name which eventually presents itself is the one I wanted. Surely there are many other features of brain functioning which are beyond the capacities of the behaviorist at present, such as the mechanism of memory. It may be that eventually the solution of all these at present so vexing questions will be found in purely behavioristic and possibly molecular if not atomic terms, but we are certainly so far from it at present that it seems to me almost arrogant to refuse to accept any help which might be given by introspection.

Introspection and the use of language in the introspectional mode need be no deterrent to a program of getting everything onto a public atomic basis as rapidly and completely as possible. In fact it may be suggestive in carrying out such a program. Suppose, for example, that in applying the introspectional microscope in the simple form now available to experiences on the limit of introspection I ask myself whether I ever have an experience of such elemental simplicity that it does not contain a recognizable component of perception. For example, am I ever aware of the flash of a firefly on a summer evening without at the same time being aware that it is a flash of *light*? Awareness that the flash is light is what I call perception. Now in attempting to imagine what the atomic description of perception involves I think it very plausible to suppose that the perception must involve some aspect of the diffusion into the surrounding structure of the brain of an excitation which was initiated at some center stimulated by an external sense organ. This "center" may be in n-dimensional space, rather than ordinary 3-dimensional space. If perception and awareness are thus always coupled, it follows that awareness is also a function of brain activity diffused through a region and not sharply localized. Such an expectation might easily be of some assistance in searching for the specific atomic or neuronic correlate of awareness or consciousness.

Until the psychological millennium arrives it thus seems to me that introspectional report has to be admitted as a proper subject for psychological study, although we may reserve judgment whether it is a fruitful topic. Once the behaviorist has admitted that introspectional report is a proper subject for psychological study he must also admit, I believe, that in particular the report of his own introspectionings is a proper topic. If one is to report his own introspectionings one has to decide how best to verbalize them. I personally find the operational dichotomy so sharp between my own introspectings and those of my fellows that I want to use a special vocabulary in reporting my own introspectings. In particular, I want to use such words as "conscious", "feelings", "sensations", and "purposes". When I use these words I incidentally give notice to my neighbor that I am referring to my own introspectings. Now the confirmed behaviorist may not attach the significance to the operational dichotomy that I do, but I believe that he is at least capable of playing my game and that I have set up no serious barrier to communication by insisting on playing my game. I believe that he is capable of playing my game because I do not believe that any intelligent individual can live in society and not discover how to interpret these words, which are continually used by everyone in their private mode. If he will play my game, then he too may use the private words "conscious", and so forth, and whenever I hear him use these words I am thereby informed that he is referring to his own introspectional experience. We have already seen that communication between individuals who each uses a special vocabulary for his own introspectings is made possible by the operation of projection.

We now set ourselves to examine some of the assumptions back of this universal operation of projection. Such an examination would be necessary whether or not we accept the convention to use certain words only in the introspectional mode. When we project, we understand the action of our fellow by imagining ourselves in his place. This involves the assumption that we and our fellow are alike. Of course we realize that we are not exactly like our fellow in all respects, but we believe that we are sufficiently alike for most practical purposes.

THE LOGIC OF AGREEMENT

To what extent has the fundamental assumption of the method of projection, that we are all alike except for small corrections, been even subjected to analysis? The validity of the assumption is certainly basic to social living together. In certain broad fields of activity the validity and the workability of the assumption is not open to question. Consensus is obtainable under a great variety of circumstances. In particular, consensus is obtainable in reporting the factual situations of daily life and also with regard to the simpler of the more complicated situations in which an element of ratiocination is superposed on the factual. Agreement is possible with regard to the operations and results of arithmetic and logic, no matter what the cultural history of the individual, provided only that he is mentally competent and has been subjected to a suitable process of education.

"Mentally competent" is an important and, it seems to me, a significant qualification in this situation. Many people are not intellectually capable of appreciating the issues involved in the more complicated parts of logic or mathematics. Furthermore, it is to be remembered that every human being is subject to intellectual limitations.

A few years ago I had an opportunity to subject the assumption of the possibility of consensus to more critical examination than is usually possible. My appointment as a University Professor enabled me to conduct a seminar in the Department of Social Relations at Harvard on the topic "The Logic of Agreement", a title suggested, by the way, by President Conant. It was my expectation that a consistent and detailed use of operational analysis would provide a technique by which agreement could be reached with regard to at least the meanings of some of the more important terms of primarily social import. The membership of the seminar was limited to seven, most of them working for the Ph.D. degree, selected after personal interviews, as being most likely to contribute. The fields of primary interest of the participants were: engineering, government, social philosophy, journalism, social anthropology, international relations, and philosophy. The meetings of the seminar were two and one-half hours in duration, once a week, during the spring term. The discussion was centered around a few concepts of social importance, such as "community", "morality", "justification", and "rights". We attempted to analyze the meaning of these words in terms of explicitly formulated operations which all could accept. In case we could not come to agreement we tried to formulate the nature of the disagreement in terms that all could accept.

The one outstanding impression that I got from the experience was of the unfathomed complexity of the verbal background of each one of us and the fact that no two backgrounds were alike. After a situation had once been analyzed at length, consensus of a sort was usually not difficult to obtain, but the major difficulty was in being sure that the analysis had uncovered all the relevant considerations. The weakness of ostensive definition became apparent — even if I and my neighbor appear to be pointing at the same thing we cannot be sure that each of us is referring to the same aspect of the thing. The ostensive definition has to be checked in an unlimited range of conditions and certainty is not attainable in a finite number of steps.

In some cases even prolonged effort did not avail to secure agreement or to isolate the sources of disagreement. A particularly recalcitrant concept proved to be that of "society". After prolonged discussion most of the members were willing to say that society is no more than the individuals who compose it, in the sense that two societies would be indistinguishable in which the individual behaviors of all their members were indistinguishable. But this point of view was not acceptable to all the members in spite of their inability to formulate the reason for their disagreement in a way that could be understood by all the others. Another vivid impression was of the amount of intellectual baggage which most people carry around with them which is not necessary for their purposes, most of which has to be discarded when agreement is desired. Occam's razor increasingly appeared as an indispensable mental tool. Contrasted with this is the statement of modern communication engineers that a certain amount of redundancy in a communication code serves a useful purpose in neutralizing the effect of "noise" and increasing the probability of successful communication. The analogy is applicable only if the excess baggage in the thinking of different people is all of the same sort — this seems to be by no means always the case.

With regard to the operational method of attack I am, if possible, more convinced than ever of its value as a tool for the analysis of meanings, both of the words which I use and of the words which I hear you use. It is, however, very difficult to discover what is the actual operational structure of the meaning system of any individual at any fixed epoch. For the act of analysis itself modifies the ideas which the individual has of what is involved operationally in his use of words, so that at the end of the discussion the individual is seeing things and accepting operations of which he was not aware at the beginning. Neither does use of the tool of operational analysis put agreement on an almost automatic basis, as I had hoped. The situation revealed by detailed analysis is so complex and individuals differ so widely that agreement is to be expected, even with the aid of this powerful tool, only after long and serious effort. In particular, seven people is by far too large a group to permit a sufficiently detailed analysis of what each has in the back of his head to justify the expectation of agreement in the time available. Moderate success might be hoped for with only one other member, but even with one, I would never be sure that I had caught all the implications of his ostentions. The situation almost demands a control of education. With a common background in childhood of an operational analysis of meanings, one might perhaps hope to get agreement in situations in which there is a background of sufficiently common experience. It appears that the *verbal* background and experiences of different people in our culture differ much more than their "objective" experiences. Especially do people differ in the implications which they read into any specific verbal form. This makes consensus, which is primarily a verbal matter, particularly difficult to achieve.

I believe that in society as at present constituted the possibility of consensus, except with respect to the simplest situations and as a first approximation, is a mirage. There is no such thing as true consensus, and any ostensible reality supposed to be revealed by the consensus does not exist. To my mind this only underlines the importance of the individual and the importance of understanding the relations of individuals to each other. It also underlines the necessity of making my own report in the first person.

THE ISSUE OF SOLIPSISM

To conclude this chapter I would like to examine the significance of the resistance which I have no doubt has been felt by the vast majority of my readers against accepting the fundamental point of view of this book. This resistance probably began with my first statement that it is necessary to get everything into the first person singular and has continued with my insistence on the unavoidably dichotomous nature of the private world of every one of us. The world which is thus presented is in the first place a pluralistic world and the numerical measure of the pluralism is the number of individuals (it has been said that there would be as many sciences as scientists), and in the second place the individual world of each of us appears as dual because of the dichotomy of the operations with which I deal with myself and my fellows. That this picture of the world would be found uncongenial appears almost inevitable when it is reflected that perhaps the one most sweeping view which the history of thought in the West has been leading up to in the last 2000 years is that the world is one. The importance of this view and its practical justification on the scale of everyday life require no argument. But to accept it and its implications in all its stark simplicity with unhumorous seriousness seems to me to betray simply bad observation of the way things are. There *has* to be a plurality of sorts, because there are many people, and there *has* to be a dichotomy of sorts because my relationship to myself is unlike my relation to everything else. The question is: how best to get this plurality and this dichotomy into my picture of the world. It seems to me that no thinking person, once his eyes have been opened, can fail to see that there is a problem here. He may of course hold that it is not an important problem and that the conventional ways of dealing with the situations, ways which have evolved under long-continued social pressure, are good enough. This is a matter of opinion — my own conviction is that the world has become so complex that the traditional methods are no longer good enough.

It has been my experience that my point of view is very likely to be damned with the epithet "solipsism". What solipsism is in the popular view may be formulated in the statement: "Only I exist and the external world is my construction". This is usually felt to be so absurd as to constitute its own refutation. Apparently, however, the implications for the professional philosopher need not be so stark or so crass as this. Thus, in a review of my *Reflections of a Physicist,* in *Science* for June 1, 1956, Professor André Mercier writes: "In reading this book I was struck by one point which I had not realized before, namely that the philosophical genre described as solipsism is really possible. Bridgman seems to me a genuine representative of that way of thought, and I respect him all the more, for his argument makes very good sense and is never offered for the sake of the argument alone, as so often happens in conventional philosophical dispute. Yet a position like this is a rare thing, and I doubt whether it has any future". In spite of enlightened sentiments like this I think it will be very hard to shake off the damning implications of the word "solipsism", and I wish that another more explicit word could be found for a point of view which is solipsistic only to the extent of feeling the need for an analysis of what one means when, on the private level, one talks about the public or the external world.

Although the world which presents itself when I view everything from myself as center has pluralistic aspects, I think this is an innocuous pluralism and one which is unavoidable in a world in which there are many individuals. On the other hand, if one is reconciled to the inevitability of describing the world from himself as center, a unity is thereby automatically restored to the world, the unity conferred by the necessity of seeing everything from a single origin. This is not the illusory unity which we formerly thought we had, but is the only unity we can use, the only unity we need, and the only unity possible in the light of the way things are.

V I I

SOCIAL IMPLICATIONS

The problem is twofold — to understand society and to decide on my own course of action in a social environment. The problem of understanding society is not different in kind from any other problem of understanding. It may be pursued in the abstract for its purely intellectual interest in the same spirit as the pure scientist pursues his subject, or it may be pursued as does the applied physicist or the engineer primarily because of the applications that may be made of the understanding. There is no sharp dividing line between the two approaches any more than there is for the scientist. Any concrete action in the social environment will depend to a greater or less extent on abstract understanding of the nature of society.

One may be interested in the abstract problem of understanding society without being interested in the problem in its greatest generality, as an anthropologist or sociologist might be. In particular, one's interest may be the special society of which he happens to be a member; this will be our interest here. In spite of the fact that the social problem which we shall encounter here is not of the greatest generality, it is by far more complex than any that we have considered hitherto. The complexities arise because we are dealing with many people interacting on each other. Here more than ever do we have to abandon the impersonal objective approach which we have found increasingly inapplicable in the progression from logic through mathematics and physics to psychology. Even more than in psychology is it difficult to make situations repeat or to execute controlled experiments. Here is a field where truly "emergent" properties occur, in the sense that when an individual becomes a member of a group he will act in ways which could not have been anticipated from an exhaustive knowledge of his behavior in an environment containing not more than one other individual. New questions arise in a social environment, such as questions of morals. When I consider the society of which I am a member, the situation becomes from one point of view even more complicated than it is in the generalized society of the anthropologist, for in the society of which I am a member I have to consider not only the public things, but also the private things. The more complicated a situation becomes, the more important is it that the description, with which any attempt at understanding must begin, reproduce as faithfully as possible what actually happens. It is for this reason that I regard a first person approach to the problem of present-day society as especially important. Whether it is a necessary approach or not we need not argue. I shall hope to show that it is at least a possible and natural approach, and that anyone can make it. The fact that this approach is possible and fruitful in such a complicated situation is to me presumptive evidence that it is, to say the least, not an incorrect approach, because the inadequacy of an incorrect approach may be expected to show more strikingly in a more complex situation.

SOCIETY THE SUM OF ITS INDIVIDUALS

It is becoming increasingly the fashion in many quarters to insist on the priority of society over the individual. Thus it is often said that the individual comes to think of himself as a person only after he has come to recognize the individuality of the people around him. His own "self" is thus a sort of construction or invention and projection inward of external "reality". The point of view is sometimes carried so far, as by Trigant Burrow and by Hans Syz in his expositions of Burrow's point of view,[1] that it results in the claim that modern man is in large measure suffering from a neurosis because the individual thinks of himself instead of society as the ultimate unit and reality. To me this is an exact inversion of the way things are. So far as modern man suffers from a neurosis I would say that it is because he does not sufficiently see things and their meanings in terms of what happens to *him*, but tries too much to get along with a dualistic point of view in which society or the state is conceived as a self-existent thing at least coordinate with the individuals who compose it. The psychologist may be right in his thesis that my idea of myself as a person came after experience with other people around me. Perhaps it is even conceivable that I did not know what my own pain was until I had observed avoidance reactions in others. The thesis of the psychologist seems most plausible when applied to language. I would be particularly willing to admit that language is a social development, and that if I had not experienced the language of my mother and father or my other fellows I would probably not be a talking animal at all. But it seems to me that all such considerations are more or less irrelevant. What matters is where I am now, not how I got here. The language which I acquired from my fellows has become the most important tool of my private thought — the overwhelmingly major part of my verbal activity is talking to myself, and even when my thinking is not consciously articulated verbally, as it often is not, the words are still pretty near the surface. The verbal tool of thought which society gave me has become entirely my own. I find that it has certain properties which limit me in my mental activities. Severe limitations are, for example, imposed by the requirement that my verbalizations have meaning.

The only rational justification that I can now find for saying that my fellows are people just like me is that I can give a behavioristic account of them which is similar in high degree to the behavioristic account which I give of myself. However I got that way, it seems to be a simple fact of observation that I now understand my fellows in terms of myself rather than myself in terms of my fellows. My fellow, I believe, understands me and his fellows in the same way. Society is a group of individuals, each thinking of the others in this way. I believe that the first person approach receives its most important application, and failure to adopt the approach has the most serious consequences, in a social setting.

The starting point in our social inquiry, as in any other discipline, must be pure description. Furthermore, it is our thesis that this description must be in operational terms — in terms of what happens. Now it seems obvious to me, and only to be said to be accepted, that if we have a complete description of the behavior of every individual in a society, meaning by "complete description" a description of all the overt behavior that is observable, we have at the same time a complete description of the society. There is nothing more to give. Two societies would be indistinguishable by me in which the behavior of all the individuals was the same.

The point of view that society is no more than the sum total of all the individuals who compose it, which seems so obvious to me, has proved inacceptable to some people, although most accept it as tautological when they see the issue. It will be remembered that this provided a topic for lively discussion in my seminar "The Logic of Agreement", and universal agreement was not attained. I think that what the nonacceptors have in the back of their heads is an idea about emergence of qualities in a group. The thesis that society can be described in terms of its individuals has, however, nothing to do with emergence. In saying this, no one is saying that when an individual finds himself in an environment with other individuals new traits in his behavior do not appear which could not have been predicted from his behavior in isolation — this may or may not be the case, but it has no effect on the thesis. It seems to me that a nonacceptor who bases his objection on some consideration such as this can only join the ranks of the acceptors when he sees the issue. But it must be confessed that there are other sorts of nonacceptors. Some of these see in society some sort of superthing existing in its own right. The personification of the state by many German political philosophers at the beginning of World War I is an example. This, it seems to me, is sheer metaphysics and fuzzy thinking, and with regret I shall have to renounce the hope of convincing such people.

It must be admitted, nevertheless, that to talk of the "state" or of "society" constitutes an intellectual invention of a sort which under other circumstances may be of the greatest utility. It often affects a most important intellectual economy, when one is dealing with a system which has some characteristic and complicated method of functioning, to invent a single name for the whole complex and to forget the details. When we talk about the state or society in this way we are employing a simplification of this sort, but I think that in this special case we often purchase the intellectual convenience at too high a price. The price we pay is to forget the detailed mechanism by which results are brought about in any specific situation. One of the most important things to remember if we hope to understand the functioning of society is that no particular situation can come to pass, no matter how desirable on general principles nor how universally acceptable, unless there is some specific mechanism by which the succession of detailed steps necessary for its realization can occur. In society the detailed steps are the actions of the individuals who compose the society. We are only too likely to lose sight of this when we attempt to simplify our thinking by interjecting some grandiose intermediate construction, such as the state, or the government, or the party. In such an atmosphere we demand impossibilities and forget possibilities and legitimate responsibilities.

It is a matter of observation that in a society there are individuals. The individuals are always "there", whatever the organization into which they may combine, or whatever their new modes of function in virtue of their organization. The situation is thus essentially different from the elementary situations of wave mechanics. The outer shell of the atom, the part that is responsible for its chemical activity, is not composed of individual electrons in the sense that the behavior of the entire shell can be described in terms of the behavior of the individual electrons. The behavior of society, on the other hand, can be described in terms of the behavior of the individuals. When dealing with society we are on the completely classical level of identifiability and individuality.

The raw material for a description of society is thus a complete description of the behavior of the component individuals. It follows that society could be completely understood if the behavior of the component individuals could be completely understood. For most practical purposes, however, we are not interested in the complete story, but are satisfied with an understanding of only some aspects of the total complex, depending on our purposes and our interests. Some of the most important aspects under which we are usually satisfied to consider the aggregate activities of a society are the economic, legal, political, and institutional, including in the latter the religious. In fact the aspects of group activity in which we are usually interested are so completely covered under these heads that we may be inclined to think of society exclusively in these terms. And associated with our particular interest, economic, political, or whatnot, there are specialized techniques, which make the individual recede into the background. The individual is, however, always there and can be uncovered if necessary.

It being the case that a complete description of all its individuals determines a society, it ought to be possible for me in our own society, in which different individuals have a high degree of equality, to discover many of the most important features which characterize our society by analyzing only my own relations to it. If the operation of projection is valid, then I may hope that my analysis will also provide, at least to a first approximation, a basis of understanding by my fellow. I cannot hope, however, that my analysis will be the same in all particulars as that of my fellow, or that the features which seem to me most interesting or important will appear in the same light to him. My emphasis will unavoidably be different from his.

In its broadest sense my society will include all my relations with other people. In some of these relations the social element, as commonly understood, will be more prominent than in others, and will accordingly be more in need of analysis. These relationships will vary in complexity; in general those relations which involve me with more than one other of my fellows will be more complicated than those in which only one other is involved. Among the latter are to be included such simple personal relations as affection or dislike, which for the purposes of this exposition I shall assume to be in need of little or no analysis. It is the more complicated group relations which will be of chief interest here.

In our analysis we shall be concerned with my present society, as I now find it as a mature man, and shall not be concerned with the history of the growth of my realization of these relationships, beginning doubtless with my relations to my mother in infancy.

Society is part of my total environment. Adaptation to society is one of the conditions of survival or of any other sort of success, no less than is adaptation to the nonsocial features of my environment. Some of the aspects of the social environment are purely physical in nature and are correlated with the fact that the individuals who compose society have physical bodies. There is no sharp line dividing my relations to my total environment into a personal part, depending on the fact that my fellows are people, and a purely physical part, including among other things the consequences of the possession of material bodies by my fellows. Sometimes it is the latter which preponderate. A man caught in a theater fire and trying to force his way to the nearest exit experiences almost exclusively the purely physical aspects of society. The situation for him is not much different from trying to extricate himself from the rushing earth of a cave-in.

The passive inertness of a group of human beings, as in a theater fire, is perhaps the simplest manifestation of a social relation which depends on the purely physical aspect of my fellows. This sort of relation is not often encountered in pure form, and we would not usually think of things of this sort as social phenomena. But there is a more active manifestation of the physical nature of my fellows which does enter into my social relations and is, I think, of much more sweeping significance than is usually appreciated. One of the earliest things I find is that with the help of my neighbor I can accomplish tasks which are beyond my own unaided strength. Two of us can move the rock which I could not move alone, and 40,000 of us can construct a great pyramid. Not only can I lift a weight with the help of John which I could not manage alone, but John and I can club together and force Peter to make me concessions which I could not exact from him by myself. This cuts both ways, for I know to my cost that John and Peter can club together to force me to act contrary to my wishes.

SOCIETY THE ARENA OF NEW FORCES

Society is the arena of new forces which do not appear so long as people function as individuals. Some of these forces are purely physical and can be measured in purely physical terms as so many pounds, as when 40,000 slaves pull on the rope that places a block of stone on a pyramid. But the more important forces are not "forces" at all in the technical sense, but are the forces which are involved in the control of people by other people. It is the questions set by the necessity for controlling this kind of force that provide the most important social questions today. This sort of force may perhaps be better described as a "compulsion" rather than as a force in the technical sense.

In society as now constructed the question of force or compulsion does not often actively obtrude itself, for most of us do not spend much time in courts of law or in arguing with policemen. But always in the background the potentiality is there, and all my relations to society are subject to the implications of the fact that society can, whenever it wishes, exercise irresistible physical force on me. All my relations to society and my programs for social action cannot avoid the implications of this fact, and any analysis of the social scene which gives less than fundamental significance to this factor can, it seems to me, be only superficial.

The mechanism by which I unite with some of my fellows against others of them may be conventionalized and ameliorated — in a modern democracy this often takes the form of the ballot box — but in spite of the amenities, the force back of the ballot box cannot be hidden. Whether I like it or not, in a modern democracy I find myself in the position of exerting force on my neighbors, either overtly by the ballot box or less obviously through such instruments as public opinion. For me, in my capacity as a member of society, one of the most pressing questions becomes to discover what principles I can accept to guide me in my unavoidable exercise of force on my neighbor. Principles of some sort I must find, if for no other reason than to expedite my decisions in the give and take of everyday life. Here decisions must often be made quickly, for reasons varying from acute physical emergency to the active impatience of my neighbor at having to wait for me to make up my mind. Not only does my neighbor demand that I make up my mind, but he demands a certain consistency in my actions, which will enable him to know what to expect, and this implies some sort of principle on my part.

It will pay to stop a bit to examine the nature of the field of force or compulsion associated with society. We need not pause for the purely physical forces, technically measurable in physical terms, except to remark that even these forces are exerted by individuals in the aggregate or else through the instrumentality of some one individual who may throw a switch or pull a trigger. We shall be more concerned with the more indirect methods of compulsion. One of the most universal of such methods is through the intermediary of man-made law. It is seldom that the compulsion exerted by man-made law is the compulsion of the direct exercise of superior physical force, but it is usually indirect, through the medium of punishment. Almost never is a man-made law enforced by the actual physical prevention of its violation. If an individual violates a law, then society punishes him. Such punishment does not wipe out the fact of violation, something that even society with its potentiality for overwhelming force cannot accomplish. Punishment does, however, serve the purpose of making a repetition of the violation less probable. Punishment constitutes an invention, the importance of which for the functioning of society requires no argument. However, it did not need a high order of intellectual ability to invent punishment, and even many of the higher animals punish their young. In application, it serves a double purpose:

the rational purpose of making less likely a repetition of the prohibited action, and the irrational purpose of relieving the outraged feelings of the people whose prohibition has been disregarded. In fact, for many people the irrational aspect seems to be the more important. It would appear that animals share this irrational aspect with human beings. Punishment for the violation of man-made law obviously does not have the inevitability associated with the laws of nature. The difference is so extreme that it is even not proper to speak of a "violation" of a law of nature. The law of gravitation is always on the job, ready to catch us whenever we jump out of a window, and it may not be violated. But any individual may, if he wishes, violate most man-made laws. Man-made law is ultimately enforced by individuals, and, if some individual is not present to enforce it, nothing happens. Everybody knows this who has driven through a traffic light on a Sunday morning. In general, society has to find an individual or individuals to enforce the law by imposing punishment for its violation. If such individuals cannot be found, the law will not be enforced. In some cases the act of enforcement may be intrinsically disagreeable for the normal individual, as in imposing capital punishment. In this case society has to offer special rewards to the individual who enforces the law. If the job of enforcement is too repulsive or too offensive to public opinion, as in the imposition of torture, then the law presently gets modified because it cannot be enforced. Except for special situations of this kind it is fortunate that in our society the ordinary job of law enforcement is so obviously for the advantage of nearly everyone that the agents of enforcement are not looked down upon, but may even have a certain prestige.

Not only does the law have to be enforced in the last analysis by the acts of individuals, but it is also created by the acts of individuals — either by an absolute monarch by his personal fiat, or by a group of individuals cooperatively in a legislature or equivalent body. Or the set-up may be such that the law is effectively made by some judge when he hands down a decision. In a modern democracy, nearly every individual in it, including myself, takes some indirect part in the law-making process. We will return later to a discussion of what this means for the individual.

Every man-made law is subject to limitations imposed by the nature of things. Not even 175,000,000 people can, for example, enforce a law that every individual shall enjoy physical comfort if there is not enough food to go around. Many people, however, do not recognize limitations of this sort and think that any undesirable situation can be remedied by the passage of a suitable law. There is a historical example in the passage by some Mid-western state in the middle of the last century of a law to the effect that henceforth the circumference of a circle should be three times the diameter instead of the mathematical and inconvenient pi times the diameter. A somewhat similar attitude is shown in the laws of a number of states which make it a crime to commit suicide. Not even 175,000,000 people can do anything to a man after he is dead.

At present there seems to be a growing sentiment among a number of sensitive people that punishment is always unjustified and should not be used as a social instrument. This sentiment is fortified by the implication of psychoanalysis that every detailed act of every individual is fully determined by factors over which the individual has no control. In this context the problem of whether to punish or not becomes a rather special subcase of the much more general problem of reconciling two patently inconsistent points of view, that of determinism and free will. It is obviously of the greatest importance to find a practical solution of this problem; otherwise we become the victims of a cancerous confusion, oscillating between the impulse to punish and not to punish.

It seems to me that we have to recognize clearly that there are here two levels of operation. There is the level of daily social life, that is, the level of free will, and there is the deterministic level. The deterministic level is, in particular, primarily the level of scientific operation. It is overwhelmingly successful on the inanimate material level, except for quantum phenomena, is less successful but still the best we have on the biological level, and on the social level has little more than the status of a program to direct action, about which we can say little more at present than that there is nothing in sight to indicate that it is a logically impossible program.

On the level of daily life and free will our great problem is to devise methods of dealing with situations in which we do not control or predict. It is a mere statement of fact that there are situations in which we make no attempt at control or prediction, and in which we disregard any ultimate possibility of such control. Such situations occur predominantly in dealing with organisms. In particular, no one of us can find either in his own consciousness or outside it factors which enable him to predict his own future behavior. We develop a language to handle this situation, in which our inability to foresee the future of ourselves or our fellows is reflected in the concept of free will, and we further develop a whole related vocabulary for situations in which we make no attempt at control or prediction. This vocabulary we apply to situations involving both ourselves and our fellows.

There is and can be no sharp dividing line between the vocabulary of determinism and that of daily life. Use of the vocabulary of daily life is an art which people acquire with varying degrees of success.

It seems to me that much of the current unwillingness to use the instrument of punishment, under conditions which would be acceptable to an enlightened social opinion, as an instrument for modifying behavior (not as an instrument of retribution or expiation, which to me is senseless and outrageous) stems from a doctrinaire insistence that our verbal edifice be a single logically consistent unit, recognizing only one level of operation. It seems to me obvious that "free will" and the "determinism" which makes questionable the justification of punishment are concepts which have to be on two different verbal levels. It is in the nature of things impossible to erect a single consistent verbal structure that is logically watertight in all respects. To act as if we could is self-defeating. For by what logic can the man who argues that punishment is unjustified because of determinism expect his arguments to affect the actions of his opponent when both his argument and the response to it were already rigidly predetermined? Pushed to its limit it can lead only to social catastrophe.

At present the only technique we have for dealing with our fellows is to say that they are similar to the sort of creature that we are ourselves. We disregard determinism when dealing with ourselves; we have to disregard it also, within reason, in our everyday contacts with our fellows.

The discussion above does not imply taking a position with regard to the question whether punishment is the most effective method of securing socially desirable behavior — this is an entirely different question.

The field of force or compulsion of society is exerted on individuals. How does the individual react? In particular, how do I react? There are two aspects to the way I react. There are the things I do and say, which are public for all to see and know, and there are the things I think but do not say, which are private. We have seen that with present psychological techniques only I can know what I am "really" thinking and feeling. Because the relations of society to me are so often relations of compulsion, it seems to me that my private thoughts, insofar as they are concerned with my private attitude toward society, are of special importance — of greater importance, for example, than my private attitude toward the law of gravitation. It may be that I find myself so thoroughly in accord with the purposes obviously back of some behest of society that I accept it without reservation, and do all in my power to see that my fellows also obey the behest. My attitude toward theft and murder are of this kind — I am against them. This does not mean, however, that I accept the punishment which society imposes for murder, in many cases capital punishment, as the best way of dealing with the matter. But in many cases the behest of society reflects some opinion of the average man with which I am not in sympathy, or which I regard as positively incorrect. An example might be the Sunday laws or, in some states, the prohibition laws. What do I do in such a situation? If I disclose my real private attitude I may be letting myself in for a great deal of unpleasantness. Since I, as an individual, am possessed of a certain low animal cunning, it is highly unlikely that I will disclose my private attitude. I will do this only if I am possessed of a genuine missionary spirit and a certain humorless belief in the importance of my own point of view. In certain extreme situations it may be that my esteem for the superior validity of my own opinions is so high that I will, for example, cheerfully go to jail as a pacifist. But ordinarily I will outwardly conform, and you will not be able to tell what I really think. As I observe your actions I infer that at least some of you also would be able to talk about your own private attitude in the same words that I have just been using about mine. This is all that either you or I need in order to be able to handle the social situations as they present themselves. In spite of this, there have been, and probably still are, situations in which some of you apparently regard it as of supreme importance to know whether I am "really" accepting a behest of society or not, and you may resort to extreme measures to find out, as witnessed by the former use of torture in judicial proceedings. We have here a special case of the idea that my state of mind is something of the same nature as, for example, the state of the weather. In the previous chapter it appeared that "state of mind" is preponderantly private in character, and that we would do well to use it only in the introspectional mode.

The emotional response by the individual to the realization that society can exert overwhelming physical force on him is almost inevitably, it seems to me, to emphasize the fact that there are some things which overwhelming physical force cannot accomplish. Compulsion by society, even 175,000,000 people, is powerless to change my private attitude. Private acceptance cannot be compelled. A realization of this is part of the armory of self-respect of the individual. Society should *expect* the individual to react in this realization, and laws and social pressure should be administered with the expectation that this is a natural way for the individual to react, in fact, so natural that he *will* react in this way, given even the minimum amount of freedom. A private attitude may smoulder underground for a long time, only to burst forth into unexpected flame when the occasion is ripe. Any compulsive control of one man by another is subject to this hazard. Private attitudes are subject to modification by education but not by compulsion.

I suspect it was some aspect of the inability of society to force the attitude of acceptance upon the individual which some of the older philosophers had in mind when they talked about the autonomy of the "will".

THE PROBLEM OF MORALS

We return now to the practical problem which confronts me in my conscious attitude toward society, the problem of formulating principles which shall govern my general behavior. The problem of finding such principles is to a large extent the problem of morals. This means that, to that extent, the problem of morals presents itself only in a social context. However, there are some people who see in morals more than my relation to my fellow and who think of morals as having absolute implications. They are accordingly concerned with such questions as the "morality" of a man's relations to his God, and in fact some people may place the entire basis for morals on this level. Without prejudicing the question whether I could find any meaning for a treatment of morals on this level, I content myself to simply state that

I shall not here regard morals from this point of view at all, but shall concern myself wholly with an examination of what is implied in the relations of people to each other. I shall seek the basis for morals in the consequences of certain relations between people. Even the man who seeks the basis for morals in the wishes of God should be able to address himself to the problem of determining the consequences of people acting toward each other in various ways, so that there should be hindrance to communication here. I shall not attempt a more precise delimitation of what is to be understood by morals, and in fact I believe that no separation is possible from other aspects of mutual relationships. What for one society at one epoch may be a matter of morals for another society may be merely a matter of esthetics or good taste.

The relations to my neighbors which have moral aspects are of an almost inconceivable variety and range of complexity. There are, in the first place, the simple relations of myself to my individual fellows. Many of these have always characterized even the most primitive societies from before the dawn of history. There are, in addition, the relations of almost limitless complexity evolving in our modern industrial world with its new mechanisms of communication and interaction which make all inhabitants of the globe potential if not actual neighbors. This is the sort of relation which is often the background for the deliberations of the United Nations.

It is a historical fact that there is a close connection between morals and institutionalized religion, although there would seem to be no necessity for such an association. The reason doubtless is that almost always some extranatural sanction is sought for a code of morals, for which the reason, again, is doubtless that society finds it easier to impose a code which is generally believed to have such extranatural sanction. It is also a historical fact that there is no newly arisen important institutionalized religion — Mohammedanism is perhaps the last, and before that Christianity, now nearly 2000 years old. The result is that the moral codes associated with the great religions were not formulated in the light of any of the rapidly growing complexities of modern societies. In particular, Christian ethics did not recognize the existence of the problems of the mutual relations of people in modern democracies, in which each individual has a measurable share in determining the action of the society as a whole. The problem for the average individual at the beginning of the Christian era was entirely different from that of the average individual today. The average individual at that time was a slave, or at best the subject of an arbitrary tyranny, and misery was his lot. The problem of immediate concern to the average individual then was how to ameliorate his own misery and how to help his fellow ameliorate his. Christian ethics is primarily the ethics of partners in misery. A society like a modern democracy would have been unthinkable to Saint Paul. He could not, therefore, envisage the new moral problems that would arise in such a society, so that, to the extent that the ethical principles of Saint Paul are applicable to modern society, it is in large part just good fortune.

To me the most important new moral problem in a modern democracy is the ethics which should control me in my capacity as a member of a majority, actual or potential, in my exercise of compulsion on my neighbor. This is the most important social problem to the discussion of which we shall address ourselves. As a preliminary it will be necessary to analyze as explicitly as possible some of the moral principles which I might adopt in my relations to my neighbors.

It is not difficult for me to find what society expects of me — my mother told me not to lie or steal and the traffic cop tells me not to pass a red light. Whether I accept or reject a moral injunction of society is closely related to the values which I attach to certain intangibles. We have already discussed certain aspects of value in Chapter V. We have seen that my values have both a public and a private component. The private component is closely related to "acceptance", but the total situation covered by "value" is much more complicated than the "yes" or "no" situations covered by acceptance. Sometimes it is not clear even to me what my values are, and on occasion I have to find what they are by contrivance. It may even occur that you are a better anticipator of what my values will turn out to be than I am myself.

In general, my values are pretty nearly coextensive with what I feel to be "good" or with what I want or like. To find my values I may make verbal experiments on myself, asking myself whether this or that seems good to me. In thus experimenting with myself, "myself" plays just as objective an external role as when I conduct an experiment in the laboratory on an impersonal object, or as when I try to find out about you by questioning you or otherwise observing your behavior.

My report on what I find by questioning myself has as much factual connotation as any other report of a factual nature. It is by no means always obvious to me in advance what my factual report will be and my inquiry into my own values often results in discovery, just as truly as does exploration in the laboratory. I try to give some account to myself of the values which I thus find, and often I can find in my past experience some feature which explains why I find this or that good or bad, as when, for example, I can trace my aversion to a certain flavor in ice cream to an unpleasant surfeit in childhood. I can see where many on my values came from — many came from exhortations by my teachers in childhood, and many came from the mores of my society in conjunction with my desire that my fellows should think well of me.

The strength of the assurance with which I can say that a certain thing is good or likable may vary over a wide range, and it may become so weak as to betoken a matter of indifference. Some of my more indifferent or weaker values may change sign under varying external circumstances, as when I find the draft from the window pleasant if I am heated after exercise, or unpleasant and to be avoided when I am cooled off. My values may sometimes be a source of pride and a feeling of superiority, as when I pride myself on my discriminating taste in literature. On the other hand, I may be ashamed of some of my values and conceal them and perhaps wish that I did not feel them. It is a matter of observation that often a resented value presently fades away. For values do change with time, and often they may be consciously manipulated to grow or wither away, although at a given instant, now, in this present, my values are as I find them, completely factual and uncontrollable.

The degree of my emotional involvement with my values varies greatly with the nature of the value. The quality of this emotional involvement also varies and sometimes is of the kind that invites use of the word "ought" or "duty". These words have a compulsive implication. The feelings that accompany them are vague and difficult to make precise — they seem to occur almost exclusively in connection with situations in which I am in interrelation with my fellows. They are, nevertheless, essentially private words. "Ought" is a feeling which *I* have and there is no method by which you can be sure that I am having it. It follows that no man may tell me my duty, although telling other people their duty is the favorite indoor sport of many, and society as at present constituted relies on this as a cement to secure stability. As I grow older I am aware of a gradual change in my attitude toward moral questions. I think less and less in terms of "ought" and "duty", and in fact now hardly use these words at all in deciding what to do. Instead of asking myself whether I ought to do this or that, I am much more likely to ask myself what will happen if I do this or that. I suspect that perhaps I never did use "ought" and "duty" so much as many of my neighbors, perhaps because in youth I did not accept the pronouncements of my teachers so uncritically as did many of my fellows. These words acquire much of their meaning in a pedagogical context.

We have said that values may change with time and be self-consciously modified. The most potent instrument for modifying values is an analysis of the consequences of acting in accord with this or that value. The consequences also have values, which may perhaps be inconsistent with the initial values. In such a case, some sort of compromise is demanded, which will result in some modification of the initial and perhaps also of the final values. There is, however, no compelling reason why values should be mutually consistent — a value system is in this respect not like a system of logic or mathematics. The reason is that the inconsistency does not enter in the same way. It is just as impossible that I should at the same time desire to please my sister and desire not to please her as it is impossible in logic that we should simultaneously have A and not A. But it is not impossible that I should at the same time desire to please my sister and desire to please my brother, although what pleases one may displease the other. Nevertheless, a value system with internal inconsistencies of this sort leads to continuous acting at cross-purposes and to frustration, and most people have enough intellectual integrity to desire as self-consistent a value system as attainable. Whence the value system may be purged by an analysis of all the consequences.

Among the consequences of my action the effect on my fellow plays a very important part, not only because of the constant possibility that my fellow may be stimulated to use force on me, but often because of the purely disinterested pleasure which I feel in securing the approval of my fellow. Whatever my reasons, it is to be expected that my actions will produce reactions in my fellow. Sometimes he reacts by deliberately attempting to modify my value system. Usually, however, in his desire to get me to act in the way he would like, he is not so subtle as to try to alter my value system, but his attack takes the cruder form of the categorical statement that I "ought" to do this or that, or that this or that is my "duty". It is not very clear what my neighbor means when he tells me what is my duty, particularly in view of my recognition that this is a private word. The most reasonable meaning I can find is that he means that if he were in my place he would feel that it was his duty to act in the way which he recommends to me. In fact, this is all that he logically *can* mean, if these are private words. And if I venture to tell my neighbor what is his duty, which sometimes I may do in moments of forgetfulness, all that I can mean is that I would feel it to be my duty if I were in his place. But I suspect that my neighbor does not usually subscribe to my thesis that "ought" and "duty" are private words, but he wants to give them some absolute meaning and believes that there are principles of right or wrong, eternal in the heavens, that determine duty and can be discovered by anyone by the appropriate method. This method may perhaps turn out to be mystical or supernatural, with religious connotations. This sort of point of view in my neighbor to me simply does not make sense, but it is incontestable that society as at present constituted does think along these lines.

It would be overly optimistic for me to expect that I could persuade my average fellow that his view of "ought" and "duty" does not make sense, but it need not be hopeless to get him to see that considerations of ought and duty are not *necessary* in establishing an acceptable value system, and that if we can get along without them we had better do so simply as a matter of good intellectual technique. I personally do not see what else I need to consider in establishing a value system than all the conceivable consequences of acting according to those values, nor do I see why I should not base my acceptance on the best compromise between all the consequences. This being the case for myself, I cannot see why you need demand anything more in setting up and criticizing your value system.

Always at the end of such an analysis, after all the consequences have been dragged into the limelight, there will be the decision whether the consequences are desirable or not. Here I think we are to a certain extent powerless and have to take things as they come. Whether I regard a certain consequence as desirable or not depends on the sort of creature I am, which is as much a fact as any other sort of fact in the present. Finding what sort of consequences appear desirable to me is one method of finding what sort of creature I am. It is true that I may be able to modify what at some future time will appear desirable to you or to me, but in the present the only attitude is acceptance of the facts as they now are. This does not mean at all that we should not attempt to analyze "desirability" or try to formulate and agree upon what constitutes desirability. Such an analysis may well react on the desirability itself, for such an analysis is merely one way of finding some of the consequences.

What now are the features in the consequences of a code of conduct or system of values which I shall regard as desirable? There are two aspects — the code as it affects you and the code as it affects me. The consequences are by no means the same with regard to their desirability for me, so that my code could very well become a double code, one for you and another for me. However, if such turns out to be the case, it is not very likely that I will proclaim abroad that there is a difference. For I have enough practical experience with my neighbor to know that I shall not be very successful in urging on him a line of conduct that I am not willing to adopt for myself. The result is that this sort of thing does not get said out loud, and the code of conduct which I publicly proclaim is a single code, the same for me and for you. You say the same for the code formulated by you. Eventually, in any particular society at any specific epoch a single public code comes to dominate, a sort of average of all our codes. This fact gives a certain naturalness to the point of view that there is something absolute back of such a code. In fact, there is something unique back of such a code which to a certain extent determines it, independent of the particular culture, namely the traits which all human beings in all cultures have in common and which condition the things which any human being will find desirable. This lends a certain degree of predictability to any code originating in this way. From this point of view the attempts of anthropologists and humanists to find a universal basis for human morals have a justification in nowise tainted by metaphysics.

The logical possibility of a single public code and simultaneous private codes different for each individual does not appear, in practice, to lead to disaster, as might perhaps be expected. For I personally find that I take satisfaction in and find it desirable to impose on myself a private code very much like that which I am willing to help impose publicly on my fellow. Part of the reason for this is doubtless my realization, based on past social experience, that this will lead to a harmonious society, which is the kind of society I enjoy living in. Part is also doubtless the purely intellectual satisfaction of adopting a code which appeals to me as satisfying artistic canons of elegance and good taste. For it is simpler, and therefore intellectually more satisfying, to find a single code according to which both I and my fellow can live than to find two. This seems to be genuinely the case for me as I judge by introspection. It also seems to be the case for a sufficient number of my fellows so that our joint action can impose this sort of code as the common code of society. This is indeed fortunate, for if it were not true it is hard to see how a society would be possible in which there was any substantial amount of individual freedom. But it is also easy for me to see that there is no inevitable reason why there should not be some individuals who take such satisfaction in aggression and self-assertiveness that they find acceptable a code of conduct completely unsymmetrical with respect to themselves and their neighbors, and which permits them to do anything they can get away with, in spite of the consequences to others. So far as such individuals are rational and accept the line of thought with regard to morals outlined above, I shall *expect* them to act in accordance with such a code. Observation of society indicates that there are probably a large number of such atypical persons, although they are in a small enough minority comparatively to permit the normal majority to control them. The society that I would like is one willing to gamble that they are in a small enough minority to permit adequate majority control. It would appear, however, that many of my fellows are not sufficiently convinced that the actual composition of the human race is like this to permit them to make this gamble with any equanimity. These are the persons who demand and impose an extranatural sanction for morals, which it seems to me can be made workable only at the price of intellectual stultification. I do not know to what extent they find this stultification desirable or even are conscious of its presence — doubtless if they were forced to articulateness they would maintain that stultification is the lesser of two evils, the alternative evil being the destruction of the human race. I myself cannot regard the human race as of such supreme and absolute importance, a point of view which need not be so shocking now as it might have been 20 years ago, now that astronomers are talking seriously of the possibility that life occurs in billions of other places in the sidereal universe. I am willing to let the human race perish if its survival must be purchased at the price of not freely using its mind. I think I would maintain this attitude even if it should prove that the possession of a mind is, in the long run, logically inconsistent with the survival of the species that has it. Pagan satisfaction in a *Götterdämmerung* is to me understandable.

It is easy to express this attitude of mine in a common idiom, which nevertheless I do not accept. It is easy to say that those who demand an extrarational sanction for morals in order to secure the survival of the race do not have sufficient "faith" that the race is so constituted that rational survival is possible. I do not find in myself what appear to me to be the traditional attributes of a faith. My willingness to gamble that the race is so constituted more nearly expresses my attitude. Aspects of this question have already been discussed in Chapters IV and V in connection with "belief".

One objection to an extrarational sanction for morals by society is that every individual in it may, in a flash of insight, discover that it is not true. As a matter of fact, this flash of insight has not in the past occurred to a significant number of individuals. The insight is more likely to occur to individuals of intelligence, and among such individuals to those who have had a favorable background in opportunity for individual thought and not too much pressure from group opinion. It seems to me that with our increasing mastery of our material environment and opportunities for individual leisure and reflection the probability is increasing that more and more individuals will have this insight. This possibility presents an element of instability in present society. The result of a general realization that society has been imposing points of view with an eye more to its own advantage than to truth may be violent when it comes. Most of us have the potential for this insight as well as the reaction to it. I think many of us had this potential in childhood more strongly than now, but it has been trained out of us. I have vivid recollections of the strength of my early reaction when I was required to do something that seemed to me intrinsically unreasonable. On one occasion I was required by my teacher to say that I was *sorry* for sticking my tongue out at my neighbor. Here was something that no one was able to exact from me because of the way things are — I knew that being sorry is a private affair over which no one else has control. Of course, being intelligent, I conformed in the presence of superior force, but I retained my self-respect by despising my teacher for a fool. It will not be good when too many people despise society for a fool for trying to impose an extrarational sanction for morals.

A similar situation arises whenever there is failure to distinguish between the public and the private words. "Sorry" as used above could have meaning only in the private mode, but it was implied by society (that is, my teacher) that it was public. This sort of situation occurs very often. The child or adolescent when confronted by society with this sort of demand sees that something is wrong, although he may not formulate it explicitly, and reacts by nonacceptance but outward conformity in the presence of superior force. It may be that here is one of the sources of juvenile delinquency. The juvenile sees that society makes demands that do not make sense. He increasingly sees the fallacy in the tactics of conventional religion. He sees that the nature of law is not what it is said to be — the thing that counts for him is what he can get away with and he sees it demonstrated that techniques can be developed for getting away with it. It is only intelligent to react in the way that the delinquent does. The only way to save the situation is by education of the emotions and through such education to modify what will appear to the juvenile to be good.

The law in this country seems to offer a curious backhanded recognition of the situation in its guarantee, in the first article of the Bill of Rights, that an individual's private thoughts and beliefs should not be unduly invaded. An example of the opposite sort of thing is the eighteenth-century law in England making a belief in antitrinitarianism a criminal matter, a law which explains some of the otherwise incomprehensible actions of Sir Isaac Newton.[2] Now the proper reason that an individual's private thoughts and feelings should not be invaded by a judicial process imposed by society is not that the individual has a "right" to the possession of his private thoughts without molestation, but that it does not even make sense for society to talk about a man's private thoughts or beliefs. How can all of you together give factual status to my belief about trinitarianism? "Private thought" is one of the relational words, not a concrete objective thing. *I* may speak about my private thoughts, but you may not speak of them in the same sense. The only possible logically consistent attitude of all the individuals collectively who together constitute society toward the private life of its individuals is a behavioristic one. The words in a code of law should be used only in their public behavioristic mode. Not only does intellectual integrity demand this, but it is also demanded by the practical consideration that it is silly to make a law that cannot be enforced in the nature of things. It seems to me that much of our legal theory has to be reformulated and our laws recast in behavioristic terms.

The view of the nature of morals which I am urging here is one in which it seems to me everyone can take part, whatever his religious convictions. Everyone can analyze what will be the consequences of adopting this or that code of conduct, without implying extrarational sanctions for the code. It is easy for all to see that a society in which uncontrolled murder or theft are rampant is an undesirable society in which to live, whether or not a prohibition of murder and theft, inscribed on tablets of stone, has been brought down by a Moses from Mount Sinai. This means that all, or nearly all, people are able to agree on the "immorality" of murder and theft on this minimum basis. It is true that some people see an additional reason for the immorality of murder and theft in their belief that it is contrary to the wishes of God, but this additional reason need not upset the agreement reached on a minimum basis. The people who want to found morals in the wishes of God may object to calling a code reached on the minimum basis a "moral" code, but this is mostly a verbal matter, and we do not all need to use the same word to describe the code reached on minimum considerations in order to agree on the course of action which we shall adopt.

What we have been doing so far in this chapter is to acquire certain insights about the sort of thing that society is and how it can function. We have seen that society is composed of its individuals — there is no superperson. Society presents a new kind of force field — in my capacity as a member of society I am acted on by forces and in turn can exert forces which do not occur in my relation to any other single individual. In my reaction to this force field I am to a large extent controlled by my values. These values are in the last analysis private, but they may be modified and changed in various ways. My relations to society are exceedingly complex and the factors which affect my behavior in any specific situation are similarly complex. In order to facilitate deciding how to behave in specific situations I find it desirable to formulate a code of behavior. Many of the issues touched by such a code are "moral" issues and the question of the nature of morality presents itself.

Such are some of the insights that present themselves with regard to my relation to society, insights which are all an outgrowth of the fundamental insight that I cannot get away from myself. They are not by any means all the insights, but for my immediate purpose they are perhaps the most important. We are now in a position to discuss what, in the light of these insights, are the characteristics of a society which has a reasonable chance of being stable and of being otherwise desirable. We begin by looking further at the question of morals.

MINIMUM CODES

It seems to me that the first attack by society on any moral question should be from a minimum point of view, that is, the point of view which involves the minimum number of restrictions and which therefore can be shared by the maximum number of people. This minimum point of view, having the potential for maximum agreement, might, in a different context, have been called a maximum rather than a minimum point of view. Such a point of view is almost essential when people of different nationalities and different religious backgrounds come together. The grounds for agreement on the desirability or otherwise of the consequences of a certain code should, in a minimum formulation, be expressed in terms which all can accept. It is a matter of experience that such a common ground can often be found, and we have, for example, international agreement on the undesirability of the white slave trade or traffic in opium. I believe that the operation of projection and the operational method in general provides a basis for finding what constitutes a minimum point of view. If, on the other hand, the operational basis does not exist, as when situations occur which have essentially extranatural implications for some people, the situation becomes much more difficult. One would hardly expect agreement between a Hindu and a Moslem on the desirability of improving the cattle of India by slaughtering the unfit, although

both might agree in their description of the purely biological consequences of such a clean-up. The Hindu recognizes extranatural consequences which for him have a desirability which for the Moslem
does not exist. However, even in this rather extreme case, it seems
to me that a minimum analysis, or at any rate an analysis in purely
operational terms, has its use and even offers the possibility of eventual agreement. Such an analysis must, however, in order to be edu-
cative effectively, exhaustively examine *all* the natural consequences,
including perhaps in this special case examination of the methods
of handling cattle in other countries than India, and discussion of
whether in fact such methods have the consequences that the Hindu
anticipates. I believe that eventually such an exhaustive analysis of
all the natural implications will often suffice to bring to light assumptions which the Hindu had not realized in his extranatural approach
and will therefore tend to lead to agreement. It must be admitted,
however, that the education demanded by such an approach will
usually be slow, and may not be accomplished in a single generation.
Meanwhile the Hindu and the Moslem and others like them can find
unsuspected possibilities of agreement in systematically exploiting an
analysis in minimum terms.

We have been saying that the method which society uses in fixing
a code of morals or conduct should be a minimum method, in the
sense that it should be assented to by the maximum number of people. It seems to me that not only should it be a minimum *method*,
but that the number of articles in the code thus adopted should be
kept to a minimum, covering only the minimum number of situations
necessary in order that society may be a satisfactory place in which
to live. The reason that I say "*should* be minimum in number" is
because I, like the founding fathers, prefer a government that governs
as little as possible. This is simply another way of saying that for me
personal freedom is one of the supremely desirable things. There are,
however, many people who do not have this feeling, and it seems to
me that the number of such people is increasing. Even such a person
can take part in our inquiry and can set himself the intellectual problem of determining what sort of society will be the result of this or
that specific code. He can also set himself the problem of finding the
minimum code that will secure a particular sort of society, whether
or not he may regard it as a desirable society. Thus such a person

can discuss what sort of code will secure religious independence for the individual, although he personally may regard only that society as desirable in which there is a state religion which everyone is required to profess. Such a person may perhaps refuse to take part in our inquiry because he may regard it as a waste of time, but he cannot refuse on the ground that it is logically absurd or is something of which he personally is incapable. And I am sanguine enough to believe that such a person, taking part in such a program, may end by finding that his original point of view becomes altered.

I now turn to the problem of explicitly formulating a code of morals or conduct which I would regard as acceptable and desirable; this will involve incidentally devising the sort of society that I would regard as desirable. My inquiry will be subject to the tacit restriction that the code or society that I devise should satisfy the minimum requirement. Since I am expressing this code in print, it is to that extent unavoidably a public code, and as such is subject to limitations. But it is to be a public code in another sense, because I shall expect it to be a code for both you and me. This is to a certain extent a matter of free choice on my part, because, as has already been said, I might have one code for you and another for me, and I might write them both down publicly. The reason that I prefer only one code has already been partially intimated — it is partly that I take a certain esthetic satisfaction in finding a single code that will apply to both you and me, and partly my realization as a participating member of society that it would be difficult to make your half of any double code of mine acceptable to you. To say this is as far as I can go in print in the nature of things — you may not ask whether I "really" act according to the public code that I say I do, or whether I do not "really" have a private code in addition. Only *I* can ask myself this question and answer it, and my answer can have no significance for you, who can only watch my behavior for overt inconsistencies.

Recognizing that everything I get from society is contributed by my fellows, a question which I have to ask myself is under what conditions I am willing to ask my fellows to make an effort in my behalf or to receive benefits from them. If I am dealing with a single individual the answer is easy — I am unwilling to ask my fellow to do something for me unless I can make a return which my fellow will regard as adequate, in the sense that he would rather make his offering to me and receive my return than not to enter into the trans-action at all. The other half of this situation, namely, that I would not be offering what I do to my neighbor unless what he gives me in return is such that I would rather receive it than not enter into the transaction at all is a matter of such obvious self-interest that it can be allowed to take care of itself and hardly needs to be formu-lated. Some such ideal as this seems to be universally recognized in dealings between individuals — a human being proves to be the kind of animal that finds this acceptable. We have here, thus, the basis for a minimum code. Doubtless this sentiment with regard to fair ex-change was subject to social evolution. In the beginning men may not have spontaneously felt this way, but may have found by long experience that the best way of getting what they wanted from their fellows was to offer a fair exchange. By now, however, a long history has made acceptance of this principle almost second nature to most people, who act in this way instinctively and who would regard any other attitude as simply not decent.

If one has vividly enough in mind that society is only a group of individuals and that one cannot receive from society without receiv-ing from individuals I think one will automatically apply to his rela-tions to society the same code of unwillingness to receive without making fair return that he applies to his relations to other individuals. Something somewhat similar to this seems to be part of the actual code of most people in present society, for most people are willing to pay for what they get provided they are asked to pay. The emphasis of this attitude is, however, different from that which I am here advocating, which is unwillingness to receive at all without some sort of payment. Personally I find that my reluctance to ask society to give me something for which I do not make fair return, or even to receive from society something for which I have not asked and for which I make no return, is so strong as to constitute almost the basic condition on which I try to conduct my relations to society. A code based on such a reluctance seems to me adapted to be a minimum code, and a society based on such a code a desirable society in which I could find it acceptable to live. Furthermore, it seems to me that the requirement of fair value returned for value received is so gen-eral and demands so little in the way of specialized point of view that it makes it a *necessary* component in any workable minimum code. More than this, the implications in a logical working out of the consequences of accepting such a code are sufficiently broad, it seems to me, to make it feasible that this should be the only requirement in a minimum code.

We now consider some of these implications. Just as there are two sides to the operation of the principle of value given for value received between individuals, namely, that not only must you esteem what I offer you fair value for what you are giving me, but I must also esteem what you are giving me fair value for what I am giving you, so there are two sides to the operation of the principle between me and society. As between individuals, I sometimes find myself in a position where I have to *insist* that my fellow give me what is my due according to the principle, and when necessary I do not hesitate to thus insist, and my other fellows usually back me up. Similarly, in my relations with society, I will not willingly nor with equanimity submit to the exaction from me by society of something for which society does not make, or at least attempt to make, adequate return. In my attempt to secure my due from society I shall employ all means legally at my disposal, and if there are no legal means I will try to change the laws, or even, if the provocation is great enough, resort to active nonconformity and rebellion. In acting so, I can fortify myself by the consideration that this is not only to my own immediate advantage, an argument which is likely to draw little sympathy from my fellows, but I can also justify my action by the long range consideration that if I, and others also, do not thus insist that our half of the relationship be respected, society as a whole will slowly degenerate into a sort of thing that none of us will find acceptable. It is, however, too much to expect that society, given the best will in the world to live up to this ideal, will be able to find a single nonpersonal code such that every individual will be equally satisfied with what society gives him in return for what it exacts from him. Difference of individual tastes constitutes a sufficient reason for this. But the individual may reasonably demand that society will accept the general principle of fair return for value received and act accordingly, on the average, taking into account the average taste of its members, and with as much flexibility in detail as is consistent with a workable social machinery.

A consistent and universal application of the principle of equal give and take between society and its members is obviously complicated because of the very unequal distribution of strength and abilities among its individuals. Always some individuals are to be expected who will be so far below the norm that they are physically incapable of making an adequate return for the mere means of existence which modern societies give them. In the more primitive societies, in which the means of existence are not so exclusively under social control, such individuals may perhaps be allowed to perish as a matter of principle. There is a certain cold logic in such a course of action which is so obvious that the society which practices it need not necessarily experience a crippling loss of morale or of effectiveness in its struggle as a group with its environment, natural or human. But usually the innate humane feelings of the individuals of a society will not allow such a ruthless application of cold logic, and somehow the stronger members band together to keep the weaker ones alive. The extent to which this is done will depend upon the stress to which the society as a whole is exposed — formerly, in a city fighting for its survival against an enemy blockade even the most elementary humane instincts were abandoned. In modern societies, however, particularly industrial societies, it is becoming increasingly the case that total production is so high that the few subnormal weaklings can be taken care of with scarcely noticeable diminution of the share of any individual. In such a situation the stronger will usually willingly accept the slight extra burden of the weaker merely because the alternative, a society in which the weaker are allowed to suffer and perish, is felt to be intrinsically undesirable and to be avoided if possible. These are minimum considerations, on which nearly all can agree. There are further considerations which appeal to many. Those who feel that the universe is run on a moral basis with the human species due for special consideration, feel that it is not a man's "fault" if he is too weak to fend for himself, and that he should not be made to suffer for his "undeserved" misfortune. Beneficent nature, however, proves insensitive to its responsibilities in this regard, so the individual takes it upon himself to redress the oversight of nature by direct action. The final result here may be the same as if only minimum considerations had been operative. It is such people who talk about a man's *right* to happiness. (Notice that the founding fathers, in the Declaration of Independence, talked only about a man's right to the *pursuit* of happiness, not about his right to happiness itself.) The idea of human rights which presents itself here is an astonishingly easy one for the human animal to 'acquire (or invent), and is about as widespread as the human race itself. It is nevertheless an astonishingly fuzzy notion, and it is very difficult to extract any precise meaning from it. Some of the consequences are distinctly undesirable. Those who have a feeling that they have a "right" in some situation are very likely also to feel that they have a right to take overt action to get what they have a right to, and they may take the most convenient means which presents itself to get their rights, with no consideration of the details of the process or of the effect on other individuals. It is this trait which the Communists are exploiting in the underdeveloped countries.

The "do-gooders" are mostly recruited from those who feel that a man should not suffer for undeserved misfortune, and that any means is justifiable to redress the oversight of nature. So sure are they of the justice of their cause that they are quite willing to, and often do, force Peter to give to Paul because Paul needs it more than Peter, and because Peter is able to give it with less inconvenience than they could themselves. It seems to me that a great deal of social legislation is of this sort, and that the instinct back of it is the instinct back of the welfare state. It is one thing to advocate a society in which every individual is assured of the minimum necessary for survival with a modicum of comfort (if feasible), and another thing to set up the ideal of "To everyone according to his needs, from everyone according to his ability" of the Marxists and the do-gooders.

THE MARXIST CODE

It will be worthwhile to pause here to examine some of the consequences of accepting the Marxist code, "To everyone according to his needs, from everyone according to his ability", because this is obviously not a minimum code, and by examining the consequences of general acceptance of this special code we can get a more vivid idea of the desirability of accepting only minimum codes. At first sight the Marxist code, at least the first part of it, appears not to be so bad, particularly for me personally, for it would obviously be pleasant from many points of view if society were constructed so as to minister to my needs. Furthermore, my fellows would presumably like it too, and for the same reason, so that I need not reproach myself for selfishness if I advocate such a code. But living in a society so constituted would have to be paid for at a price, and the question is whether, after detailed analysis, I am willing to pay it. The price would be paid both in the way society would act toward me and in the way in which I would be required to act toward society.

In the first place, I personally do not like to have things given to me merely because I need them. The casual and unsystematic gifts of family life and between friends which betoken affection I like, and I like them even more when the gift thoughtfully satisfies a need, but the need must be the incidental and not the primary reason. When, however, the personal relationship is absent and I am receiving impersonally from society I have the strongest aversion to receiving on the basis of my need, but feel that the only self-respecting basis is that of value returned for value received. Many of my fellows have the same sort of feeling, and the reluctance to accept charity is a pretty deep-seated human trait. But the opposite and inconsistent trait is also widespread. The desire to get something for nothing is almost universal — so universal that one might be tempted to try to make it the basis for a universal minimum code. Now willingness to receive according to need and without making return is pretty closely related to the willingness to get something for nothing and is doubtless the reason that this appeals to so many people. The situation here is obviously by no means simple or straightforward. The desire to get something for nothing is only a special case of the desire to pay no more than is necessary, and this is usually regarded as on the whole commendable and evidence of only ordinary intelligence. No normal human being would refuse to accept a piece of good fortune, such as the discovery of an oil well in his back yard. It is only when such good fortune involves the misfortune of someone else that people begin to have qualms and scruples. Even here there are shades of difference; most people would be glad to pick up and keep a hundred dollar bill found blowing about the street, provided they could not find the original owner, and this in spite of the fact that their good fortune is someone else's misfortune. As a general rule, however, such things do not happen, and most of what we get has to be paid for. In any event, anything that we get has to come from somewhere — if it comes from my neighbor I regard the situation as demanding more consideration than if it drops from the sky or gushes from the ground.

I think the reason so many people are willing to take what they can get from society so much as a matter of course is that their imaginations are not vivid enough to see the details or to realize that most things come from other people. All this of course applies to material things — it does not apply to an intangible such, for example, as mutual confidence, which grows with the mere having and practice of it. I think that the scientist, and perhaps the physicist in particular, is a little more likely than the layman to appreciate that the material things of society are limited and have to come from somewhere, very often from a man's fellows. Experience with such natural laws as the conservation of matter and the conservation of energy are conducive to this realization.

All these considerations are one aspect of my reluctance to make my need the justification for what I allow myself to take from society. Another element in the situation which I find distasteful is that if I expect society to satisfy my needs I must usually *ask* society to give me what I need. For need, except for such universals as food and shelter, is a private matter, and you cannot know my needs unless I tell you. By the same token, if, as a member of society, I am going to give to my fellow according to his needs, he must tell me what his needs are. This puts me in a distasteful relation to him. I do not like to tell him what I need and I expect of him that he will not like to tell me what he needs. If he does tell me, as too often happens, I am likely to react by not liking the man who thus acts in a way which I do not like. But I want to like my fellows, and a society in which this is difficult is to that extent undesirable. Furthermore, experience shows that I have to guard against abuse of his privilege by my fellow and I do not like to be in the attitude of questioning and checking what he tells me, yet I have to do this as a matter of self-protection and self-respect. Then there is the question how far I shall go in trying to satisfy the needs of my fellow which he tells me about, in view of the fact that needs are so different in individual cases and are subject to no natural upper limit. Needs grow with the gratification, and a millionaire may really need his large income as much as the day laborer does his television set.

Put in a nutshell, perhaps the most fundamental reason why I do not like a society in which need is recognized as having precedence is that such a society is incompatible with the self-reliance, independence, and dignity of the individual which I value above material comfort.

Now let us look at the other half of the code — the requirement of "from everyone according to his ability". I certainly do not like this requirement when applied to myself. Perhaps one of the chief reasons I do not like it is that it implies your right or privilege to dictate my actions, something which I always resent in my neighbor and which I will accept only if there is some compensating good. In this case the implications are particularly obnoxious. Whose ability is it anyway, mine or yours? You certainly cannot claim, if my ability is greater than the average (and it is only this situation that I am worrying about, not the situation where my ability is less than the average), that society (meaning by that *you*) is in any way responsible for my greater than average ability. By what effrontery then do you expect to horn in on my good luck? Any attempt at justification, and there will certainly be many who will attempt to justify it, will involve in the background the ideal of an equalitarian society in which all individuals are equalized in every conceivable regard, not only in their opportunities, but also in the pleasure and the satisfaction which they take in their lives. In such a society every natural difference will be leveled so far as possible — the man of naturally gloomy disposition will be given more than his share of the total goods of society at the expense of his more cheerful fellow until each finds existence equally acceptable (or equally intolerable), for is it the fault of the gloomy man that his disposition is naturally as it is, and if it is not his fault, why should he suffer for it and why should his more fortunate fellow not be willing to help in the compensation?

There is no limit short of the grotesque to such an equalitarian social philosophy. It seems to me that acceptance of such a philosophy implies a willful refusal to recognize what is perhaps the most fundamental characteristic of the way things are with human beings. Human beings *differ*, in tastes and temperaments and, most importantly of all, in abilities. It is futile and for me undesirable to hope to wipe out these differences by artificial compensation. A workable society has to be based on acceptance of the fact of these differences. It is for the individual to find how to live as best he can with his own individual characteristics. This is necessary not only on practical grounds, because there is no acceptable method by which other people can do it for the individual, but for me it is also a matter of sheer self-respect. This is the way I feel about it myself, and I expect my fellow to feel about it in the same way for himself.

In the actual working out of the equalitarian philosophy in any social code of which I am aware, the equality seems to be on the pretty low plane of creature comfort. Why is your desire for material comfort so commendable a thing that it should automatically enlist my sympathy and cooperation? Or why should I make sacrifices so that you may have your comfort? In my own case I have not regarded material comfort for myself as such a prime requisite, but have put ahead of it (within reason) an interest in intellectual matters, in particular the desire to understand the workings of nature to the extent made possible by physical research. By what right shall anyone tell me how much of my ability in research I shall devote to the service of my mediocre fellow in order that he may enjoy his "bread and circuses"? Some of my fellows, as well as I, seem also to hold material comfort in relatively low esteem as shown by their artistic activities or even their delight in miscellaneous intellectual activity for its own sake. In general, I regard a man's brain as a higher organ than his body, and the skillful exercise of it as automatically worthy of greater admiration and sympathy.

The most fortunate of all facts for the human race is that there are individuals in it of more than average, and even sometimes of supreme, ability. But no individual in the race, nor the race as a whole, has done anything to secure this fortunate occurrence and accordingly has no claim, except the claim of superior physical force, on the individual who manifests the unusual ability. For me, the ability of such an individual is his own, to do with as he pleases, subject only to the universal requirement that he return to society more than he takes. In most cases it turns out that he makes a far greater return, and this is where the fortunateness of the situation for society lies. But neither I nor society has a right to the unusual ability and, in the society which seems good to me, may not coerce its possessor. Even in pure self-interest society should not try to coerce ability, for it may easily be driven underground. In fact something like this is not uncommon today in academic circles, where a man who desires opportunity for research will often be driven to conceal any administrative ability that he may have.

THE CODE OF VALUE FOR VALUE

We return now to our problem of formulating the minimum conditions to be satisfied by a Utopian society in which due regard is paid to the conditions imposed by the nature of society in general and, in particular, by its relations to the individuals who compose it. So far as such a Utopia as ours is different from any of the other Utopias which have been invented in the past, I think it will be in the explicit recognition of the unavoidable dichotomy in each of us between the public and the private.

Such a society will in the first place be constructed on the assumption that the normal individual in it will not wish to take from society (that is, his fellows) anything for which he does not make return. And since making an exactly equivalent return for what he gets is an impossible ideal, each normal individual will strive to return to society somewhat *more* than he takes. In this way society on the whole and in the long run is assured of being a going concern, continually progressing. The obverse of this is that no individual in this society will, after his eyes have been opened, willingly take part in any operation by which society takes by force from any individual or group of individuals more than society as a whole returns to the same individual. For such an operation between individual and individual would not be acceptable, and the fact that society intervenes does not obliterate the fact that the relationship is still essentially between individual and individual.

So much for the broad outlines of the code. In the detailed working out of it all sorts of questions arise, to some of which I now turn. In the first place how shall the individual know whether he is returning to society more than he is taking, and in what units shall he measure either his own contribution to society or the contribution of society to him? The classical theory of economic action would maintain that this mostly takes care of itself automatically. In a free market exchange will not occur unless each party to the transaction is satisfied. The salary which society pays me for my services is set at such a figure that society would rather have the services than the salary, which means that from the point of view of society I am giving a little more value than I take, whereas I would not be accepting the salary unless I would rather have my salary than my services, which means that from my point of view I am receiving a little more value than I give. Now this easy classical picture is oversimplified from several points of view. In the first place, it is not "society" which pays me my salary, but an individual or group of individuals within society. It is sufficient that *they* think they are making a good bargain, and there is no mechanism by which their opinion can reflect the average opinion of all the individuals who compose the society. In the second place, the market which determines my salary is not a "free" market except in the tautological sense in which it used to be said that a man is free and always freely chooses that course of action which, *all things considered,* he prefers to take. To say this is to say exactly nothing. It is a wry sort of freedom to be able to choose whether to eat or to starve, and this is precisely the sort of freedom that has been offered to the individual all too often in our industrial age.

The classical picture does not represent the whole situation, and the value to society of the contribution which an individual can make is too complex a thing to be determined by any simple criterion or to be measured in any single or simple set of units. The criterion of the market place doubtless affords a crude standard, which in the majority of cases gives the correct answer within what a physicist would call an "order of magnitude", but in any specific case there are a multitude of more complex factors to be taken into account.

In a society as complex as ours the contributions which an individual can make are often intangible, and by the same token the value to the individual of what society gives him may often reside in some intangible, not measurable in terms of salary. The values to be attached to these intangibles in setting up the balance sheet will to a large extent depend on ideals and motives and purposes. These are often so vague that all the individual can ask himself is "Will the world be a better place for my having lived in it?", with no sharp answer to what "better" really means. There can be no absolute answer, but at any epoch the answer will depend on the contemporary temper of society. Furthermore, there is no mechanism by which the general temper of society can become articulate, with the result that it is often the individual concerned who has to decide for himself whether he is making a worthwhile contribution. The individual does not have to accept unreservedly the mood or the criterion of the average of his fellow men, but he can try to modify it in the direction which he himself conceives to be better, and live his individual life in full integrity in clear-eyed recognition of what he is doing. If society does not like what he is doing, he is free to take the consequences. I take it to be a matter of fact and observation that some men are constituted so that they will act in this way, as witness the conscientious objectors. This is one of the ways things are with respect to the human race. Whether such behavior on the part of the individual is "rational" or not we do not discuss. In the meantime we do not have to go to the extreme of martyrdom to recognize that society often moves in such a direction that it values less and less highly the contribution which some individual is able to make, and that in self-defense the individual may be driven to try to modify the attitude of society so that it will esteem his own contribution more highly. Not only is this true of the individual, but it is true of whole classes of individuals.

There are several examples of this sort of situation in our present-day American society. Perhaps the most obvious is that of the teachers. In the last thirty years there has been a progressive worsening in the apparent valuation which society places on the teaching profession, and the teacher is getting an ever smaller share of the material goods of our society. The change is to a certain extent not intentional and is partly an incidental result of a change of remote economic factors, but it has by now reached such a stage that the loss of economic reward is producing, as it almost always does, a loss of general social esteem and prestige, with the result that we are faced with a serious shortage of teachers for the new generation. Whether society is intelligent enough or whether a mechanism exists capable of acting rapidly enough to rectify the situation does not yet appear. It is now easy to see that if the teachers as a class had had some organization by which they could have called attention early enough to the change of trend, and if they could have secured some action to counteract it, it would have been to the advantage of all, society and teachers as well. It is also easy to see that, with things as they were this was a most unlikely sort of thing to have happened. For a movement of this sort must have started with some individual. Put yourself in the place of that individual. How much of his time should he devote to it? What are the chances that he will reap any individual benefit from it in time to do him any good? How willing is he to encounter the cynicism of society toward any individual who backs an enterprise that will benefit him personally? How much does he love his fellow man anyhow? And how much of a missionary is he? It is easy to see that in our society as at present constituted the chances are small that any movement such as this, no matter how much needed, can get started. Perhaps a change of attitude in all of us will be needed. In the meantime we can be a little less cynical toward anyone who has the hardihood to trumpet the value of his own contribution to society.

Another example of much the same sort, but cutting deeper than the example of the teachers, is the change of attitude toward all activity of purely intellectual interest. It has become a commonplace that the present generation is anti-intellectual — the statement has been made in official reports to the President. This is perhaps no more than a working to the surface, as is almost inevitable eventually in a democracy, of the deep-rooted aversion of the average human being to using his mind.

What are people who are interested in the intellectual life and who do not regard a society as a good society unless there is opportunity for intellectual activity and companionship going to do about it? It seems to me perfectly obvious that the intellectual people in self-defense should get together and try to modify the attitude of the average man. It is too much to expect that an active taste for intellectual activity can ever be developed in more than a small fraction of people, but by presenting a clearer picture of what the intellectual life involves it should at least be possible to develop a little more tolerance toward those who are interested. There is one line of attack which I think offers some promise. I believe that the average man genuinely admires unusual ability, whether it is physical skill and dexterity or intellectual accomplishment. If the average man could be made to see that often an intellectual pursuit demands unusual ability, and that often such pursuits are not even open to average ability, I think he would prize unusual intellectual ability a little more and would be willing to make his contribution toward encouraging the development of intellectual interests among those who are capable of them. I believe that he can be made to take pride in a high level of intellectual accomplishment in his own society.

Again there is the difficulty of mechanism. Where is the machinery by which the intellectuals can band together and start a campaign to so modify society that it will esteem more highly the contributions which they can make? As society is now constituted it is mostly a matter of chance whether such a movement ever gets started or not. It is fortunate that society, like the statistical systems of pure physics, is subject to continuous spontaneous fluctuations, and sometimes a fluctuation occurs of such a nature to provide a needed corrective or even to initiate some desirable novel trend in society. But as matters now stand the whole thing is too much a matter of chance. Again there is at least one moral that stands out. If the individual wants to play a part in modifying society in the direction which seems good to him (and the good *can* be good only from the point of view of individuals) he must discard his diffidence and not hesitate to urge what seems good to him, even if in so doing he is urging something from which he personally will profit. There seems to have been a gradual change of attitude in this country in the last 175 years toward the propriety of the individual acting in self-interest. It must be remembered that the founding fathers based our Constitution on the explicit hypothesis that each class of our society would not hesitate to act in its own interest — the resulting edifice would represent a sort of equilibrium between conflicting interests, which, it was hoped, would secure the ideal of the "greatest good for the greatest number". But, now, with the high-minded man made to feel that it is reprehensible for him to urge his own interest and with the low-minded man feeling no such compunction, the inevitable result is a deterioration toward the level of the lowest, a deterioration which it seems to me we are now witnessing. Such deterioration is particularly hard to avoid in a democracy. In the past, democracies have not been stable over too long intervals. In the starting anew after some catastrophe democracies have presented their most favorable aspects, and unusual ability has found its opportunity. It is a genuine problem to avoid the deterioration in a democracy which has been stable a long time.

SCIENCE AND THE SCIENTIST

There is one aspect of the intellectual life and the attitude of society toward it which demands special consideration because some of the features which it presents are new and society has no precedent for the way it should act. This concerns the place of science and the scientist in society. The scientist is a comparatively late arrival on the human scene. The reason for this does not greatly concern us; perhaps the most important reason is the cumulative nature of scientific knowledge. Each new step depends on all the preceding steps and could not have been taken until after the preceding steps had been taken. A result is the explosively expanding science and the associated technology which we are now witnessing. The technological consequences are by many regarded as the most important, particularly at the present epoch. It seems to me, however, that another aspect of the situation has more important long range implications. The scientist is an unusual sort of human being of which there have not been many in the past; he is interested in something which has little appeal for the average man. The scientist wants to understand how things go, merely for the sake of understanding and irrespective of the practical use to which the understanding can be put. He so much wants to understand that he prefers to find out even the unpleasant things rather than not find out at all.

It is only comparatively recently that the development of society has been such that the scientist has been able to find himself. In so doing he has discovered a new kind of good, the good of understanding for its own sake. The discovery that this is a good could perhaps have been as little anticipated as that earlier discovery of the human race about itself, namely, that it responds emotionally to music and finds it good. However it got that way, there is no denying that a fraction of the human race now recognizes a new good — the good of finding out about things, in particular finding out new things, and understanding them.

The scientist thus having discovered a new kind of good, he, and through him others, will henceforth impose a new kind of criterion as to whether a society is good or not. The criterion is whether society is a place in which there is opportunity for acquiring understanding and whether such understanding is prized. Because the point of view is new, it is almost unavoidable, if society as a whole is to acquire the new outlook, that the scientist himself urge the human worth and dignity of knowledge and understanding for their own sakes, simply because he is in the best position to appreciate what is involved. I believe that too few scientists appreciate this situation or, if they do, are too much deterred by diffidence or fear of the cynicism which they know greets any effort in which a component of self-interest can be detected. The matter is acquiring a certain urgency, for as part of the general anti-intellectualism of the present is to be detected a special and growing hostility to the scientist — at least this was undeniably the case before the appearance of the Sputniks.

With the appearance of the Sputniks there has been an abrupt reversal of the popular attitude toward the scientist, who is now regarded as the potential savior of his culture. It is now felt that there cannot be too many scientists and it is regarded as one of the most pressing questions to find how to modify our system of education to produce more of them. The reasons for the reversal of attitude are for all to see. These reasons are superficial and short range; they certainly do not imply anything so fundamental as a reversal of the growing tide of anti-intellectualism. I can see no evidence of growing esteem for intellectual ability and achievement in other lines as a result of the increased regard for the scientist. Because the popular reaction is superficial and for the wrong reasons, I think the serious-minded scientist cannot help regarding the present turn of events as calamitous from the long range point of view of the scientist and society's finding how to live together. I believe that all the deeper issues involved in the relation of the scientist to society are as they were before. I have therefore decided to leave the rest of this section as it was written before the Sputniks — the issues here presented are still with us and have to be faced even if there are new ones. In any event, the newer issues are mostly beyond the intended scope of this book, issues such, for example, as the best methods of stepping up the education of scientists, including the effect on the recruiting of young scientists of their realization that science and scientists have now become the most important instrument of national rivalry. It may well be that a sensitive young man will not want to be used as an instrument of such a rivalry.

The pre-Sputnik growing hostility to the scientist is partly explained by the reaction against the atomic bomb and partly as general resentment against the necessity for revising the social outlook imposed by modern general technological improvement. Revision of outlook is obviously demanded, and to make this revision, careful thinking is necessary. Now if there is one thing that the average man does not like to do it is to use his mind, especially when he is forced to it. On the other hand, the one thing that the scientist and those temperamentally like him like to do *is* to use their minds. We have here a clash of temperaments, which we have always had with us, but which is now accentuated, while at the same time the need for some sort of reconciliation becomes more pressing because of the increasing part which the scientist is coming to play in modern life.

One aspect of this clash of temperaments is the clash between science and religion. I think it is a mistake to play down this clash, as do many, but I believe on the contrary that we have here a real opposition between outlooks and assessments of what constitutes the good, which we must somehow find how to live with because both are equally human traits.

How shall the scientist react to this situation? He may, in the first place, purely as a matter of self-interest, try to educate his nonscientific fellow so that he will see what science is like and what it involves, to the end that he too may become convinced that one of the things which makes a society good is that science should flourish. The individual scientist who in this way tries to educate his fellow to the value of science may legitimately claim that in so doing he is at least partially fulfilling his self-imposed obligation to return to society more than he takes. For, according to his own standards, increased appreciation of the value of science contributes to the betterment of society. He need not apologize for using his own standards, because in the last analysis this can never be avoided. The amount of time which any individual scientist thus devotes to educating the public to the value of science will evidently vary greatly with the individual. Some can do this more effectively and with less sacrifice of scientific activity than others, and some will view the importance of such education as relatively greater than others. In fact, it may well be that any one particular scientist may take no part at all in such a campaign of education, but may nevertheless make his return to society of more than he takes out.

Whatever the variation from case to case, it seems to me that there is one clean-cut minimum requirement on the scientist here. Unless the scientist publishes the results of his researches so that they are accessible and can contribute to the general growth of knowledge his labors are ineffective. From the point of view of society they might as well have not been made at all, and from the point of view of the individual they are merely a form of self-indulgence. If ever use of the word "duty" is justified, and we can certainly usually get along without it, I would be tempted to use it in this connection.

It is easy to determine whether this minimum requirement of publication has been satisfied in any particular case, and once it has been satisfied the scientist is more or less automatically assured that he is on the way to making his proper return to society. But there is more to it than this, because the value of published scientific results varies greatly and may not be measured in terms of pages. There are good scientists and not-so-good scientists. In a properly educated society the contribution of the good scientist will be of more value than that of the not-so-good scientist and accordingly his debt to society more easily paid. I think there is no absolute method for dealing with this situation. However, I believe that society, from its own point of view, may be content to leave the matter to the control exerted by the natural ambition of nearly every scientist to be as good a scientist as possible and as highly esteemed by his colleagues as possible, and to the competence of the judgment by his fellow scientists of the worth of the work of any individual. For professional judgment of worth is keen and informed and sometimes ruthless.

CONFORMITY AND ACCEPTANCE

So much for the problems presented to the individual by his desire to return to society as much as he takes or, even, to be on the safe side, to return more than he takes. It seems to me almost un-avoidable that within limits the individual has to be his own judge in this matter. If there is too glaring a discrepancy between what the individual and society regard as fair return for value received there are mechanisms by which correction can be made, as the individual knows only too well. What now is the individual to do when he regards a demand of society as unjustified and one that he is not willing to accede to? No sharp dividing line can be drawn between the economic demands of society and the more intangible sorts of social pressure, which, at the extreme, merge into questions of "conscience". We have seen that the individual does not have to conform and cannot be made to, except outwardly. Whether in any particular case he will conform or not depends on whether he is willing to pay the price that conformity involves, that is, whether nonconformity is worth it to him. The extreme of nonconformity is, of course, presented by martyrdom. To me martyrdom is plain silly. If my neighbor manages to get me into such a position that he can exercise overwhelming physical force on me and chooses to use this force to exert pressure on me to say that I believe what he believes, I am perfectly willing to go through the motions and lie for him, despising him for a fool for thinking that anything I say can change the way things really are or can change what I really believe. I would certainly have acted as did Galileo if I had been in his position. It seems to me that people who are willing to become martyrs or who admire martyrdom in others take themselves with a deathly seriousness and subscribe to a Platonic conception of the independent existence of abstract principles of morality, a point of view to which I have already paid my respects.

Fortunately the issue of conformity in these days, except perhaps where there is a Gestapo, is seldom pushed to the extreme of martyrdom. Nevertheless there must be numberless examples in which the individual outwardly conforms but inwardly does not accept — I can say this by looking at myself. The question for the individual now becomes what form his inward nonacceptance shall take. There are obviously degrees of nonacceptance. At the extreme it may lead to embitterment against society, resulting perhaps in passive withdrawal into oneself and passive noncooperation, or it may take the form of active sabotage. Now, for the average human being, embitterment is not a pleasant attitude to have. In fact, I think that for the individual, one of the most important of all things is to avoid embitterment. The intelligent individual will, if possible, react to his nonacceptance of a social demand in a less extreme way than by embitterment. It is quite possible for a man who does not accept the demands of society to endeavor to change the demands of society by working within the legal framework. Public opinion recognizes this as a right and respects a man who thus operates. Public opinion also allows a man to proclaim his nonacceptance if he nevertheless stays within the law. With these possible outlets the average human being will not usually regard the acceptance of a demand of society as of sufficient importance to be worth either fighting or getting embittered about, and he will outwardly go along with what is expected of him without making too much fuss.

Whether a man is embittered or not by his nonacceptance of a demand of society which he thinks unjustified may be determined in large degree by the spirit in which society (that is, his average fellow man) makes the demand. What this spirit is can be judged much more accurately by an active member of the society than by an outsider. This is one of the reasons why, for instance, an American will put up with things in American life which to a European seem incomprehensible. The McCarthy situation presents an example. In this country many articles of social legislation seem to me ill-advised and based on crooked thinking, but nevertheless reflect a kindly concern for the well-being of the underprivileged. Such legislation can be and is tolerated without bitterness by a man who thinks it is dead wrong and even if it is contrary to his own interest. This attitude of tolerance toward otherwise ill-advised legislation, provided the underlying motives are on the whole believed to be kindly, is, I think, rather characteristic of this country. From the long range point of view, however, I do not believe that all the consequences of such a tolerance are desirable, because it results in a gradual drift toward mediocrity.

THE EXACTIONS OF SOCIETY

So far we have been considering our minimum code of mutual exchange of value from the point of view of the individual. Now let us look at it from the point of view of society and, in particular, from the point of view that society will not exact from any individual anything for which society does not make adequate return to the individual. Since any action of society is only the action of the individuals who compose it, this requirement can be met only if the individuals whose joint activities constitute the action of society see to it that it is met. In our democratic society this means you and me. The mechanism by which you and I can help ensure that this requirement is met is, if we are ordinary citizens and not members of a lawmaking or judicial body, by the ballot box directly, and indirectly by influencing public opinion through our contacts with our fellows or by direct contact with our legislators.

The nature of the exactions and restrictions which society imposes on the individual vary through a wide range and is not always such that the principle of value returned for value received can obviously apply. Examples of such cases are the laws against obscenity or indecent exposure or the Sunday laws. Even here, however, the criterion of value returned for value received can be made to apply by stretching matters a little. Thus the return made to the man who is deprived of the privilege of exposing himself indecently (assuming that he regards this as a privilege) is the assurance that he will not be subject to the unwelcome experience of witnessing the indecent exposure of other people (assuming that this is an unwelcome experience). Now it is particularly obvious from this example that general prohibitions of this nature can be justified only from the point of view of the average opinion and temper of society and not necessarily from the point of view of every particular individual. For in this example the individual who suffers the deprivation is not the same as the individual who receives the reward, for one may assume that in general an individual who likes to expose himself indecently does not regard the exposure of others as unwelcome. Even here, however, the other broad principle controlling the exercise of compulsion by society still applies, namely the principle that no individual will concur in the exaction by society from any other individual of something which he would be unwilling to exact of him in their relation as individuals. This obviously applies here, because the normal individual in our society would not hesitate to resent and prevent by direct action indecent exposure of another individual. Some actions of this sort are so instinctive and taken so much as a matter of course that they are felt to require no explicit justification. We are here down to bedrock — it is a fact that in certain situations a human individual will and does exert force on his individual fellow. One of the things that we are trying to do with our minimum code is to ameliorate some of the consequences of these bedrock facts, which are often undesirable, even if not in the particular example above.

Among all the forms of compulsion which society exerts on the individual I single out for detailed discussion two as among the most important — these are the imposition of taxes and the imposition of military service. Both of these forms of compulsion we have had so long that they are accepted with a certain fatalism, and it is seldom that an examination is made of what should be the principles governing such compulsion or whether the principles are actually being followed. It is, furthermore, evident enough that society is not a completely free agent in this matter, but is subject to the natural limitations. If society is to provide certain facilities for its members, the means now provided by taxes have to come from somewhere. Or if a particular society is to secure itself from aggression from without, often someone has to fight for it.

TAXATION

Let us first consider the question of taxation. The question is: how shall we ensure that society does not take from a man in taxes more than it returns to him in some other form? The question is not often raised, nor does one often find concern expressed that a satisfactory answer be found. In this country, in particular, taxation is a pretty hit or miss affair, with the only obvious guiding principle being to raise the most by taxation with the minimum squawking, the total amount of squawking being measured in terms of votes. As might be expected in such a haphazard situation, the laws of chance ensure that some of our taxation satisfies the principle of no taxation without adequate return, and some does not. An example of a tax which satisfies the principle is a gasoline tax, when honestly administered. What society gives the individual in this situation is use of the highway system. The value of this use to the individual will, other things being equal and on the average, be proportional to the amount of use. The amount of use is proportional to the number of miles driven, which again, and on the average, will be proportional to the number of gallons of gasoline consumed. Hence when the individual pays to society an amount proportional to the number of miles he drives, he is receiving from society something commensurate with what he pays. However, this equitable return is obtained only in the large and on the average. A meticulous application of the principle would doubtless demand consideration of individual cases and individual adjustment. One individual may be in a position to make greater return to society by his use of the roads than another. For instance, I think it would be universally agreed that a physician makes more return to society in his use of the roads than does a man on a fishing expedition, and a good argument could be made for making the physician pay a smaller gasoline tax than the fisherman or anyone else who drives for pleasure only. Although the justice of this claim may be recognized, what prevents honoring the claim in practice is simply the mechanical difficulty of devising a system which should make the discrimination without involving a prohibitive amount of expensive paper work and red tape. People recognize the existence of limitations of this sort and are willing to put up with individual inequities, provided the matter does not involve too much hardship, and provided they do not feel singled out for individual discrimination.

Another tax of the same sort, less specialized, is a sales tax in general. Roughly and on the average the value of what society gives a man is measured by the use he makes of the facilities offered by society, and there is a rough parallelism between this and what he buys. We have here, therefore, a method of roughly ensuring that what a man pays in taxes is measured by what he gets. The exclusion of certain articles, such as bread, from the sales tax, can be justified by the general principle that society will, for reasons already discussed, undertake to ensure to every individual a certain minimum without exacting any repayment.

In general, a tax on goods purchased or on the use of a public facility, the amount of tax being proportional to the amount of use, will automatically achieve the result that what a man pays is proportional to what he gets. Going still further, an income tax, in which a man pays a fixed proportion of his income in excess of the minimum which society allows him, also achieves the same end, roughly and on the average. For in an economy roughly in equilibrium a man's income will be mostly spent, so that to tax his income is roughly to tax him for what he buys, which is thus roughly a sales tax, which again is roughly a tax on the use of public facilities. A tax on income is, however, not in all respects equivalent to a tax on use. For ideally the income is already a return for the contribution made by the individual to society, and to tax it is to give with one hand and take back with the other. Such a procedure is to be justified only by such practical considerations as that, for example, the contribution which an individual makes for which he is rewarded by income is usually not in such a form as to be utilizable by society for its immediate purposes. Society cannot build roads with the education which a teacher imparts. From this point of view an income tax constitutes a correction on the transaction between the individual and society which is in the main covered by his income.

The same remark applies to any sort of taxation. A tax is a correction on the transaction between the individual and society covered in the main by the mechanism of the market place. The correction is necessary because all the needs of society are not taken care of by the market place. Now corrections are a usually necessary accompaniment of any human transaction, but if the transaction has been skillfully arranged the correction should be small. The fact that the correction on the largest incomes is so large that it almost equals the income itself raises the suspicion that the underlying economic mechanism has been, to say the least, ineptly designed. A physicist would perish from mortification if the necessary correction to his first approximation turned out to be 92 per cent, as it is for the top incomes.

So much for the average. The individual with abnormally large income requires special consideration. In general he is not able to, or as a matter of fact does not, spend all his income on living, but accumulates it and usually plows it back into capital investment. Such investment is for the advantage of society, so that a strict application of the principle of *quid pro quo* demands that the proportional part of his income which is syphoned off in taxes should be less for the man of large income than for the average.

All these considerations suggest that if there is one method of taxation which does *not* satisfy the principle of *quid pro quo* it is the graded income tax. Nevertheless this form of taxation has become so firmly embedded in public acceptance in this country since the sixteenth amendment that it is like tilting against windmills to try to alter the public temper. I shall, nevertheless, permit myself the luxury of a few remarks. In the first place, acceptance of such a principle of taxation marks a step toward acceptance of the communist ideal of the welfare state. Having gone as far as we have along the road, I fear there is no logical stopping place short of the complete acceptance of the welfare state principle, which Marx expressed in his famous slogan to which we have already paid our respects.

So far as there is any explicit attempt to justify the graded income tax it is a disguised form of the minimum squawking principle, masquerading under the more high sounding slogan of "taxation according to ability to pay". "Ability to pay" is here measured in terms of loss of material comfort occasioned by paying the tax. The concealed ideal is the equalitarian ideal of an equal share in material comforts for everyone, irrespective of contribution to the creation of the comforts. This ideal is to be attained even if it can be reached only by taking away the possessions of those who have and giving them to those who have not. In fact, one frequently hears the argument in justification of this kind of taxation "All these socially desirable things have to be paid for somehow, and where else can the money come from?" It used to be thought that a man had to reconcile himself to not having certain things, particularly if the only way he could get them was by stealing.

To me the thing that is hardest to bear is the obvious inequity of it all. I do not expect my neighbor to give to me of his goods because I need them more than he does — why should society compel me to give of my goods to society because society needs them more than I do, society being only all my neighbors together? Every time I pay my income tax I smart under a sense of unfairness as keen as that of the old militant suffragette, denied the right to vote merely because of her sex. I feel exploited and discriminated against on the basis of superior ability and industry. It is hard to keep away the bitterness. So far as I have been able to keep away the bitterness it is because I believe the fundamental instincts of the men in our streets are still humane and kindly, and that they act in the way they do because their appreciation of the broader and longer range implications is obscured by the shorter range outlook and their desire to get something done quickly.

Fairness and justice is almost never mentioned in what public discussions there are of the graded income tax, but the argument is almost always based on expediency or public advantage. Often those who oppose a tax will venture to say that it is against public interest to discourage initiative by putting a discriminatory tax on special ability or industry. It is recognized that by discouraging initiative the morale of those with special ability is undermined, so that they will be less likely to make their special contribution, but the only reason recognized why their morale should not be undermined is that it is against public interest, not that it is unfair.

So much for what appear to me to be the broad outlines of the graded income tax situation. Sometimes other and special justification is offered for a confiscation of high incomes. This is often expressed in the argument that the great power conferred by an unusually high income is against the interests of society. This argument was doubtless more pertinent formerly than now. Organized labor has acquired sufficient influence so that it is able to neutralize most of the undesirable results of the power sometimes associated with large incomes. If there are still socially undesirable potentialities associated with unusually large incomes, then, it seems to me, they should be dealt with by special legislation, as, for instance, by forbidding a man to directly hire more than so many men or to own more than so many acres of grazing land or oil land, or by prohibiting other undesirable sorts of manipulation in amassing a large fortune. There are obvious difficulties in protecting any specific danger area, but a clever lawyer should be able to think up methods without resorting to throwing out baby and bath together. I suspect that a number of the undesirable features in our culture are the result of insufficient cleverness in our lawyers.

It will relieve my feelings a little, and perhaps yours also, to mention instances in which it seems to me that our lawyers have not been sufficiently clever. I am outraged by the fact that a man has no legal redress for false imprisonment. If I as an individual had made a mistake of this kind in dealing with my fellow I would expect to make some attempt at restitution. I cannot accept with equanimity the position that I have no corresponding obligation when the society of which I am a member makes a corresponding mistake. The legal position here seems to be that it is impossible to devise a method of making redress for false imprisonment without violating the principle of "sovereignty", and that all legal machinery is unavoidably subject to imperfections of some sort, which in extreme and exceptional cases may result in such things as false imprisonment, and that the individual has to pay for the privilege of living in society at all by taking his chances that such a thing will happen to him. I believe that if lawyers were cleverer the burden of the chance that such a thing might happen could be made to fall on society as a whole and not on the unfortunate individual. Another matter in much the same category is the impossibility of suing the government for violation of contract, or other similar infraction of ethics, without the consent of the government.

This sort of thing would be completely inacceptable between individuals. The answer of the lawyers is that the individual could not sue on his own initiative without violating the sovereignty of the government, a concept without which it seems no acceptable theory of the process of government can be set up. It seems to me that an acceptable theory of government is too high a price to pay in return for something which allows the possibility of violating elementary sentiments of justice and fairness. I would prefer to get along with no theory at all and meet each special situation on its own merits, something which the individual is capable of doing, although it doubtless offends the legal mind.

MILITARY SERVICE

We now consider the second of the two important social compulsions, military service. Military service and war are associated with emergency and stark issues of survival in which the pressures on the individual are so great that he will act as the immediate necessity pushes him, with little attention to long range considerations, either of policy or rationality. In this area it is particularly evident that what society does is only the aggregate of what its individuals do. I imagine that from the point of view of human society taken as a single unit and from the long range point of view resistance to aggression is seldom justified. It was Hillary Beloc who said that from the point of view of his time and generation it was a calamity that Napoleon had not been successful in bringing all Europe under his domination. For if he had, all the temporary and local hardships would have disappeared, united Europe would have achieved peace and stability, and there would have been no World Wars. The same can be said in principle for the Communist ideal of a world united under Communism. But human society is not a unit and there is no mechanism by which a long range point of view can be made to prevail against a short range view. In particular, I at this moment am going to act in such a way that the prospect for me during the rest of my life is as favorable as possible. "Favorable" means favorable, *all things considered,* including the ideals and the intangibles. You, I judge, are going to act in the same way. I suspect that both of us would have opposed Napoleon, and felt virtuous in so doing. In situations of acute emergency, as when a band of raiders from a foreign country threatens my life, ideals and intangibles, either long or short range, get pushed into the background, and I act as my own survival demands. I will, if necessary, apply force to you to compel you to act to secure my own survival. Fortunately for both of us, when you so act you are often acting to secure your own survival also. However, in applying force to compel you to cooperate in saving my life, I seldom argue or attempt any formal justification — that is just the way I act in such circumstances.

Such we may imagine to have been the state of affairs in a primitive society when everyone seized the nearest weapon to repel a hostile raid. In our complex society the picture has changed. We can generally see the danger in advance and have more time to react rationally. The job of defense has become a professional matter, performed by a small minority of all the members of society. In a modern society, on the average, when any individual votes that a certain class of the citizens, generally the young able-bodied men, shall assume the job of defending the whole society, he is generally voting that someone else risk his life in order that he himself may live in safety. To the average human being, particularly if he thinks about it, this is a most distasteful sort of thing to do, and it has to be justified by soul-searching analysis. The physical facts and necessities of the situation are obvious enough. Only the able-bodied young men are physically capable of entering the front lines of combat where there is special danger to life. If the enemy is to be repelled and the country saved only the young man can do it at the risk of his own life. But who am I to compel my young neighbor to accept my ideal that my country is worth dying for? This is not for everyone a completely self-evident proposition. As a matter of fact in our society the chances are good that any particular young man will both feel that his country is worth dying for and will recognize the physical necessity that it is he who has to take the risk of dying. Why, then, should I not deal with the matter on a volunteer basis and give any particular young man a choice whether he will risk his life for me or not? I think the answer is that it should be put on a volunteer basis if it is feasible. In earlier times this was feasible. There used to be enough young men who, for one reason or another, whether pure patriotism or sheer love of adventure, were willing to run the risks of fighting. But with the very large armies demanded by the last few wars there are not enough young men who are willing to make the sacrifice or to take the long preliminary training necessary to acquire the techniques demanded by modern war. Compulsion has to be put on the young men, therefore. I, as an individual, have to take part in this compulsion. Nevertheless, such action on my part is inherently distasteful. It violates my fundamental principle that I will not, in my capacity as a member of society, exert force on my neighbor which I would not be willing to exert on him directly, as individual to individual. For certainly I would not be willing to demand of any particular young neighbor that he risk his life for mine. Why am I willing to do it here, then, and why are my neighbors willing?

It is, I think, evident that we are here confronted with a genuine dilemma, that we cannot simultaneously follow all the principles of conduct which seem good to us, and that some sort of compromise is necessary. This compromise will to a large extent be dictated by the inherent physical limitations in the situation. Perhaps the most important such limitation is that it is only the young men who are physically able to fight in the front line. This cannot be avoided. How, then, shall the rest of us conduct ourselves? It seems to me that the only decent way for the rest of the community to act is for everyone else to devote himself to making such contribution as he can to the common effort to ward off the common danger. This means universal compulsory service for everyone in wartime. The ideal would be for everyone to find the niche in which he could make the most effective contribution. The mechanism by which this can be accomplished will not be easy to devise, and should preferably be thought out in advance of the necessity.

Universal compulsory military service in time of war has actually been proposed as a solution at various times, for instance, by Granville Clark during the last war, but public sentiment has not been ready for it. The thing requires to be thrashed out in public discussion. I think such discussion is capable of making the average man feel that it is not decent for him to be exacting from the young men something in which he is not taking part himself to the best of his ability. When he gets this point of view the promise of Roosevelt to organized labor at the beginning of the last war that they could fight the war without lowering their standards of living, and the willingness of labor to act on this assurance, will both appear equally contemptible.

There is a corollary of the ideal of universal service which has consequences which I think are applicable even if universal service is not itself adopted. This is that no able-bodied young man should be *allowed* to enter the front line of combat or otherwise to risk his life if he is capable of making a greater contribution somewhere else. Great numbers of such cases arose during the last war in connection with men of specialized technical competence which involved long training or special abilities. The way the situation was met was on the whole satisfactory, and grew more satisfactory toward the end of the war, but the opposition to this point of view was serious enough to raise real problems. Only too often a local draft board took the position that true democracy demanded that everyone in it, which in practice meant everyone in the special age and sex group of the young men, share the danger of being shot at, and that possession of the ability to make an exceptional contribution was no reason why a man should be exempted. To me this point of view does not make sense — it reminds me too much of the old idea of punishment as retribution and for its own sake — an eye for an eye and a tooth for a tooth. And too often the ugly specter of naked envy could be sensed in the background.

Along with the attitude toward the draft discussed in the last paragraph, some people adopted what appears to be a curious perversion and inversion of this attitude. This was the attitude that society does not have the right, by applying special exemption, to force any young man into a position where he might be subject to the scorn of his fellows or to his own self-reproaches for not sharing their dangers with them. That is, it was regarded as an inalienable right of a man, to be exercised even during the emergency of war, to share their dangers with his fellows. We are told that in Russia they did things better — there a young man regarded it as a matter of pride if he was singled out as being too important for society to run the risk of losing him.

Universal service in time of war, with everyone making the contribution for which he is best fitted, with no one permitted to improve his status at the expense of his fellows, appeals to me as the best compromise. But I clearly recognize that even this solution has not avoided for me the unwelcome exercise of force on my neighbor to compel him to adopt my point of view in preference to what may be his. Here, my point of view is that loss of freedom and dictation of my activities by the enemy are intrinsically so bad that fighting to prevent them is preferable. Of the two evils, fighting appears to me to be the lesser. But there are people with diametrically opposite views — Ghandi was one such who at the beginning of the last war would have surrendered India to Japan if Japan had invaded it. In this sort of situation I do not hesitate to impose my point of view, by force, if necessary. In so doing I am at least consistent, for what I am saying is that there are some evils which are worse than the exercise of force. Accordingly I apply force to my neighbor to prevent him from acting according to his worse ideal. The nature of force being what it is, it is I that will win unless the people who feel like Ghandi are so numerous that they nullify their opponents by the sheer weight of their dead bodies. The English encountered a situation something like this in India with passive resistance. Passive resistance by its nature cannot succeed unless backed by an overwhelming majority of the individuals in a large society — otherwise it eliminates itself like any other mutant unfitted for survival.

There is one curious exception to the consistency with which society enforces the majority point of view that there are some things worse than the exercise of force and which justify society's fighting on occasion. The exception has to do with the conscientious objector. In our society and in some others the claim of a man that his conscience will not permit him to fight is usually received with respect. Such claims are of course particularly likely to be fraudulent, and society has to take special means to be sure that the claim is genuine. If the claim is accepted as genuine it is usually honored — in earlier times by outright exemption from all military service and recently more usually by substitution of something else for military service. The nature of the criteria applied to ensure that a claim is "genuine" would repay special study as shedding light on what people mean by the "reality" of a man's state of mind. We shall not stop for this analysis, but ask rather why it is that society honors a man's claim that conscience forbids him to do this or that. The reason a man does not fight does not affect the enemy and the country is just as likely to be overrun no matter what the reason why its people fail to resist. Why then does society accept the plea of the objector? The reasons seem to be complex. In the first place I do not think the claim would be honored if there were so many objectors that they constituted a factor of any military importance. Neither do I think that the claims of the objector would be honored unless the objector himself were willing to go to extremes to maintain his "right" to act according to his conscience. If he is willing to undergo imprisonment or martyrdom there will be enough tender-minded individuals in the community to exert pressure against enforcement of legal penalties. But I think the chief reason the conscientious objector gets as much consideration as he does is because of the religious involvements of the concept of conscience in the mind of the average man. The notion that conscience is the voice of God directly speaking to one is widely held — I was brought up with it myself. Also a great many people feel that a claim of religion takes precedence over any claim of society or the state, or even over any claim of self-survival. There are enough such people to secure special treatment for the conscientious objector. Objection to public military policy on any other ground than the religious, on the other hand, gets short shrift. Bertrand Russell's pacifism in World War I on the purely intellectual ground that war in general is stupid received peremptory reward by imprisonment, with no consideration whatever for the validity of his argument.

I think there are many aspects of the way in which our society at present handles the military service situation which are unsatisfactory, and I think the public realizes this and manifests all the evidence of bad conscience in the matter. One of these signs is that many act as if drafting a man and putting him into uniform automatically confers on him the status of hero. Much more widespread is the feeling that society owes a special debt of *gratitude* to its soldiers. This made sense when armies were recruited by volunteers, but it seems to me not to make sense with drafted armies. If I had served in uniform I do not believe that I would expect society to be grateful to me for doing what I could not avoid, any more than I expect society to be grateful to me for paying my taxes. This, however, is not the feeling of the majority of our veterans, and they have turned themselves into a pressure group, exploiting this instinct of gratitude on the part of the rest of society, an instinct which seems to me to betray a bad conscience in the realization that the philosophy of the draft has not been properly thought out.

OTHER MINIMUM CODES

We have now proposed our minimum code and discussed how it will work out in two situations of great social importance, taxation and compulsory military service. This is not the only possible minimum code. Our code honors the reluctance of the average individual to exert force on his neighbor for his own advantage, either directly as individual to individual, or indirectly through the medium of social action. An entirely different sort of minimum code is also possible, a code recognizing the primacy of force and allowing the stronger to impose his will on the weaker. There is no logical reason why one code should be adopted rather than the other. It seems, however, to be a fact that the human animal has turned itself into the kind of animal that on the average has an instinctive aversion to letting naked force have free play. He may not have been this kind of animal in the beginning, but the aversion to unrestricted force may well have been bred into him by the elimination of societies in which naked force was not controlled. Cooperative enterprise is more effective in protecting a community against external aggression than a policy of every man for himself. The average man has become such a creature that if he were adrift on the open ocean in a lifeboat where cannibalism was the only resource he would prefer to have the next victim selected by lot rather than that the next victim should be the weakest of the survivors, in spite of the fact that the latter is perfectly logical, and conceivably preferable from the long range point of view of the race.

Now although aversion to the use of naked force has been bred into the average man in such situations as suggested above, the aversion is not so logical or universal as to raise in me any delusions about the likelihood of my minimum code getting actually followed in any contemporary society. Men will still use force if the provocation is great enough and if they can argue that the end justifies the means. People are particularly likely to think that the end justifies the means if the end is altruistic. The bandit who robs the rich traveler and gives to the poor is a popular hero. There is something of this spirit in the average man, and he is in fact rather proud of it. So long as this spirit is in the ascendant there is little hope of getting rid of the graded income tax. The best hope would seem to be to so raise the average economic status that the average man comes to identify himself with the rich traveler rather than the pauper. It is said that this situation has already occurred in New Zealand where the dock workers had become so opulent as a result of their monopoly of the boat-unloading privilege that they exerted political pressure to try to abolish the graded income tax. There are perhaps faint signs of the beginning of something of this sort in this country.

The code that I have been proposing is truly a minimum code in that it makes no effort to control many of the functions of society which are at present subject to legal control. It seems to me that society tries to formally control, by means of its laws, too many sorts of thing. Popular sentiment has ways of getting results which are effective and more flexible in expressing the current local social sentiment. For example, among the issues which I believe should not be subject to legal control is book censorship. In those cases where public sentiment is not strong enough to exercise effective control I believe it is questionable whether any formal control by law should be permitted, particularly when it is realized that such legal control is often representative of some minority interest, which has been made effective by some accident of the interplay of pressure groups.

The inherent probability that society may eventually evolve into something controlled by the sort of minimum code suggested above depends almost entirely on whether the average human being possesses the requisite emotional composition. He must have an instinctive aversion to self-assertion at the expense of others, particularly when that self-assertion is brought about by the exercise of physical force. He must be capable of taking a certain esthetic emotional satisfaction in the elegance of a code with a unified point of view — a code in which he himself is treated on the same basis as everyone else, that is, a code in which he asks no special favors. He must have a certain probity which makes him unwilling to deceive himself or to cheat in any other way, even if he knows that no one is looking and he can get away with it. He must have a passionate admiration for supreme ability and accomplishment. But, in addition, he must be intellectually capable of never forgetting that he cannot get away from himself. He must either have acquired an adequate understanding of the nature of his own intellectual processes, or he must regard the acquiring of such understanding as the most important intellectual problem. Whether the human race has within it the emotional and intellectual possibility of evolving into this sort of being does not now certainly appear, but I like to be optimistic. It is, however, in any event obvious that such an evolution will not occur without well considered self-direction and that suitable education will be necessary.

Finally, we return to consider some of the questions connected with man-made law. The importance of these questions is obvious, because law is the most universal and the most important of the instruments by which society exerts compulsion on the individual.

Since the laws of society take their origin in the acts of individuals, in particular myself, the primary question for me is: To what sorts of law will I allow myself to be a party? The question for you is similar. The question is to be answered in the light of all the insights available, in particular, the insights which I have been trying to emphasize in this book.

In the first place, I will not attach as much importance as do apparently a good many professional lawyers to getting all law formulated into a verbally consistent edifice. No one who has been through the experience of modern physics or who has acquired the point of view of this book can believe that there can be such an edifice, but it seems to me that nevertheless I can sometimes detect an almost metaphysical belief in the minds of some people in the possibility of such an edifice. If one needs specific details to fortify his conviction that there is no such edifice, plenty can be found. There is, for example, the inability of lawyers to agree on a definition of law — definitions have been proposed varying all the way from the pragmatic, positivistic definition of law as that which gets enforced by social action to the highly idealistic definition as that code which is in accord with divine principles and the divine will. All sorts of nebulous situations arise in practice — what to do about contradictory laws, how to treat conflicts of authority, how shall questions of interpretation be decided, what is the legal status of constitutions or other instruments purporting to limit the scope of law? The situation here for the lawyer resembles somewhat the general situation for the scientist. We have seen that in the popular view the scientist assumes that nature operates according to certain broad sweeping generalities. This is paraphrased by saying that the scientist must have "faith" that there are natural laws. We have not accepted this view. It seems to me that a better description of how the scientist operates is to say that he adopts the *program* of finding as much regularity as he can in the operation of nature, without any prior commitment to how much he will find. So too it seems to me that here the lawyer should and can make no prior commitment about the possibility of erecting a self-contained self-consistent verbal legal edifice, but that all he can strive for is as self-contained and logically consistent an edifice as he can erect. Only his case is from one point of view much worse than that of the physicist, because there is no present evidence to compel the physicist to abandon his program of ultimately getting complete order into everything that he finds, whereas the lawyer knows perfectly well, or should know, that his ideal is definitely not attainable, and that all he can do is to do his best.

A realization of this will, I think, make the lawyer less insistent on the demands of legal theory, which after all means only a verbally consistent edifice, and more willing not to insist on theoretical perfection at the expense of some other claim that should have precedence, such as the claim of justice in the case of false imprisonment. In the face of a situation like this the claims of legal theory leave me cold.

The question which started our inquiry now broadens itself. It becomes, not what sort of laws am I willing to be a party to, but, rather, under what circumstances am I willing to be a party to the exercise of force on my fellow through law? In trying to answer this question I realize that there are certain limitations to which any formulated code of rules is subject, some of these being limitations of verbal origin, and some of a more inexorable physical nature, which rule out certain subjects from any legitimate lawmaking activity whatever, although it is not possible to set limitations on what the lawmaker may say is law. We now consider some of these limitations.

Consider in the first place the question of language. There is a certain cross-connection and interrelation between the language in which a code of law is formulated and the subjects which can properly be touched by such a code. For our present immediate purposes we attend to only one aspect of the law, its aspect as a command of society to the individual. When society issues its commands I also, in my capacity as a member of society, am to that extent issuing my commands. As an individual I recognize certain limitations on the sort of command I allow myself to issue; the commands in which I take a part as a member of society will be subject to the same limitations. For example, as an individual I will not command my child to be "sorry" — as a member of society I will not issue any command that presumes or pretends to dictate the private mental attitude of anyone. The reason is much more deep-seated than any mere scruple such as finds its expression in the Bill of Rights, and it ultimately rests on the ineradicable operational dichotomy between the public and the private modes of such words as "sorry". If, following the suggestion of this book, it is agreed to emphasize this operational dichotomy by using words like "sorry" only in the introspectional mode, then there is an immediate reaction on the language in which any law can be expressed. For when I as an individual take part in the commands which society issues, it is the conduct of other people that I am prescribing, and in talking about the conduct of other people I shall use no introspectional words, but only those with a completely public behavioristic meaning. You will do the same. The resulting law, being a sort of average of the commands of all of us, will therefore contain no introspectional words. The resulting verbal edifice of codified law will be couched in as severely behavioristic language as the most ardent behaviorist could desire. The reason is not any idealistic reason, connected with a more or less metaphysical conception of human rights and human dignity, but the severely logical reason that this is the only thing that makes sense.

One of the first results of accepting the view that law must be formulated in behavioristic language will be the disappearance of such legislation as, for example, that of the Japanese just before the last war, who attempted to attach a criminal status to the thinking of "dangerous thoughts", or to the eighteenth-century law in England, already mentioned, making a belief in antitrinitarianism a criminal matter. I believe that there will be many repercussions on present legal practice here. There is the comparatively trivial matter of the oath taken on the Bible preliminary to giving testimony in court. This has in actual practice degenerated into little more than a trick which serves the purpose of legalizing prosecution for perjury. The hollowness of the form will, I believe, presently become so obvious and so distasteful that it will be abandoned. The lawyer will probably be able to invent a way of simply declaring that under certain conditions lying or perjury is an actionable matter, without the necessity for any cooperation from the individual. I believe that in the same way other oaths, such as the teachers' oath, will also presently be abandoned.

In much the same category is the present practice of making criminal responsibility depend on the ability to distinguish right from wrong. It was already suggested in the last chapter that the concepts of right and wrong essentially can have meaning only in the introspectional mode. It seems to me therefore that the use of these words must be given up and that some more behavioristic method of defining criminal liability must be discovered. Similar questions arise in trying to find a legal definition of what constitutes "cruelty", either to animals or to people. One's impulse is to use the word "suffer" in framing the definition, but suffer is obviously an introspectional word and some other definition must be found.

A law framed in behavioristic terms is the only type of law which has the property that violation of it can be established in clean-cut "objective" terms. Hence, ultimately, it is the only sort of law that is enforceable. Now everyone, the law giver as well as the subject, can see that a nonenforceable law is stultifying and therefore not to be promulgated. Here is a second reason why law should be framed in behavioristic terms.

The question of "loyalty" presents somewhat similar issues. Present-day social sentiment demands, from the individual, loyalty to the average opinions of the group of which he happens to be a member. In the writings of some lawyers I have found, in accordance with this, the implication that society has the right to demand loyalty to its laws on the part of its individuals. It seems to me that "loyalty" is essentially a private introspectional word. I know when I have the feeling of loyalty, but you may not know what my loyalties "really" are, and can only guess at them on a probability basis by observing my behavior. Loyalty has a large component of "acceptance", but it is more intimate and personal. Loyalty is something which I bestow, but which you may not command. I am loyal to the various groups to which I voluntarily attach myself, but I resent the assumption of a national group to command my loyalty to all its purposes, in the formation of which I had no part, because of an accident of birth. I do not attempt to command the loyalty of my fellow to me, and I resent it when all my fellows presume to command my loyalty to them. It seems to me that so long as the overwhelming force which society can exert plays as large a part as it does at present, loyalty can be only a small component in the attitude of the individual toward law, and lawyers should not expect it. I believe that loyalty will not become an important ingredient in the attitude of the average individual toward the law until he takes a much more influential role in the formulation of law than he does at present, and until he is allowed much greater mobility in moving from group to group than at present, a mobility which has been decreasing rather than increasing since World War I.

The ultimate result of behavioristic laws will be to enhance the freedom and the dignity of the individual. For example, freedom of religious conviction will not present itself, either positively or negatively, as a subject for law. From this point of view it would appear that the characteristic emphasis of English and American law on the freedom and dignity of the individual has been a more or less fortunate accident. Historically, we have had a deep-seated instinctive and emotional bias to focus importance on the individual, but for the wrong reasons. I believe, however, that a rational foundation can be found for the course of evolution that our legal institutions actually took. Perhaps when we become more conscious of the rational foundation we can expect accelerated progress toward the self-realization of the individual. Perhaps even countries like Japan or Russia, adopting an operational behavioristic attitude toward law, will gradually modify their attitude toward the individual.

There is another direction in which man-made law is subject to limitations as inexorable as those with regard to dictating the inner thought of the individual. The inescapable physical limitation here is that the past is irreversibly gone and that nothing can be done to change it. Any law which disregards this is an empty grammatical form. In the light of this, and from one point of view, a retroactive law is intrinsically impossible. For, if one wants to define law as the command of society, then retroactive law is impossible in the sense that society cannot issue a command that something shall be done in the past. Neither I as an individual nor society as a whole can command anyone to do something yesterday. But if one wants to emphasize the enforcement-punishment aspect in his definition of law, then retroactive law is at least possible, because I can make a law now saying that if someone did not do some particular thing yesterday he shall be punished today, and such a law can be enforced. This is the sense in which retroactive law is usually understood. The deep-seated aversion with which retroactive law of this kind is regarded is because it violates elementary sentiments of fair play and justice and is peculiarly liable to abuse in the hands of whatever faction is temporarily in the ascendant. To me a retroactive law indicates two things, both discreditable. In the first place, it indicates a willful refusal to face the facts and admit that there are some things which not even all-powerful society can do. In the second place, it indicates bad sportsmanship on the part of society. Society was not clever enough or far-sighted enough to anticipate how certain things would turn out, and now that they have turned out contrary to expectation it wants to go back and take it out on the individual who perhaps was cleverer than society. Going off the gold standard in 1933 represents this kind of retroactive legislation. Such conduct would certainly not be acceptable between individuals, and I do not propose to take any greater part in it than I can help in my capacity as a member of society. In fact, my aversion is so strong that I think I would not have recourse to retroactive law under any circumstances whatever.

In recent times perhaps the situation in which retroactive law has aroused most discussion has been in connection with the German Nazi war criminals. The lawyers were confronted here with admittedly an exceedingly difficult situation. The most elemental and sacred of human instincts had been flagrantly violated and an outraged public opinion demanded that something be done about it. The lawyers apparently regarded it as of the utmost importance that some way be found which should be dispassionate, orderly, and so far as possible in accordance with accepted legal practice. In these terms the situation was an essentially impossible one. Some lawyers argued that the best way of dealing with it was to accept frankly the necessity for retroactive laws, and punish now for violations of laws which did not exist at the time of the violation. This apparently was not acceptable to the consensus of legal opinion. A course of action was finally adopted which to an outsider seemed to involve highly casuistical argument, which purported to avoid retroactive law, but which in fact did not. The casuistry and the retroactive nature of the action, in fact if not in word, left a most unpleasant impression on me. I would far rather have come out into the open and merely said that there are some things that so violate deep-seated human instincts that we will resort to naked force to express our outrage, and we are going to shoot you now, in anger, because we are able to. I think in the long run it would have been all to the good to let people see that the irresistible force which society can exert on its individuals is in fact something prior even to law. And the man who relies on words written in a law book in the face of forces like this is simply a fool and blind to the way things are.

VIII

IN CONCLUSION

We now find ourselves, at the end of our long analysis, in a position to offer a tentative and partial answer to the problem dimly shadowed forth in the Introduction, namely, to find the source of the weakness or ineptness in all human thinking. We have commented more than once on the fact that the succession of topics as we have analyzed them has been a succession in which the individual plays a continually more important role and first person report becomes increasingly necessary if we are to hope even to describe faithfully what occurs. As the culminating step in thus emphasizing what happens to the individual I have suggested the desirability or even the necessity of restricting the use of such words as "conscious" to the introspectional or private mode as distinguished from the public behavioristic mode. The necessity for some such convention in the handling of our verbal tools suggests what I believe to be at least one of the fundamental troubles with the way all of us handle our minds. This trouble arises from the fact that all of us as individuals are compelled to use in our thinking tools which were fashioned by and for society rather than for the individual. The average individual does not appreciate how brazenly the cards have been stacked against him in the evolutionary process. Up to now evolution has been concerned with the species, not with the individual. If the individual is ever to emerge, it can be only by some relaxation of present pressures, perhaps when the species has been perfected as far as possible by the conventional evolutionary process and something transcending the evolutionary process appears on the scene.

The individual has remained the forgotten man, in spite of the pious slogans of democracy or our repeated assertions that society exists for the individual. On the contrary, up to the present society has in fact almost completely dominated the scene, particularly the intellectual scene, at the expense of the individual. As the individual stands today he is the creature of society. This is coming to be increasingly recognized and talked about — not only is it recognized as a fact, but there seems to be a growing sentiment that this is the way it *ought* to be, and many profess that they are glad to accept it. As an illustration there is the thesis of Trigant Burrow, already commented on, that modern man is suffering from a neurosis because he thinks of himself too much as an individual and identifies himself insufficiently with society. I have stated that it seems to me that there is indeed a neurosis, but exactly opposite in nature, a neurosis arising from a domination of the individual by society so complete that the individual is, among other things, continually frustrated in his attempt to describe with simple integrity what happens to him with the verbal tools vouchsafed him by society. I have no doubt that the majority of people find the concept implied in the statement "only I am conscious" entirely unintelligible, so completely has any possible freshness of perception been atrophied under the bludgeoning of society. As part of the same picture, when the individual realizes that he cannot get away from himself, he will see that his most important personal problem is to find his springs of conduct within himself, a vision of which very few people are capable.

The inadequacies of our traditional intellectual tools are most manifest when we deal with the opposition between ourselves and other people as distinguished from the opposition between ourselves and inanimate things.

It is easy to see how things got this way. The infant in his attempt to adjust to his environment *has* to accept the methods employed by his culture. Not only is the infant not developed enough intellectually to be able to subject these methods to a critical examination, but he has time only to acquire as quickly as he can some method which will meet the necessities of the moment. It is thus almost inevitable that he adopt the methods which the people around him use, that is, the methods acceptable to his society and culture. Now the methods which have survived in any society are subject to one control which dominates so overwhelmingly that it casts into eclipse practically all other considerations. This is the control based on the requirement of survival of the society. If the method does not satisfy this requirement the society that uses it gets automatically eliminated, and with it all its component individuals. Now the brute requirement for survival is not a discriminating requirement, so that it comes about that anything goes, so long only as this one need is met. This need is by no means coextensive with the needs of the individuals of which the society is composed, and in fact is often directly opposed to them. It would indeed be a miracle if there were not an opposition here. Survival of the race requires the survival of the individual up to the time when he has reproduced himself by procreation, but the individual wants to survive longer and furthermore has many other needs. It is true that some of these needs will also be automatically satisfied in society in virtue of the fact that society is the sum of its individuals. If, for example, every individual strives for a higher standard of living it is probable that the standard of living of the society as a whole will be high. It seems to me that most of the needs which are more or less automatically filled by society are on the "material" plane. One reason is that nearly all people feel the same material needs. Having agreed on the need it is usually not difficult to agree on means for meeting it. Everyone agrees that it is nice to have enough to eat and to have good roads to drive automobiles on, and everyone knows that to get these things land has to be planted to crops and roads bulldozed. Although the individual can regard society in the long run as a pretty effective arrangement for satisfying his material needs, this does not mean by any means that the interests of society and the individual are identical even on the material plane. Wherever there is personal aggrandisement of the individual at the expense of others the conflict of material interests is manifest. The impulse to such personal aggrandisement is one of the commonest human traits, all the way from the bully in school to the tyrant or dictator.

However, it is on the intellectual plane that the mechanism which secures adaptation of society to the needs of its individuals is least effective and where failure to meet the needs of the individuals concerned most serious. The principle reason for this is perhaps the simple fact that so few individuals feel or express such intellectual needs. Perhaps the most pressing intellectual need of the individual is simple integrity. Society, on the other hand, has no need for integrity except insofar as it conduces to social stability. The result is that the individual can have no assurance that the intellectual tools which he has inherited from society are of such a nature that he can use them with integrity, or that he can acquiesce with integrity in the social philosophy which society expects him to accept. Not only is there no *assurance* that the individual can practice his intellectual life with integrity in the context afforded by society, but it seems to me to be a fact of observation that such integrity is well-nigh impossible with the present make-up of society. If the contemporary individual wants to live a life of intellectual integrity he pretty much has to do it on his own. Society as a whole is not interested in this and in fact is often positively hostile. There are so few other individuals interested in it that there is little or no public discussion of how to solve the problems, few books get written on the subject, and there is no cumulative body of practice on which the individual can build. Furthermore, the individual himself usually does not come to a realization of all this until he has matured and relaxed sufficiently from the pressure of making things happen in the material world to be able to devote leisurely thought to it. Contrast this with the situation in physics — where would physics be today if every new physicist had to start by himself from scratch? It will be a long time before the individual fully emancipates himself from his intellectual thralldom to society, and therefore a long time before the individual can effectively emerge. Perhaps the process may be accelerated somewhat as leisure becomes more general, and perhaps, even, this book may help a little.

I now propose to make an explicit list of situations in which it seems to me that the individual will find it difficult to use with integrity the intellectual tools which he receives from society. I shall also list situations in which the social philosophy which he is supposed to accept cannot be acquiesced in with integrity.

It may be well first to attempt to clarify what I mean by "integrity". It is in the first place an attribute of the individual, and, as I shall use it as applied to myself and by projection to others, an attribute of which I am conscious. This is not the sense in which it is sometimes said that a "well integrated" person has integrity. The word is also sometimes used in a more impersonal sense, as for instance when a process of logic may be said to have integrity, but this usage is rare and is nearly synonymous with "soundness", and I shall not use the word in this sense. There is a connection with soundness, however. If I were aware that a certain process in logic were not sound and if I continued to use it, I would not be acting with integrity. Because of the implication of awareness it does not make sense to speak of society as having integrity. Although society as such cannot have integrity, nevertheless certain actions by society may have the same effect as would actions which performed by an individual would connote lack of integrity. For me, integrity in the individual implies "intellectual honesty", but it is more than this. It is a frame of mind. Integrity demands that I *want* to know what the facts are and that I *want* to analyze and to understand my mental tools and know what happens when I apply these tools to the facts. The flesh being frail and life short and there being many other things to do I have to make some sort of compromise with the demands of integrity. But there is one thing which I may not do and retain my integrity — if I have a new vision of something which I did not appreciate before, I may not try to put the vision back and pretend that I did not have it and refuse to admit that there may be consequences. Now it is often difficult to think through the consequences of a new vision, and often one simply does not have time. It seems to me that the individual who finds himself in such a situation can only react with diffidence — "humility" is not quite the right word. And it is to be continually kept in mind that new visions do occur, both to the individual and to society. Intellectually the human race is still young, and even without any evolutionary change in its intellectual capacities, it has many new intellectual experiences ahead of it.

Let us now consider in detail some of the characteristics of the mental tools, and this means mostly the verbal tools, which I have received from society which make it difficult for me to practice intellectual integrity. We have discussed many respects in which the traditional tools are imperfect; each of these imperfections is a potential danger to my integrity to the extent that I have not thought through how best to adapt myself to the imperfection. Some of these imperfections are not due to any "fault" of society, but would appear to be intrinsic in the nature of things, before which society is as powerless as the individual. Furthermore, some of the characteristics of our mental tools which reflect something intrinsic in the nature of things are not to be classed as imperfections at all, at least until someone has a bright new idea. Among such perhaps are to be reckoned the commitment of our speech to the three-dimensionality of space and the forward flow of time. Among the characteristics which perhaps reflect something intrinsic in the nature of things and which we would perhaps be more inclined to rate as imperfections is the inability of language to deal with self-reflexive situations as we would like. Language has to be handled with the greatest circumspection if we are to avoid paradox, as is well known with regard to some of the situations in elementary logic. A special case of the self-reflexive situation is afforded by introspection. There are great difficulties here — I have tried to meet some of them by the device of using certain primarily introspectional words only as "relational" words, but this device does not meet all the demands. For example, we have seen that it is extraordinarily difficult to get into words what I mean by the "quality" of my sensation of red, but there is nevertheless something pretty definite here to which nearly everyone responds. It may well be that we are here trying for something which is intrinsically unobtainable, for we are trying to get into words, which are the instrument of communication, that which cannot be communicated. We are up against it — we cannot talk about it without using some noncommittal word like the "that" of the last sentence, whereas introspection discloses no "that". One of the most serious consequences of this ineptness of words in dealing with introspection is that it makes it so difficult to formulate satisfactorily the fundamental introspectional insight that I cannot get away from myself.

The hand of society is not especially obvious in these various specific ineptnesses of our verbal machinery. But it is not so obvious whether society has or has not played a role in casting our communication and thinking into the mold of words at all. The use of words may perhaps be inevitable because of the construction of the individual brain. Now words have certain characteristics that are so limiting that they may well be called imperfections. For example, words are static as used in language to convey meaning, and a sentence in general has no meaning until it has been completed. But recognizable mental activities occur during the utterance of the sentence, and these activities are very difficult to get into words. It is not now obvious whether in the predawn of history the human race took a fork in the road which committed it to the use of the mechanism of words with their static meanings instead of a fork which might have allowed it to reproduce more faithfully the fluent character of things as they are.

The formative hand of society is no less obvious in the way in which the individual thinks about the future in general, particularly events after his own presumptive death. Society has a continuity which the individual does not, so that society finds a utility in the conventional concept of an objectively existing future which the individual does not. I have not always found it easy to hold myself to a realization that any meaning which I have a right to ascribe to the future is to be found in things which happen to *me, now*. The conventional tool of language is not adapted to make this easier.

Other examples could be given — in fact examples could be drawn from most of the instances discussed in this book in which a conventional concept leaves something to be desired. However, enough has been said to show that the individual has not played a very large role in the development of many of the concepts which he uses, and that these concepts themselves are not particularly well adapted to the needs of the individual. In all these instances the role played by society has been more or less incidental and the final result has been rather in the nature of an artifact of the total situation. There are many situations, however, in which the role played by society is more active, and indeed where the role played by society, if it had been played by an individual, would not have been called innocent. We have seen that the control exerted by the survival motif is so overwhelming that social philosophies get accepted and forced on the individual with no regard to their truth. Such disregard of truth in the behavior of an individual would hardly be said to exemplify integrity. Although the property of integrity can hardly be associated with the action of society as a whole, it must be remembered that the total activity of society is compounded of the actions of its individuals. I cannot believe that society has accepted casuistical arguments in the past without some individuals knowing that they were casuistical and condoning them, it may even be because of considerations of the common good. If there have been such individuals in the past, and history makes it evident that there have been, I cannot concede that they have been acting with integrity.

Let us now look at some of the situations in which society asks the individual to subscribe to a philosophy which he cannot accept with integrity. These often occur in connection with the rationalizations which society asks the individual to accept for its mores and codes of conduct, that is, for its values. It seems to me that one of the most sweeping dicta which society asks the individual to accept is the dictum that in the long run, and from the broad point of view, all things considered, the interests of society and the interests of the individual are identical. This dictum played an appreciable role in my own bringing up. Such a dictum may have been tenable with the assistance of the concept of a future life in which the individual may expect to be rewarded or punished in accordance with the social value of his actions on earth. But without such a supernatural mechanism, the dictum is just plain not true, and anyone would be a simple fool to accept it, to say nothing of integrity. Even if such a crude supernatural mechanism is not used, the importance to society of getting its individuals to accept the values of society is obviously so great that all sorts of pressures are put on the individual to see his own values through the eyes of society. The values of society are presented to the individual as having an absolute quality that for some reason demands their acceptance by the individual. In their social context values get thought of simply as *values*, without qualification, forgetting that a value has to be a value *for* someone. Now if anything is obvious to the individual it is that his own values have nothing of the absolute about them, but are continually changing with time, and therefore for this reason alone cannot possibly be identical with the values of society. But this is something that society, for obvious reasons, feels that it cannot let the individual say out loud, and does all in its power to prevent. Integrity in the thinking of the individual demands that he recognize this situation. Whether integrity also demands that he speak his thought out loud is a matter for the individual to decide.

It is not difficult to understand the mechanism by which the values of society acquire a degree of absoluteness. For when I talk about a value of society I am talking about a sort of average or least common denominator of the values of all my fellows. And when my neighbor talks about a value of society he is talking about a similar average, which he obtains by the same sort of process that I did, except that my value appears in his average and his own drops out, whereas in my case the converse happens, my own value dropping out and his appearing. When society consists of many individuals, the two averages, that of my neighbor and myself, are so nearly alike that the differences may be disregarded, and the "value" of society emerges as something absolute in the sense that all individuals come to approximately the same result. Furthermore, a value thus generated has considerable stability in time, a much greater stability than do my own personal values. The reason is simply that the average over the community is the average over all age groups, and the relative numbers in the different age groups have stability, although the individual members of each age group are in a constant state of flux. The values of society thus come to have a certain stability and "objectivity". This is no reason, however, why the individual who thinks about the matter should accept them.

The situation presented by values is typical of the general situation. Society feels that it cannot permit free discussion of many topics, and wherever this occurs the integrity of the individual is threatened. The instances could be multiplied. Perhaps the supreme example of an insight which the individual must be prevented at all costs from saying out loud, and the utterance of which constitutes the supreme *lésé majesté* against society, is that the individual is free to accept or reject in his inmost heart any demand of society. Society will go to any length to prevent people from realizing this — it is my personal opinion that some of the roots of juvenile delinquency may be found here; at least I can see how I might have been forced into delinquency by such treatment.

The institution of nationalism is one that society at present expects the individual to accept without discussion. It is easy to imagine the social furor which would greet a proposal to discuss seriously the question "Why *should* I be patriotic?" The word "subversion" would often be heard in the clamor. Politics within the nation affords many instances. In a country such as ours it is the common opinion that anyone born to be a citizen of the country is by that very fact committed irretrievably to a defense of its political institutions as the best possible. It is regarded as pretty close to treason to suggest that one's own political institutions are capable of improvement. The workings of such a philosophy are particularly obvious in a time like the present. Everyone of us in this country should be re-examining our fundamental political suppositions to see how they stand up under the altered technological conditions of our times and to find ways of modifying them if it should appear desirable. Instead of this, because of rivalry with Russia, every citizen of this country is expected to defend the institutions of this country as better in every possible way than those of Russia. The disadvantages of a set-up as inflexible and as frozen as this would seem obvious without argument. So long as this inflexibility remains, the only way in which the human race as a whole and from a long range point of view can be expected to progress is in those few moments of flexibility when an old political system breaks down and is replaced by another. This occurred during our American Revolution. If we are not able to achieve greater flexibility it may happen again to us, in reverse. And if it is Russia that dominates after the next break-up, it will in turn happen to Russia, unless Communism achieves a flexibility of which it gives no present hint. In the meantime, and from the point of view of the individual, it is evident that the political arena is no place for the practice of individual integrity. It seems to be more and more the case that political success is achieved at the cost of personal integrity.

The pressures are hardly less compelling in the field of ethics. It is expected that every individual will esteem the indefinite preservation and welfare of the human race as the supreme good and value for him personally, even if racial survival has to be purchased at the price of not being allowed to use one's mind freely. It is also often assumed that the ideal of service to others or to the race in general is the highest motivation that an individual can have for conduct. The usual rationalizations for these values must, I think, strike the critical individual as pretty crude, but the individual is nevertheless expected to accept them. The difficulty of maintaining integrity in an atmosphere like this is obvious. It is not easy for the individual to be continually questioning and rejecting the consensus of his fellows.

In spite of the generally unfavorable social atmosphere I do not believe that the difficulties of achieving a satisfactory intellectual integrity on the social level are overwhelming, for it is usually pretty clear when a demand made by society fails in intellectual probity. It must be kept in mind that in saying this I do not imply that integrity need be pushed to the point of martyrdom. Some individuals may feel that their integrity demands martyrdom, but such integrity is of another sort, not intellectual integrity. In fact, martyrdom may sometimes be evidence of just the opposite of intellectual integrity, involving a willful refusal to see things as they are.

Intellectual integrity is always an affair of the individual. For the individual, that is, for me, there are other situations in which the practice of intellectual integrity is incomparably more difficult than in the situations presented by society. For I know that my intellectual tools are defective, but I have to continue to use them. What am I to do in a situation like this? This book is part of my answer.

REFERENCES

CHAPTER I

1. Dagobert Runes, *A Treasury of Philosophy* (New York: Philosophical Library, 1955).
2. Adelbert Ames, Jr., *Visual Perception and the Rotating Trapezoidal Window* (Psychological Monographs, vol. 6, no. 7; Washington, D.C.: American Philosophical Association, 1951). William H. Ittleson and Hadley Cantril, *Perception, a Transactional Approach* (Doubleday Papers in Psychology; New York: Doubleday, 1954).

CHAPTER II

1. H. Poincaré, *The Foundations of Science* (New York: Science Press, 1929).
2. Jason Xenakis, *Methodos 6* (1954), 299–329.
3. Charles W. Morris, "Foundations of the Theory of Signs," *International Encyclopaedia of Unified Science* (Chicago: University of Chicago Press, 1955), vol. 1, pp. 78–137.
4. Alfred Tarski, "The Semantic Conception of Truth," *Philosophy and Phenomenological Research 4* (1944), 341–376.
5. W. V. Quine, *From a Logical Point of View* (Cambridge, Mass.: Harvard University Press, 1953).

CHAPTER III

1. A. Cornelius Benjamin, *Operationism* (Springfield, Ill.: Charles C. Thomas, 1955).
2. Arthur G. Walker, Axioms of Kinematical Relativity, Report of International Symposium on the Axiomatic Method (Berkeley, Calif.: 1958), 144.
3. Mortiz Schlick, "Meaning and Verification," in Feigl and Sellars, eds., *Readings in Philosophical Analysis* (New York, Appleton-Century-Crofts, 1949).

CHAPTER IV

1. See, for example, chapter IV in my book, *The Nature of Physical Theory* (Princeton, N. J.: Princeton University Press, 1936).
2. Susanne K. Langer, *An Introduction to Symbolic Logic* (2nd ed.; New York: Dover, 1953).
3. P. W. Bridgman, "A Physicist's Second Reaction to Mengenlehre," *Scripta Mathematica 2* (1934), 3–29.

4. Rudolf Carnap, "The Two Concepts of Probability," *Philosophy and Phenomenological Research 5* (1945), 513–532.

5. Ernest Nagel, "Principles of the Theory of Probability," *International Encyclopaedia of Unified Science* (Chicago: University of Chicago Press, 1955), vol. 2, pp. 341–422.

6. Henry Margenau, "The Role of Definitions in the Physical Sciences, with Remarks on the Frequency Definition of Probability," *American Journal of Physics 10* (1942), 224–232. "On the Frequency Theory of Probability," *Philosophy and Phenomenological Research 6* (1946), 11–25.

7. S. S. Stevens and H. Davis, *Hearing, Its Psychology and Physiology* (New York: Wiley, 1938).

CHAPTER V

1. Ernest H. Hutten, *The Language of Modern Physics* (London: Allen and Unwin, 1956).

2. Norman R. Campbell, *Measurement and Calculation* (London: Longmans, Green, 1928). Harold Jeffreys, *Scientific Inference* (Cambridge, England: The University Press, 1931). This is the first edition; there is a second edition with much altered subject matter. S. S. Stevens, "Mathematics, Measurement and Psychophysics," in S. S. Stevens, ed., *Handbook of Experimental Psychology* (New York: Wiley, 1951).

3. Henry Margenau, "Can Time Flow Backwards?" *Philosophy of Science 21* (1954), 79–92. R. P. Feynman, "The Theory of Positrons," *Physical Review 76* (1949), 749–759. Hans Reichenbach, *The Direction of Time* (Berkeley, Calif.: University of California Press, 1956). Adolf Grünbaum, "Das Zeitproblem," *Archiv für Philosophie 7* (1957), 165–208.

4. L. L. Whyte, "Dimensional Theory: Dimensionless Secondary Quantities," *American Journal of Physics 21* (1953), 323–325. "On the History of Natural Lengths," *Annals of Science 10* (1954), 20–27.

5. P. W. Bridgman, *The Nature of Some of Our Physical Concepts* (New York: Philosophical Library, 1952), 14.

6. See, for example, page 150 in *The Logic of Modern Physics* (New York: Macmillan, 1957).

7. William Bender, *An Introduction to Scale Coordinate Physics* (Minneapolis: Burgess, 1958). Also, "The Nature of Scale Coordinate Geometry," *Proceedings of the South Dakota Academy of Science 35* (1956), 232–265.

8. Ernst Cassirer, *Determinism and Indeterminism in Modern Physics* (New Haven, Conn.: Yale University Press, 1956).

9. Max Born, "The Conceptual Situation in Physics and the Prospects of Its Future Development," *Proceedings of the Physical Society 66* (1953), 507.

CHAPTER VI

1. W. S. Hunter, "Biographical Memoir of James Rowland Angell," *Biographical Memoirs of the National Academy of Sciences 26* (1950), 191–208.

2. B. F. Skinner, *The Behavior of Organisms: An Experimental Analysis* (New York: Appleton-Century-Crofts, 1938).

3. D. B. Silversmit, "Freedom of the Will, An Experimental Approach," *ETC 14* (1956), 50–52.

4. See reference 2 of the Introduction.

5. Anthony Flew, "Motives and the Unconscious," in vol. 1 of *Minnesota Studies in the Philosophy of Science* (Minneapolis, Minn.: University of Minnesota, 1956).

CHAPTER VII

1. Trigant Burrow, *The Neurosis of Man* (New York: Harcourt Brace, 1949). Hans Syz, *Trigant Burrow's Thesis in Relation to Psychotherapy, Progress in Psychotherapy* (New York: Grune and Stratton, 1957).

2. I. Bernard Cohen, *Franklin and Newton* (vol. 43 of the Memoirs of the American Philosophical Society; Philadelphia: American Philosophical Society, 1956). I. Bernard Cohen, "Newton's Personality and Scientific Thought," *Actes du XIIIᵉ Congres International d'Histoire des Sciences*, (Florence: September 3–9, 1956), 195–201.

INDEX